James B. Welsh

Radioactivity
and
Nuclear Physics

BY

JAMES M. CORK

Professor of Physics, University of Michigan

THIRD EDITION

D. VAN NOSTRAND COMPANY, Inc.

PRINCETON, NEW JERSEY

TORONTO   LONDON

NEW YORK

D. VAN NOSTRAND COMPANY, INC.

120 Alexander St., Princeton, New Jersey
257 Fourth Avenue, New York 10, New York
25 Hollinger Rd., Toronto 16, Canada

*All correspondence should be addressed to the
principal office of the company at Princeton, N. J.*

First Published February 1947

Four Reprintings

Second Edition, June 1950

Three Reprintings

Third Edition, May 1957

PRINTED IN THE UNITED STATES OF AMERICA

PREFACE TO THE THIRD EDITION

Since the previous edition of this text was written, significant advances have been made in many areas of Nuclear Physics. Accelerators have produced particles with phenomenal energies and present designs are aimed at still higher goals. Classical detectors have been improved and supplemented by such newer devices as multichannel scintillation spectrometers and liquid bubble chambers. The properties of the various types of mesons and their interactions have been more clearly established. In addition to the discovery of the antiproton, positive evidence has been found for the existence of the last of the theoretically expected fundamental particles, the antineutron. Predictions have been made and confirming experiments carried out regarding the failure of the long established principle of the conservation of parity in nuclear reactions.

To cover these many advances together with the well established domains of modern nuclear theory, several additional topics and a new chapter on the nucleus have been introduced. Mathematical developments have been limited to an understanding of the subjects presented. Original references in the literature are appended to assure proper historical development. It has been the aim in the text to include material satisfactory for an introductory course in Nuclear Physics at the upper undergraduate or beginning graduate level. Problems of varying degrees of difficulty are at the end of each chapter. The inclusion of the many tables of significant nuclear data should make the text a useful handbook for workers dealing with radioactivity in allied fields.

The author acknowledges with deep appreciation the many private communications received containing late data and figures dealing with current researches, together with permission for their use.

JAMES M. CORK

April, 1957

CONTENTS

CHAPTER 1

NATURAL RADIOACTIVITY

1.1. The Periodic Table. As early as 1815, W. Prout,[1] an English physician, advanced an interesting hypothesis suggesting a genetic relationship between the elements. Measurements already made at that time indicated that, if the atomic weight of hydrogen be taken as unity, then the weights of many other elements were almost, but not exactly, integral numbers. Prout suggested that these differences from whole numbers were experimental errors and that hydrogen was a mother substance out of which all other elements were built. Thus an atom of oxygen was considered as being made of 16 atoms of hydrogen.

In 1864, J. Newlands [2] observed that, when the elements were arranged in the order of their symbol weights, the tenth was similar, chemically, to the second; the eleventh to the third, and so on. This generalization, although ridiculed when first proposed, has been termed the Newlands law of octaves.

In 1869, D. Mendelejeff [3] in Russia, and L. Meyer [4] in Germany, apparently independently, published almost identical tables, arranging the then-known elements in vertical and horizontal columns. The elements in any vertical column behave similarly, chemically. From left to right along a horizontal row the elements change from those with pronounced alkaline properties to those with strong acid characteristics. The properties of the elements both physical and chemical are functions of their atomic weights and many of these properties exhibit a periodic variation.

[1] W. Prout, Thomson, *Ann. Phil.*, **6**, 269 (1815).
[2] J. A. R. Newlands, *Chem. News*, **10**, 94 (1864).
[3] D. Mendelejeff, *J. prakt. Chem.*, **106**, 251 (1869).
[4] L. Meyer, *Ann. Chem. Pharm.*, **7**, 354 (1869).

When the periodic table was first published, many spaces in it were left vacant. By 1895, 65 elements had been identified and classified. The elements as recognized at the present time are shown in Table 1.1. Starting with hydrogen as atomic number one and arranging elements in a numerical sequence of increasing weight, the heaviest element is atomic numer 101, called mendelevium, and every intervening number is represented by an element. The position of the element in this sequence is termed its atomic number, and is represented by the symbol Z. It will be seen that this number represents the number of negative electrons in the outer orbits of the atom and hence also the number of positive charges in its nucleus. It thus determines the chemical behavior of the element. The nine heaviest elements, whose atomic numbers are 93, 94, 95, 96, 97, 98, 99, 100, and 101 have been made from uranium by induced nuclear transmutations.[5] The rare elements, technetium 43, prometheum 61, astatine 85, and francium 87 were all first made by nuclear reactions.

For each atomic number or element there may be atoms having one or more different atomic weights. These various atomic weights are termed isotopes, and for any element they differ among themselves approximately by small integral numbers of mass units. The isotopes for a given element always occur with a fixed relative abundance, with the exception of helium, lead, and certain others, such as strontium and argon which are sometimes products of radioactive decay.

1.2. Atomic Weights, the Chemical and the Physical Scale. A scale of atomic weight measurement has been developed based upon the relative combining weights of the elements in chemical reactions. In this scale, oxygen is taken as a standard, with an assigned value of exactly 16.00000. The corresponding value of hydrogen is 1.00785.

[5] G. T. Seaborg and J. G. Hamilton, *Science*, **102**, 556 (1945); *Chem. Eng. News*, **23**, 2190 (1945); S. Thompson, A. Ghiorso, K. Street, and G. Seaborg, *Phys. Rev.*, **77**, 838 (1950); *Phys. Rev.*, **98**, 1519 (1955); L. Magnusson, M. Studier, P. Fields, C. Stevens, J. Mech, A. Friedman, H. Diamond, and J. Huizenga, *Phys. Rev.*, **96**, 1576 (1954).

TABLE 1.1. THE PERIODIC TABLE OF THE ELEMENTS

	I	II	III	IV	V	VI	VII	VIII			0
I	1H HYDROGEN										2He HELIUM
II	3Li LITHIUM	4Be BERYLLIUM	5B BORON	6C CARBON	7N NITROGEN	8O OXYGEN	9F FLUORINE				10Ne NEON
III	11Na SODIUM	12Mg MAGNESIUM	13Al ALUMINUM	14Si SILICON	15P PHOSPHORUS	16S SULPHUR	17Cl CHLORINE				18A ARGON
IV	19K POTASSIUM	20Ca CALCIUM	21Sc SCANDIUM	22Ti TITANIUM	23V VANADIUM	24Cr CHROMIUM	25Mn MANGANESE	26Fe IRON	27Co COBALT	28Ni NICKEL	
	29Cu COPPER	30Zn ZINC	31Ga GALLIUM	32Ge GERMANIUM	33As ARSENIC	34Se SELENIUM	35Br BROMINE				36Kr KRYPTON
V	37Rb RUBIDIUM	38Sr STRONTIUM	39Y YTTRIUM	40Zr ZIRCONIUM	41Nb NIOBIUM	42Mo MOLYBDENUM	43Tc TECHNETIUM	44Ru RUTHENIUM	45Rh RHODIUM	46Pd PALLADIUM	
	47Ag SILVER	48Cd CADMIUM	49In INDIUM	50Sn TIN	51Sb ANTIMONY	52Te TELLURIUM	53I IODINE				54Xe XENON
VI	55Cs CESIUM	56Ba BARIUM	57La LANTHANUM	72Hf HAFNIUM	73Ta TANTALUM	74W TUNGSTEN	75Re RHENIUM	76Os OSMIUM	77Ir IRIDIUM	78Pt PLATINUM	
	79Au GOLD	80Hg MERCURY	81Tl THALLIUM	82Pb LEAD	83Bi BISMUTH	84Po POLONIUM	85At ASTATINE				86Rn RADON
VII	87Fr FRANCIUM	88Ra RADIUM	89Ac ACTINIUM								

RARE EARTHS

LANTHANIDE

58Ce CERIUM	59Pr PRASEODYMIUM	60Nd NEODYMIUM	61Pm PROMETHEUM	62Sm SAMARIUM	63Eu EUROPIUM	64Gd GADOLINIUM	65Tb TERBIUM	66Dy DYSPROSIUM	67Ho HOLMIUM	68Er ERBIUM	69Tm THULIUM	70Yb YTTERBIUM	71Lu LUTETIUM

ACTINIDE

90Th THORIUM	91Pa PROTACTINIUM	92U URANIUM	93Np NEPTUNIUM	94Pu PLUTONIUM	95Am AMERICIUM	96Cm CURIUM	97Bk BERKELIUM	98Cf CALIFORNIUM	99E EINSTEINIUM	100Fm FERMIUM	101Mv MENDELEVIUM		

Studies in band spectra indicated that oxygen did not consist of a single isotope, as had at first been suspected.[6] A careful investigation with the mass spectrograph confirmed the prediction that, in addition to the isotopes of mass 16, there were also traces of isotopes of masses 17 and 18. Now, if it be assumed that the mass of the abundant isotope of oxygen is exactly 16, then isotope 17 is found to have a mass of 17.004534 and an abundance of 0.04%; and isotope 18, a mass number of 18.004855 and an abundance of 0.20%. On averaging these quantities, a value for the atomic weight of oxygen, on what is termed a "physical" scale, is 16.004411. It thus follows that the atomic weights on the physical scale are in the ratio of 1.000275 to 1, to the corresponding weights on the chemical scale.

The isotopes are now regarded as if built from hydrogen atoms and neutrons. The neutron is a neutral particle whose mass on the "physical" scale is 1.008986. Thus oxygen 16 is equivalent in structure to the sum of eight hydrogen atoms and eight neutrons. The eight electrons of the hydrogen atoms constitute the outer orbital electrons of the normal oxygen atom, while the eight hydrogen nuclei or protons combine with the eight neutrons to form the oxygen 16 nucleus. The A particles within the nucleus are termed *nucleons*, whether they be neutrons or protons. An isotope of a particular mass number is sometimes called a *nuclide*.

1.3. Isotopes, Mass Defect and Binding Energy. With the precision now attainable in mass spectroscopy, it is possible to express the mass of an isotope to six significant figures. Similarly, the relative abundance of the isotopes comprising an element has been accurately determined.

The interesting observation has been made by Aston that elements of odd atomic number have only one or two components, whereas elements of even atomic number may have several, in some cases as many as eleven, isotopes. This fact is il-

[6] W. F. Giauque and H. L. Johnston, *J. Am. Chem. Soc.*, **51**, 1436, 3528 (1929).

lustrated by Figure 1.1, which represents the isotopic distribution in the odd-numbered element manganese and the even-numbered element tin whose atomic numbers are 25 and 50.

Isotopes having an even atomic number Z and an even number N of neutrons are most abundant in nature, 164 of the approximately total number 242 being so constituted. Only six

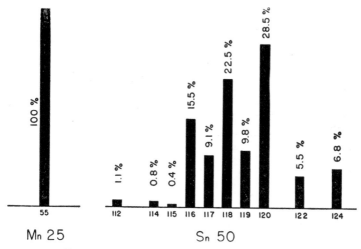

FIG 1.1. Isotopic distribution in manganese and tin.

of the natural isotopes have both odd atomic numbers and odd numbers of neutrons, namely, H^2, Li^6, B^{10}, N^{14}, K^{40}, and Lu^{176}. The distribution of the natural isotopes is shown graphically in Figure 1.2 in which the atomic number Z appears as abscissa and the neutron number N as ordinate.

On the mass scale in which 16.0000 represents the abundant isotope of oxygen, the mass of the abundant isotope of hydrogen is 1.008145, and of helium, 4.003873; and for the neutron, the mass is 1.008986. Now, it is clear that if the heavier elements be regarded as constructed from the lighter components, the masses do not seem correct. For example, two neutrons plus two hydrogen atoms have a mass of 4.034262 instead of 4.003873, as is found for helium 4. This apparent loss in mass of 0.030389 mass units is termed the "mass defect" and is extremely important in determining the relative stability of the element and the energy exchange in nuclear reactions. Similarly, for oxygen, eight hydrogen atoms plus eight neutrons

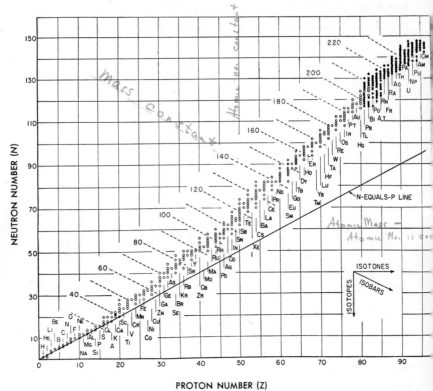

Fig. 1.2. Proton number versus neutron number for the stable isotopes.

might be expected to have a mass of 16.137048 instead of 16.0000, i.e., a mass loss of 0.137048. The mass loss per nucleon in the packing or build-up of the oxygen nucleus is then one sixteenth of this value, or 0.008565 mass units.

From relativity theory an equivalence between mass and energy is postulated, so that the mass defect per nucleon, such as 0.008565 mass units for oxygen, is expressible as 7.984 million electron volts (Mev) per nucleon. This mass defect per particle for any element represents a tightness of packing and is thus called its "binding energy" per nucleon. Figure 1.3 shows graphically the binding energies for various elements through-

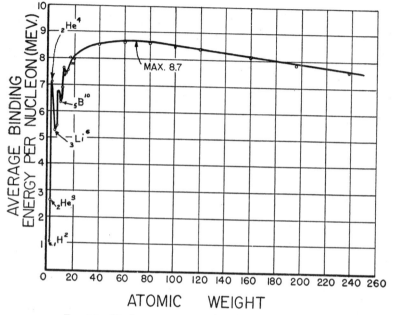

Fig. 1.3.   Binding energy per nucleon for various elements.

out the periodic table. For the light elements a periodicity is apparent. For elements whose atomic weights are greater than 20, the value varies only slightly from 8 Mev, reaching a maximum of 8.7 Mev at atomic weights around 70, and decreasing slowly to 7.6 Mev per nucleon for the heaviest elements. The stability of an element is directly related to its binding energy.

Since the binding energy per particle is approximately constant, the total binding energy of an isotope is approximately proportional to its total number of nucleons A. This may be regarded as evidence for the nature of the forces that act between particles within a nucleus. Since the neutrons and protons are either neutral or positively charged, Coulombian forces could only be repulsive in nature and yield a negative binding energy. Gravitational forces can play only a minute role in the binding. If a distance between centers of 10^{-13} centimeter be assumed and the mass of neutron and proton be each taken as 1.66×10^{-24} gram, then this binding energy per pair due to Newtonian gravitation is only about 10^{-30} electron volt. It is apparent that a short-range attractive force must exist between nucleons regardless of their electric charge. Since the binding energy in light nuclei exhibits maxima for $A = 4, 8$, and 12 nucleons, the combination of two neutrons and two protons must form a very stable group. Each nucleon must effectively interact only with its immediate neighbors and for this group of four a condition of saturation exists. Heavy nuclei have sometimes been regarded as built up of such subgroups. Had the interaction forces been of a classical nature, the total binding energy would have varied directly as A^2, and the binding energy per nucleon should have increased linearly with A instead of being constant. Such shortrange nongravitational nonelectric forces known as "exchange" forces have been treated with some success in modern theory.

1.4. Packing Fraction. The deviation in the atomic masses of the various isotopes from integral numbers on the "physical" scale was first pointed out by Aston. He defined a quantity for a particular isotope known as the "packing fraction" (P.F.) as follows:

$$\text{P.F.} = \frac{A' - A}{A} \times 10^4 \qquad (1.1)$$

where A' is the true "physical" isotopic mass and A is the number of nucleons in the isotope. For oxygen 16, $(A' - A)$ is zero and hence also the packing fraction.

For other elements the P.F. may be positive or negative; thus for helium 4, nickel 58, and uranium 238 the values are +9.68,

−8.36, and +5.26, respectively. These values for a number of isotopes throughout the periodic table are shown graphically in Figure 1.4. The periodicity observed in the binding-energy curve for light nuclei is apparent here in an inverted position. A close relationship exists between the binding energy (B.E.) per nucleon and the packing fraction (P.F.) for any nucleus. By inserting the numerical atomic masses for the neutron M_n

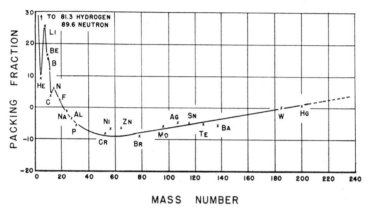

MASS NUMBER

FIG. 1.4. Packing fractions for the elements.

and for the hydrogen atom M_h in the equation for the binding energy, it follows that

$$B.E. = \frac{ZM_h + NM_n - A'}{A}$$

$$= 0.008986 - 0.000841 \frac{Z}{A} - P.F. \times 10^{-4}$$

(1.2)

expressed in atomic mass units per nucleon, where Z is the atomic number, A is the total number of nucleons in the nucleus, and A' is the true atomic mass.

When a very heavy isotope such as plutonium 239 undergoes nuclear fission such that two lighter elements result, the total energy released per fission may be calculated by using either the relative packing fractions or the binding energies. For example, if one of the isotopes formed is iodine 135, it alone would contribute a gain in binding energy of about 0.8 Mev per nucleon or, in total, 108 Mev for the 135 nucleons. Similarly from the packing fraction curve, a change from $+4$ to about -4.5 occurs for each of the 135 nucleons of this isotope or a net change of about 0.1147 atomic mass units, or 108 Mev.

example

It is equally apparent from Figures 1.3 and 1.4 that if the intermediate elements could be synthesized from the very light isotopes then an enormous release of energy would result. Such a process is termed nuclear "fusion" as opposed to fission. Although it has long been thought to be of only academic interest, it has now been demonstrated to be possible.

1.5. Isotopes, Isobars, and Isotones. As previously stated, those nuclei which possess a common atomic number Z, but are different in mass, are termed *isotopes* of the element, there being one isotope or nuclide for each particular mass. For any particular element the isotopes are shown in Figure 1.2 as circles along a vertical line. If the total number of nucleons is the same in atoms of different atomic number, such nuclei are called *isobars*. In Figure 1.2 isobars are represented by lines of negative slope. Nulei which have the same number of neutrons, N, regardless of their charge Z, such as hydrogen 2 and helium 3, are called isotones. In those elements for which N or Z are equal to 20, 50, 82, or 126, called "magic" numbers, an unusually large number of isotones or isotopes are found to exist. It is probable that for these numbers there occurs in the nucleus something analogous to the closure of shells in the atoms of the noble gas elements.

1.6. Abundance and Properties of Uranium and Thorium. Because the subject of radioactivity owes its origin to uranium and thorium, and because of the very important role these elements are certain to play in the future world economy and world peace on account of nuclear fission, it is of interest to know something of their abundance and distribution. Uranium was first discovered in 1789 by Klaproth, and in 1841 the metal was first prepared by Peligot, by the reduction of uranous chloride (UCl_4). The metal has a specific gravity of 18.7, an atomic weight of 238.07, a melting point of 1150° C., and atomic number 92. Thorium was discovered by Berzelius in 1828. The metal has a specific gravity of 11.2, an atomic weight of 232.12, a melting point of 1845° C., and atomic number 90.

It has been estimated that uranium is present in the earth's crust up to about four parts in a million, while thorium is about three times as abundant. The most common natural form of uranium is pitchblende, which is really an oxide of uranium, $U(UO_4)_2$. This ore is usually found in pockets or veins in sedimentary rock. Carnotite is a yellow crystalline powder consisting of a vanadate with uranium, sometimes up to 50%. Thorium is often found associated with the rare earth elements. Monazite is a cerium phosphate, $CePO_4$, containing up to 10% thorium and about 1% uranium. Chalcolite, a green crystal, is a phosphate of copper and uranium. Orangite, thorite, and sodite are silicates rich in thorium. Thorianite is an oxide containing about 65% thorium and 10% uranium. Samarskite is a tantalate of rare earths, particularly yttrium, containing uranium and thorium.

These ores of uranium and thorium are widely distributed throughout the world and it would appear that no important nation is without a supply of this critical material. Under the incentive of government subsidies American production of ore has increased enormously, with a current annual output in excess of three million tons.

1.7. Discovery of Radioactivity. While studying the phosphorescence of various materials in 1896, Henri Becquerel [7] was led to the discovery of radioactivity. He noticed that from several uranium salts an invisible radiation was emitted, capable of traversing thin layers of opaque materials and affecting a

[7] H. Becquerel, *Compt. rend.*, **122**, 501, 689 (1896), et seq.

photographic plate. After a lapse of several months, during which time the uranium salts were kept in complete darkness with no apparent diminution in their ability to activate photographic emulsions, Becquerel concluded that the radiation was not phosphorescent, that is, it was not dependent upon any primary exciting radiation. It was also observed that the air close to the uranium salts was electrically conducting so that a charged electroscope could be discharged.

In 1898, G. C. Schmidt [8] and Mme. Curie [9] independently observed that similar radiations were emitted by compounds of thorium. Madame Curie noted further that cerium, niobium, and tantalum gave similar slight activities and that yellow phosphorus was very active, whereas red phosphorus was not. These mistaken conclusions were made because only the apparent ionizing property of the substances was observed, and humidity changes in the electroscope produced a similar effect.

Madame Curie noted that natural pitchblende $U(UO_4)_2$ was more active than pure uranium oxide and that natural chalcolite $(Cu + U)SO_4$ was more active than the same substance when prepared in the laboratory. She made a further careful check on the radioactivity from various compounds of uranium and thorium and found that the activity was proportional solely to the amounts of uranium or thorium present regardless of their state of chemical combination. Thus she decided that the radioactivity must be an atomic phenomenon. These observations led to a tireless search for the source of the increased activity in the natural ores. As a result it was found possible to isolate from the pitchblende a sulfide of bismuth having an activity 400 times greater than that from the same quantity of uranium. Pure bismuth sulfide was shown to be completely inactive. It was therefore assumed that a new element was present with the bismuth. This element was called polonium.[10]

[8] G. C. Schmidt, *Ann. Phys. Chem.*, **6.51**, 141 (1898).
[9] Mme. Sklodowska-Curie, *Compt. rend.*, **126**, 1101 (1898).
[10] P. Curie and M. Sklodowska-Curie, *Compt. rend.*, **127**, 175 (1898).

From another portion of the pitchblende residue it was found that an exceedingly active barium chloride could be fraction-ally precipitated. The atomic weight of barium in this sepa-ration was noted to be greater than the usual value. With this precipitate it was possible to darken a photographic plate in one-half minute, whereas several hours would have been re-quired by the same amount of any other compound of thorium or uranium. It was therefore assumed that another new ele-ment was present, associated with the barium. This element was called "radium," [11] from the Latin *radius*, meaning ray.

1.8. Properties of the Radiation. In announcing the discov-ery of X-rays in 1896, W. Roentgen reported quite completely and accurately on their properties. On the other hand, the prope;ties of the radiation emitted by uranium and its com-pounds were not at first correctly recognized. It was rightly concluded that this radiation rendered gases electrically con-ducting and that it would traverse layers of opaque materials. It was, however, incorrectly concluded that the radiation could be reflected by a mirror and refracted in a glass prism in the same way as ordinary light. It was further reported that when identical radiations were passed through two plates of tour-maline, in one case with axes parallel and in another case with axes at right angles, extinction occurred in the latter case and not in the former, just as for ordinary light. The radiation was also incorrectly reported to be strengthened when the uranium was exposed to an electric arc.

Becquerel was not alone in making observations which had later to be corrected. Two years later, G. Schmidt, in an-nouncing the discovery of the radiation from thorium, asserted that the radiation was refracted by a glass prism in the same manner as ordinary light.

In 1899, it was shown independently by Giesel [12] and by S. Meyer and von Schweidler [13] that the radiation could in part

[11] P. Curie, Mme. P. Curie, and G. Bémont, *Compt. rend.*, **127**, 1215 (1898).
[12] F. O. Giesel, *Ann. Phys. Chem.*, **69**, 834 (1899).
[13] S. Meyer and E. von Schweidler, *Phys Z.*, **1**, 90 (1899).

be deflected and resolved by the application of a strong perpendicular magnetic field.   P. Villard showed that the portion
of the radiation not deflected by the magnetic field would in
part traverse thick layers of matter.[14] The deflected part of
the radiation behaved like electrons and was termed *beta radiation.* The entire remaining undeflected part was at first termed

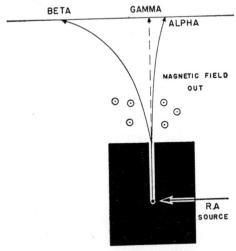

F<small>IG</small>. 1.5.   Resolution of the radiation from a radium source.

alpha radiation. In 1903, Rutherford showed that if the magnetic field was sufficiently strong the alpha radiation also could
be deflected, behaving as if positively charged.[15]   R. Strutt
found that a component of the radiation was highly penetrating
and was undeflected even in the strongest electric or magnetic
fields.[16] This component was termed *gamma radiation* and was
believed to be similar in nature to X-rays.

The resolution of these three radiations emanating from a
specimen of radium placed at the bottom of a small drill hole
in a lead block is shown in Figure 1.5.   In this figure the mag-

[14] P. Villard, *Compt. rend.*, **130**, 1178 (1900).
[15] E. Rutherford, *Phil. Mag.*, **5**, 177 (1903).
[16] R. J. Strutt, *Proc. Roy. Soc.*, **72**, 208 (1903).

netic field is directed out of the paper, and the beta particles, being negatively charged and of small mass, are strongly deflected to the left. The alpha rays were ultimately shown to consist of the nuclei of helium atoms stripped of their outer electrons and hence positively charged. The undeviated beam is electromagnetic radiation of extremely short wavelength. Substances that emit any of these radiations are said to be "radioactive," and the science dealing with all phases of the phenomenon is termed "radioactivity."

In summarizing, the radiations from a fairly strong sample of radium may:

a. Render gases conducting, as shown by the ability to discharge a charged electroscope,

b. Cause materials to fluoresce, particularly those commonly used with X-rays, such as platino-barium cyanide, zinc sulfide, and calcium tungstate,

c. Affect photographic plates, as does ordinary light,

d. Traverse material layers, opaque to ordinary light,

e. Develop heat continuously in any matter absorbing the radiation,

f. Produce helium in the containing tube in an amount increasing directly with the time,

g. Develop helium outside the gas-tight container, if the walls are very thin.

h. Develop another heavy gas, radon, within the sealed container in amounts proportional to the time. This gas when isolated is also found to emit radiation and ultimately vanish, leaving a leadlike deposit, and

i. Kill any living organism on exposure, if intensity is sufficient.

1.9. Atomic Disintegration. Until 1902, studies had been confined to the properties of the radiation and to the discovery of new sources. It was, however, generally thought that the radiation was an invisible fluorescence due to some unidentified primary excitation. It was subsequently noted that any substance, kept in the proximity of a radioactive body for some time, became radioactive. This induced radioactivity could be modified by subjecting the material to heating or by placing it in a vacuum. In 1903, Rutherford and Soddy demonstrated that the induced radioactivity was really due to a gas arising in the original radioactive body as a consequence of its radioactivity and diffusing away into its surroundings. On passing the gas through tubes immersed in liquid air this emanation from thorium condensed at a temperature of $-120°$ C., and the corresponding emanation from radium at $-150°$ C.

It became increasingly clear as numerous natural radioactive bodies were isolated that certain genetic relationships existed between them. Thus for the first time evidence was at hand that the atoms of an element, which from their very name were regarded as indivisible, must, in the radioactive process, disintegrate. Every uranium atom could in succession eject several light particles, each time leaving a new residual atom.

1.10. The Fundamental Particles. If by "fundamental particle" is meant an elementary unit that under no condition can be transformed into one or more other particles, then no fundamental particle exists. At various times it has seemed certain that such entities as protons and electrons might be so regarded. On further investigation it must be concluded that within a nucleus or on suitable collision, protons transform into other particles, and electrons form from and convert into photons. There are certain elementary particles, however, which, although transmutable among themselves, seem to serve as the building units for more complicated matter.

These particles are as follows:

a. Electrons. Electrons are particles whose electric charge is indivisible and of value -4.8021×10^{-10} electrostatic unit. At small velocities they possess a mass which expressed in atomic mass units is 0.00054862 and in grams is 9.19×10^{-28}. The term "electron," with the interpretation now accepted, was first used by Stoney.[17] Credit for proof of the existence of these particles is usually given to J. J. Thomson.[18] Streams of the particles in motion in a discharge tube are called cathode rays. When ejected from a radioactive body they are termed beta rays. As the velocity (v) of the electrons increases so as to approach the velocity of light (c), 3×10^{10} centimeter per second, the mass (m) of the electrons increases above their mass (m_0) at slow velocities, according to the equation

$$m = \frac{m_0}{\sqrt{1 - \left(\dfrac{v}{c}\right)^2}} \tag{1.3}$$

This change in mass with velocity was first experimentally demonstrated by W. Kaufmann in 1902.[19]

b. Protons. Protons are the positively charged nuclei of hydrogen atoms that have been stripped of their orbital electrons. Since each complete hydrogen atom is electrically neutral and possesses a single orbital negative electron, then the electric charge of the nucleus is positive and equal in magnitude to the electron. Protons were first observed as positive "canal" rays in a discharge tube, in 1886 by Goldstein.[20] Twelve years later, W. Wien [21] determined the ratio of their charge e to their mass m. The value of e/m, although highly inaccurate, was found to be the same regardless of the kind of gas in the discharge tube and was very small compared to the value of e/m found by J. J. Thomson for electrons. In a more accurate study of the canal rays, Thomson [22] noted that he sometimes observed a value of the order of 10,000 electromagnetic units per gram which was considerably larger than the value reported by Wien. At other times he found a value only half as large and, with

[17] G. J. Stoney, *Sci. Trans. Roy. Soc.*, Dublin, **4**, 563 (1891).
[18] J. J. Thomson, *Phil. Mag.*, **44**, 293 (1897).
[19] W. Kaufmann, *Gott. Nach. Math-phys.*, **5**, 219, 296 (1902).
[20] E. Goldstein, *Berlin. Ber.*, **39**, 691 (1886).
[21] W. Wien, *Berlin. Phys. Gesell. Verh.*, **16**, 165 (1897); **17**, 10 (1898); *Wied. Annal.*, **65**, 440 (1898).
[22] J. J. Thomson, *Phil. Mag.* VI, **13**, 561 (1907).

helium gas in the tube, a value only one fourth as large. This was interpreted as meaning that in the stream of canal particles both atomic and molecular hydrogen ions were present. The molecule of double mass had lost only one electron. Similarly the helium atom had lost only one electron.

c. Neutrons. Neutrons are particles whose mass is only slightly greater than that of the hydrogen atom and whose electric charge is zero. Their discovery is attributed to Chadwick [23] in 1932, although it might be claimed that his disclosure was possible only because of the investigations of W. Bothe and H. Becker [24] and of I. Curie-Joliot [25] and F. Joliot.[26] These experiments will be described later. The neutron has no orbital electrons and, being uncharged, it is influenced by other atoms only at very close range. Consequently it will traverse thick layers of heavy elements with little loss in energy. This lack of charge also makes it difficult to detect the neutron by any direct method. The atomic mass of the neutron is 1.008986, which is equivalent to 1.67454×10^{-24} gram.

d. Positrons. Positrons are particles exactly like electrons in mass and magnitude of electric charge but they differ in that their charge is positive in sign. In making cosmic-ray studies in 1932 with a vertical Wilson cloud chamber provided with a strong magnetic field, C. D. Anderson [27] noticed certain tracks whose curvature was in a direction opposite to that of the usual electrons. This could conceivably occur by the reflection of negative electrons (see Figure 6.6*A*). Excluding this possibility, the conclusion could be drawn that the paths were those of positively charged particles. They were at first thought to be protons but on further investigation Anderson announced [28] them to be positive electrons or "positrons." In nuclear reactions, to be described later, these particles are very commonly

[23] J. Chadwick, *Nature*, **129**, 312 (1932).
[24] W. Bothe and H. Becker, *Z. Physik*, **66**, 289 (1930).
[25] I. Curie-Joliot, *Compt. rend.*, **193**, 1412 (1931).
[26] F. Joliot, *Compt. rend.*, **193**, 1415 (1931).
[27] R. A. Millikan and C. D. Anderson, *Phys. Rev.*, **40**, 325 (1932).
[28] C. D. Anderson, *Phys. Rev.*, **43**, 491 (1933).

emitted. Their life span is short, lasting only during their transit which is usually less than a microsecond. In their absorption in matter they behave [29] quantitatively like negative electrons.

e. Neutrinos. Studies of the energy distribution of the beta radiation emitted by a radioactive substance showed it to be continuous. This result presented certain fundamental difficulties. Most evidence indicated the existence of definite energy states within the nucleus; hence any emission should have involved definite discrete energies, instead of a continuous distribution. The interpretation seemed to offer only two alternatives. These were, namely, to relinquish the principle of "conservation of energy" as applied to intranuclear processes or to postulate the existence of a nondetectable, yet energetic, particle which is emitted with each beta particle, so that the sum of the two energies is a constant. This particle is assumed to have a rest mass much smaller than the electron. It is usually regarded as zero, and hence it travels with essentially the speed of light. Many experiments of an indirect nature have attempted to prove the existence of the neutrino.

By observing [30] the paths of the recoiling heavy chlorine nuclei in a cloud chamber containing radioactive Cl, in gaseous form, their momenta could be determined. This was found in most cases not to be equal and opposite to the momentum of the electron. The conclusion in this case and in many similar experiments favored the existence of the neutrino. More elaborate experiments to identify the neutrino by capturing it in flight will be described later in Chapter 6.

f. Mesons. In 1935, H. Yukawa [31] presented a theoretical discussion of the short-range forces acting between a neutron and a proton in the nucleus. In accounting for beta disintegration he was led to a prediction of the existence of quanta of mass about one tenth that of the proton.

[29] B. R. Curtis, *Phys. Rev.*, **53**, 986 (1938).
[30] H. R. Crane and J. Halpern, *Phys. Rev.*, **53**, 789 (1938).
[31] H. Yukawa, *Proc. Phys. Math. Soc. Japan*, **17** 48 (1935).

In 1936, Anderson and Neddermeyer observed [32] among their many cloud chamber tracks several traces of particles whose penetrating powers were much greater than would have been indicated by their radii of curvature, had they been electrons. Many subsequent investigations have revealed a great complexity in the characteristics of these particles. They differ as to mass, electric charge, and mode of decay. The lightest has a rest mass that is 206.6 times that of the electron, whereas the heaviest is about 2400 times as large. These are described in detail in Chapter 10.

g. Photons. Electromagnetic radiation in many ways displays a corpuscular nature. In 1905, Einstein proposed [33] the now famous photoelectric equation

$$hv = \tfrac{1}{2}mv^2 + P \tag{1.4}$$

The product of the Planck constant h and the frequency v represents the energy of the incident photon, and $\tfrac{1}{2}mv^2$ is the kinetic energy of the escaping electron which required an energy P to release it from the surface. Since at impact the momentum as well as the energy must be conserved, the incident photon must have possessed both energy and mass and hence momentum. Einstein later formulated this postulate as: "Every quantity of energy of any form whatever represents a mass which is equal to this same energy divided by C^2, where C is the velocity of light, and every quantity of energy in motion represents momentum."

It was seven years later before this relationship was experimentally verified.[34] In nuclear reactions the photons or gamma rays may possess very large energies. On occasion they are found in their passage through matter to disappear entirely. On their death they give rise to an electron pair, that is, both

[32] C. D. Anderson and S. Neddermeyer, *Phys. Rev.,* **50,** 263 (1936).
[33] A. Einstein, *Ann. Physik,* **17,** 132 (1905).
[34] K. T. Compton, *Phil. Mag.,* **23,** 579 (1912); A. L. Hughes, *Phil. Trans. Roy. Soc.,* **212,** 205 (1912); R. A. Millikan and J. R. Wright, *Phys. Rev.,* **34,** 68 (1912).

a positive and a negative electron.   It is therefore reasonable to include photons as fundamental particles.

h. The Antiproton.   It had long been suspected that there should exist in nature a particle of protonic mass, but with negative charge.   Positive evidence [35] for the reality of this particle has finally been reported in the studies of the disintegration products arising from the bombardment of a Cu target by 6.2 Bev protons in the Berkeley bevatron.   To produce a proton-antiproton pair with their rest mass sum of 3660 times that of the electron, should require a minimum energy of 1.866 Bev.   However, to satisfy both the conservation of momentum and energy, at impact, it follows that the incident proton energy expected to be necessary is greater than 5.4 Bev.   In practice it may be much less due to particle motion within the nucleus as will be described later.

i. The Antineutron.   The last of the many fundamental particles needed to give complete symmetry to the array found in the universe, namely, the antineutron, has now been detected.[36]   On bombarding a beryllium target with the 6.2 Bev beam of protons in the bevatron, many disintegration products arise.   By magnetically separating the resultant particles and examining the uncharged beam, occasional extraordinarily large bursts of energy ($\sim$2 Bev) occur.   The interpretation of this as evidence for the existence of the antineutron is given later under "Neutrons."

1.11. The Decay Constant and Half-life.   In 1900, from a solution of uranium, Crookes [37] precipitated a carbonate which, although free from uranium, possessed an activity many times as great.   At the same time the residual uranium solution lost its ability to affect a photographic plate.   A similar separation was carried out on thorium by Rutherford and Soddy.[38]   Be-

---

[35] O. Chamberlain, E. Segré, C. Wiegand, and T. Ypsilantis, *Phys. Rev.*, **100**, 947 (1955).

[36] B. Cork, G. Lambertson, O. Piccioni, and W. Wentzel, *Phys. Rev.*, **104**, 1193 (1956).

[37] W. Crookes, *Proc. Roy. Soc.*, **66**, 409 (1900).

[38] E. Rutherford and F. Soddy, *Phil. Mag.*, **5**, 445, 574 (1903).

cause of their unknown character, the active substances thus separated were called uranium X and thorium X, respectively. The strong initial activity of these separated substances was found to decrease rapidly, while at the same time the parent substances appeared to regain their original activity. These changes with time, as noted by Rutherford for both uranium

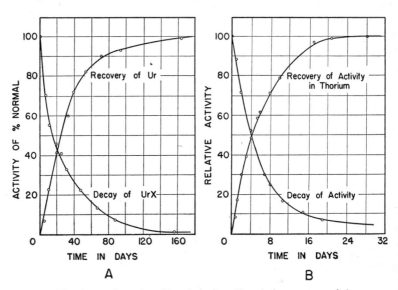

FIG. 1.6. The decay of uranium X and thorium X and the recovery of the parent materials.

and thorium, are shown in Figure 1.6. The form of the decay curves suggested a logarithmic decrease of the number of active particles. This follows the assumption that the number of particles ΔN disintegrated in a time Δt, is proportional to the total number of active particles N and the time Δt and to a probability constant λ defined by the equation

$$\Delta N = -\lambda N \Delta t \qquad (1.5)$$

It is evident that λ may then be defined as the relative number of particles disintegrating per second, and has the dimensions of reciprocal seconds. By assuming an initial number N_0 at $t = 0$, then on integration of equation 1.5 it follows that the number N of particles remaining after the lapse of time t is

$$N = N_0 e^{-\lambda t} \tag{1.6}$$

Now if $\dfrac{N}{N_0}$ be set equal to $\frac{1}{2}$, then on taking logarithms it follows that

$$\log_e 2 = \lambda t = 0.693 \tag{1.7}$$

so that the half-life, $T_{\frac{1}{2}} = \dfrac{0.693}{\lambda}$ second. This quantity is very generally used in describing radioactive emitters. From equation 1.6 it follows that if the intensity of any radioactive source of single-valued half-life be plotted logarithmically against the time, then a straight line of negative slope results, as shown in Figure 1.7. If a radioactive source emits radiations decaying according to several different half-lives, then the analysis may be carried out from such a semilogarithmic plot by subtracting in succession the straight-line plot for the longest half-life remaining. An example of this kind is shown in Figure 1.8, representing a certain radioactive indium consisting of three activities having half-lives of 54 minutes, 72 seconds, and 13 seconds. On subtracting the straight line representing the 54-minute activity, a residual curve having a straight end segment results. This represents the 72-second activity, and after its subtraction a single straight line remains for the 13-second activity.

The activity along the recovery curve in Figure 1.6 is more complicated. Starting with N_U uranium atoms with a disintegration constant λ_U, then the loss per second is

$$\frac{dN_U}{dt} = -\lambda_U N_U \tag{1.8}$$

This loss of uranium atoms represents a corresponding gain in

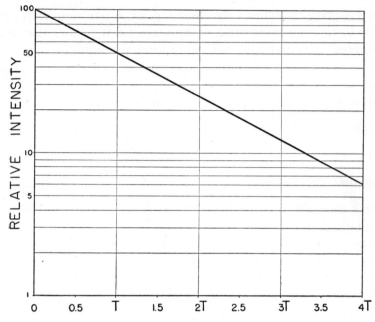

FIG. 1.7.   The logarithmic decay of radioactive source.

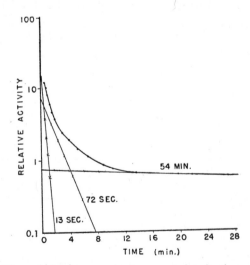

FIG. 1.8.   The analysis of a composite decay curve into its three components.

the daughter substance A, which in turn loses a number $\lambda_A N_A$ per second so that the net change per second in A is

$$\frac{dN_A}{dt} = +\lambda_U N_U - \lambda_A N_A \tag{1.9}$$

A solution of equations 1.8 and 1.9 gives for the number N_A at any time t

$$N_A = \frac{\lambda_U N_U}{\lambda_A - \lambda_U} [e^{-\lambda_U t} - e^{-\lambda_A t}] \tag{1.10}$$

The disintegration constant λ_U is very small compared to λ_A and after a sufficiently long time t, $e^{-\lambda_A t}$ becomes equal to zero. Assuming that the change in N_U is negligible, then equation 1.10 may be transformed to read

$$\frac{N_A}{N_U} = \frac{\lambda_U}{\lambda_A} = \frac{T_{\frac{1}{2}}(A)}{T_{\frac{1}{2}}(U)} \tag{1.11}$$

This means that the daughter substance is in equilibrium with the parent and the numbers of particles of the two substances are in the same ratio as their half-lives. Much use will be made of this fact in later discussions.

The reciprocal of λ is the time required for the intensity to drop to $\frac{1}{e}$ or $\frac{1}{2.7}$ of its initial activity. This time may be shown to be the "mean life" for the initial particles.

During any interval of time dt, a number N of the initial particles N_0 will still exist, and a number dN will disintegrate, all having lived for the time t. Hence the total time lived by all initial N_0 particles may be found by integration. The "mean" life will be this total time lived, divided by N_0. Thus

$$\text{Mean life} = \frac{\text{total time}}{N_0}$$

$$= \frac{1}{N_0} \int_{t=0}^{t=\infty} t \, dN = \frac{\lambda N_0}{N_0} \int_{t=0}^{t=\infty} t e^{-\lambda t} \, dt = \frac{1}{\lambda} \overset{*}{} \tag{1.12}$$

* Note: $\int x e^{ax} \, dx = \frac{e^{ax}}{a^2}(ax-1)$.

Hence the mean life of any group of particles is 1.44 times the half-life. Its relationship to the half-life for any emitter is shown in Figure 1.9.

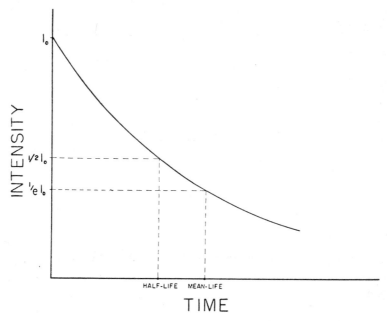

FIG. 1.9. Showing relation between half-life and mean-life.

1.12. The Uranium-radium Family. Following the discovery of polonium and of radium in 1898 and the notion of atomic disintegration, numerous other radioactive bodies were isolated and identified. Each substance was characterized by a particular half-life and the emission of a particular type of radiation, with definite energy limitations. Among these may be mentioned the discovery of actinium in 1900 by Debierne;[39] of radiolead by Hofmann in 1904;[40] and of ionium, the direct parent of radium, by Boltwood in 1907.[41]

[39] A. Debierne, *Compt. rend.*, **130**, 906 (1900).
[40] K. Hofmann, L. Gonder, and V. Wolf, *Ann. Physik*, **15**, 615 (1904).
[41] B. B. Boltwood, *Nature*, **76**, 544 (1907).

Uranium exists in nature in the form of three semistable isotopes of mass 234, 235, and 238, and relative abundance 0.006%, 0.71%, and 99.28%, respectively. Each emission of an alpha particle with its mass 4 and positive charge of two units thus lowers the mass and in reducing the charge by two units leaves a new residual element standing two below that of the parent in the periodic table. The emission of a beta particle with its negative charge and negligible mass is thus equivalent to adding a positive electronic charge to the nucleus. This results in a new element, standing one space higher in the periodic table. Elements of different atomic number are usually separable chemically. In this way continued investigations revealed the fact that the atom of uranium of mass 238 and atomic number 92 is the parent of an entire series of elements of descending atomic weights. In its continued disintegration eight alpha particles and six beta particles are emitted. The final residual atom is an isotope of lead of atomic weight 206 and atomic number 82.

Many of the intermediate products, at their discovery, were given names which, although significant at that time, have now become misleading and do not express the nature of the isotopes they represent. For example, uranium X_1 is not an isotope of uranium but rather of thorium; uranium Z and uranium X_2 are protactinium; and radium C and radium E are isotopes of bismuth. This genetic development from the uranium isotope of mass 238, including the half-lives of the intermediate radioactive isotopes, is shown in Figure 1.10. In addition, the neutron-induced isotope leading to the element plutonium of atomic number 94 is included.

The half-life of uranium 238 is about 4.5×10^9 years, which means that the disintegration constant λ which is $\dfrac{0.693}{T_{1/2}}$ has the value 4.9×10^{-18} per second. Hence a gram of pure uranium 238, which contains 2.53×10^{21} atoms, will give rise to $2.53 \times 10^{21} \times 4.9 \times 10^{-18}$ or about 12,400 disintegrations per second. The half-life of radium, whose mass is 226 and atomic number 86, is now known to be about 1620 years but until recently it was believed to be 1590 years. Hence the disintegration constant has been assumed to be 1.385×10^{-11} per second, and the 2.665×10^{21} atoms in one gram will give rise

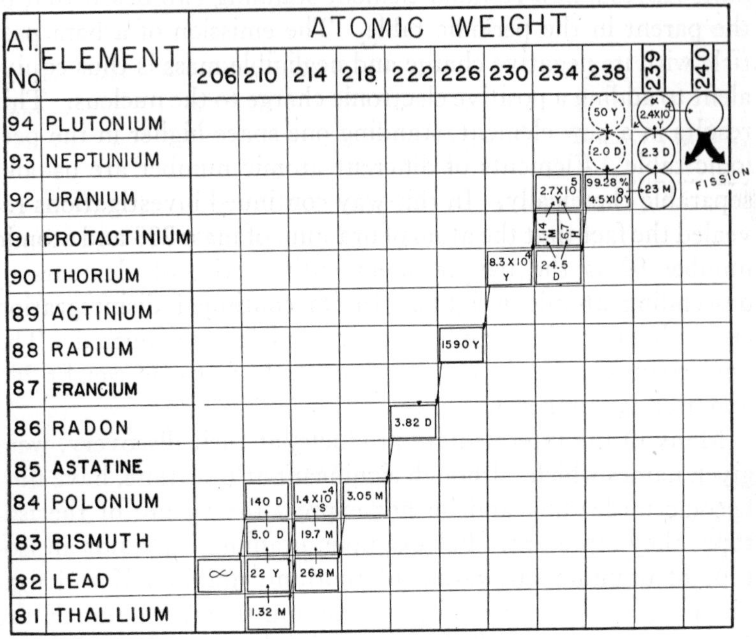

FIG. 1.10.   The uranium-radium family.

to 37.0×10^9 disintegrations every second. This number is important in current definitions of the curie, a unit used to express the strength of radioactive sources.

1.13. The Uranium-actinium Family. Another series of radioactive elements genetically related among themselves has been shown to be derived from the less abundant uranium isotope of mass 235. This parent isotope has a half-life of 7.1×10^8 years and emits in succession seven alpha particles and four beta particles. The final residual atom is an isotope of lead of mass 207. The nature of the intermediate products is quite similar to the atoms in the parallel radium series. For example, the element of atomic number 86 is a gas called actinon, much like the corresponding element in the radium series, radon. This sequence of elements is shown schematically in Figure 1.11.

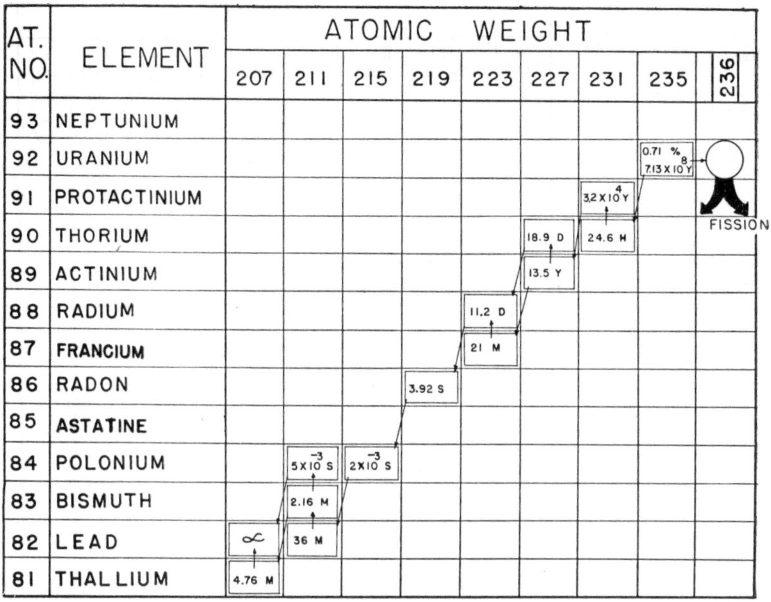

AT. NO.	ELEMENT	ATOMIC WEIGHT								
		207	211	215	219	223	227	231	235	236
93	NEPTUNIUM									
92	URANIUM								0.71 % 7.13 X 10^8 Y	◯
91	PROTACTINIUM							3.2 X 10^4 Y		FISSION
90	THORIUM						18.9 D	24.6 H		
89	ACTINIUM						13.5 Y			
88	RADIUM					11.2 D				
87	FRANCIUM					21 M				
86	RADON				3.92 S					
85	ASTATINE									
84	POLONIUM		5X10^{-3} S	2X10^{-3} S						
83	BISMUTH		2.16 M							
82	LEAD	∝	36 M							
81	THALLIUM	4.76 M								

FIG. 1.11.   The uranium-actinium family of radioactive atoms.

1.14. The Thorium Family. Another independent radioactive series has been identified, based upon the single natural isotope of thorium, whose mass is 232 and atomic number, 90. After the successive emission of six alpha particles and four beta particles the emitting atom becomes an isotope of lead, of mass 208. The element of atomic number 86 in this series is also a gas, called thoron. The thorium family, including the half-lives of the intermediate elements, is shown schematically in Figure 1.12. Thorium itself has a half-life of 1.389×10^{10} years.

Many of the intermediate products in all three families emit gamma rays in addition to the alpha or beta particles. The gamma radiation from thorium (C + C′) has been extensively used where a high energy source was desired. Its radiation is concentrated largely in a single-emission energy of 2.62 Mev.

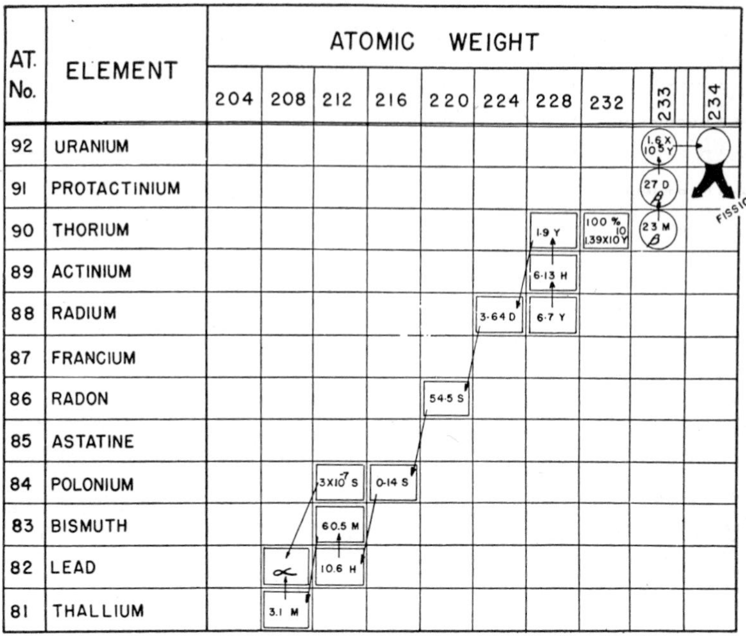

AT. No.	ELEMENT	ATOMIC WEIGHT									
		204	208	212	216	220	224	228	232	233	234
92	URANIUM									1.6×10^5 Y	(fission)
91	PROTACTINIUM									27 D	
90	THORIUM							1.9 Y	100% 1.39×10^{10} Y	23 M	
89	ACTINIUM							6-13 H			
88	RADIUM						3·64 D	6·7 Y			
87	FRANCIUM										
86	RADON					54·5 S					
85	ASTATINE										
84	POLONIUM			3×10^7 S	0·14 S						
83	BISMUTH			60.5 M							
82	LEAD		∝	10.6 H							
81	THALLIUM		3.1 M								

FIG. 1.12.   The thorium family of radioactive elements.

1.15. The Neptunium Family. An observation of the masses of the members of the three radioactive families, already described, reveals the fact that in each family the atomic masses are characterized by numbers representable by the term $(4N + a)$. Thus in the uranium-radium family, N may be any integral value from 51 up to 60, and a has the value *two* so that the series is sometimes called the $(4N + 2)$ series. In a similar manner the actinium family constitutes a $(4N + 3)$ series, and the thorium family is represented by $(4N + 0)$ or $4N$. The absence of a $(4N + 1)$ series seemed to be an oversight of nature.

With the production of uranium 233, a complete new radio-active family has been found [42] which satisfies the $(4N + 1)$ relationship. This series is called the neptunium family and is shown in Figure 1.13. It is noteworthy that, unlike the other

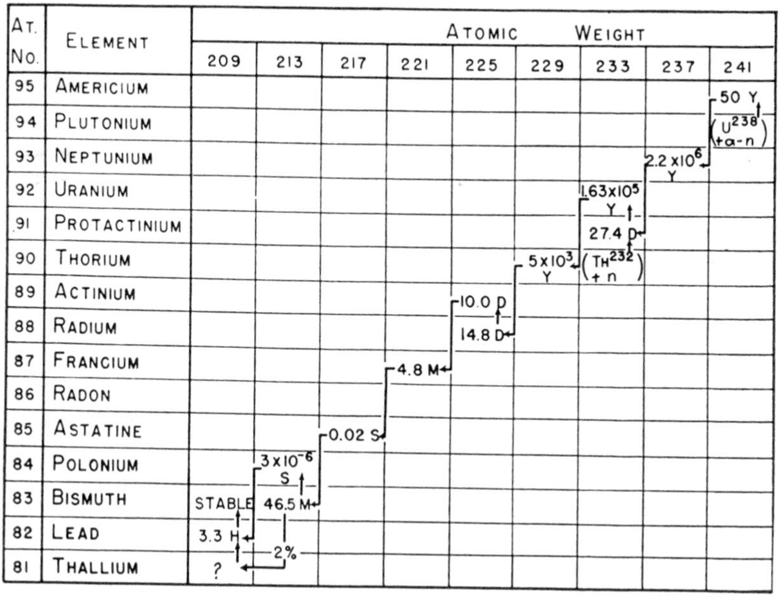

At. No.	Element	Atomic Weight								
		209	213	217	221	225	229	233	237	241
95	Americium									⌐50 Y
94	Plutonium									(U238 +a-n)
93	Neptunium								2.2x10⁶ Y	
92	Uranium							1.63x10⁵ Y		
91	Protactinium							27.4 D		
90	Thorium						5x10³ Y	(Th232 +n)		
89	Actinium					10.0 D				
88	Radium					14.8 D				
87	Francium				4.8 M					
86	Radon									
85	Astatine			0.02 S						
84	Polonium		3x10⁻⁶ S							
83	Bismuth	STABLE	46.5 M							
82	Lead	3.3 H								
81	Thallium	?	2%							

Fig. 1.13. The neptunium or $(4N + 1)$ series.

families which terminate in lead, the final product is an isotope of bismuth of mass 209. It also differs in another respect in that there is no radon or gaseous member in the family.

1.16. The Age of the Earth and Radioactivity. The development of helium as a product formed in the aging of uranium, offers a method of estimating the age of the uranium. Assumptions must be made regarding the retention of the helium

[42] F. Hagemann, L. Katzin, M. Studier, A. Gioret, and G. Seaborg, *Phys. Rev.*, **72**, 252 (1947); A. English, T. Cranshaw, P. Demers, J. Harvey, E. Hincks, J. Jelley, and A. May, *Phys. Rev.*, **72**, 253 (1947).

formed and the fact that no other source of helium is present. It is usually assumed that helium will be retained in rock when the temperature has fallen below about 1000° C. Thus, knowing the about of helium recovered for each gram of uranium present, it is possible to compute a minimum value for the time elapsed since helium began to be formed. The decay constant for uranium 238 as now observed is 4.9×10^{-18} per second. The possibility exists that originally other isotopes of uranium with their greater disintegration constants were relatively more abundant. Assuming, however, that the isotope 238 was always preponderant, then the half-life of 4.5×10^9 years can be used. Since each disintegrating atom yields eight alpha particles and in one half-life, half of the particles disintegrate, it follows that an original gram of uranium will in one half-life produce $\frac{16}{238}$ or 0.0674 gram of helium. This quantity would represent 376 cubic centimeters under standard conditions of pressure and temperature. It is apparent that if retained in pockets in the ore to this extent it will be under high pressure and hence apt to escape. For this and other reasons, ages computed by the helium method are regarded as too low. The transformation of uranium during one half-life may be represented as

$$1 \text{ gram uranium} \rightarrow 4500 \text{ million years} \rightarrow \begin{cases} 0.5 \text{ gram uranium} \\ 0.0674 \text{ gram helium} \\ 0.4326 \text{ gram lead } 206 \end{cases}$$

A knowledge of the excess Pb^{206} over that in nonradiogenic lead could allow the age determination of a mineral. Extensive investigations of ores from various terrestrial sources have been carried out. The results of such studies seemed to indicate for the earth's crust a maximum age of about 2800 million years. Similar results were obtained in minerals having an excess of lead 208, derived from the decay of thorium.

It is now believed that this estimate of the age of the earth's crust is too low. Rubidium 87 whose abundance in normal rubidium is 27.8% is unstable and decays by beta emission to strontium 87. This isotope in normal strontium has an abundance of 7.02%. By carefully noting the relative abundance of strontium 87 in rocks that contain rubidium, as well as the absolute amount of Rb, then $\left(\dfrac{Sr^{87}}{\text{all Sr}} - 0.0702 \right) \times 100$ yields the percentage of the Sr due to Rb decay. The half-life of Rb 87 had been assumed to be 6×10^{10} years and using that value the results obtained did not agree with the lead or helium determinations. More recent measurements [43] indicate that the half-life of Rb 87 is 5×10^{10} years and with this value fair agreement is obtained with the results of the U-Pb technique. This method should have some advantage in that the Sr is less apt to be lost from the parent rock. While the rock ages can be correlated with their geologic formation, an extrapolation indicates that the age of the earth's crust is of the order of 4500 million years. Such ages have been observed directly for meteoric rock.

1.17. The Measurement of Radioactivity. (a) *The Curie.* It is apparent that with the present extensive use of radioactive materials some agreement must be made regarding the units used in measuring the activity. Radium itself is usually used as a chloride, and the active content can be expressed in grams. Since a radium sample will soon generate products with which it is in equilibrium, then these separated products, although very minute in mass, will have a radioactivity comparable with that of the parent radium. Consequently a unit, now known as the "curie," has been recognized; as originally defined it was the amount of radon in equilibrium with one gram of radium. From their comparative half-lives, namely 1620 years and 3.82 days, this amount of radon would weigh only 6.35 millionths of a gram, and under standard conditions of pressure and temperature would occupy only 0.640 cubic millimeter. On pump-

[43] L. Aldrich, G. Wetherill, G. Davis, and G. Tilton, *Bull. Amer. Phys. Soc. Series III*, **1**, 31 (1956).

ing off this gas an additional amount will re-form according to a growth curve as shown in Figure 1.6.

When the radon is in equilibrium with the parent radium, each would have the same number of disintegrating atoms per second. It is now known that this number is about 36.8×10^9, but because of the earlier error in the half-life of radium the value 37×10^9 is accepted and no attempt will be made here to introduce a revision. It has accordingly now become common practice to express the radioactivity of any specimen, regardless of the type of emission, in terms of the number of disintegrating atoms per second in the source. Thus a millicurie of radiophosphorus, which emits no gamma radiation whatever, is that quantity of radioactive material in which 37 million particles are disintegrating per second. Certain anomalies arise from such a definition. It often happens that a single disintegrating atom in quick succession emits more than one particle or gamma ray. Thus each atom of radiocobalt of mass 60 emits two strong gamma rays in its disintegration. Since any gamma ray usually has sufficient energy to traverse completely the detector, it is evident that the ionizing effect of a millicurie of radiocobalt would be twice as large as the ionization produced by a similar source of another isotope in which only a single gamma ray is emitted per disintegration.

(*b*) *The Roentgen or "r" Unit.* Gamma radiation may be detected by the same technique as that employed in measuring X-rays. A unit known as the "r" unit, after W. Roentgen, the discoverer of X-rays, has long been recognized in X-ray practice. This is defined as the amount of radiation that will, on passing through pure air under standard conditions, produce one electrostatic unit of ions, of one sign, per cubic centimeter. It is evident that this is no measure of the total energy of the radiation, but rather of its absorptivity. In fact, the lower the energy of the photons comprising the radiation, the greater would be the ionization per centimeter of path.

The ionization produced by a photon is accomplished by

tearing away and energizing electrons, from the neutral atoms of the traversed gas. At relatively low energies this is accomplished by two processes known respectively as the photoelectric effect and the Compton effect. On the average a photon produces only about 1.5 ion pairs per centimeter of path in normal air, compared with about 50 pairs per centimeter for beta particles and 30,000 pairs per centimeter for alpha particles. In r units, a gram of radium supplies at a distance of 1 centimeter an ionization equivalent to 480 r per second. The gamma radiation alone amounts to about 2.4 r per second. One of the most direct methods for measuring the ionization produced, and hence the number of r units, is to allow the radiation to pass through the gas between the oppositely charged plates of a condenser, usually cylindrical in form. The fall in potential times the electrical capacity in electrostatic units divided by the volume gives the "r" value.

(*c*) *Rad*. Although only about 14 electron volts are necessary to produce an ion pair in air, in practice a photon seems to lose about 35 ev for every pair formed. The excess work appears in the kinetic energy of the particles. To induce a charge of 1 ESU in 1 cm^3 of normal air, means the production of 2.08×10^9 ion pairs or an energy expenditure of 72.8×10^9 ev, which is equivalent to 0.116 erg/cm^3. Since there are 770 cm^3 of normal air in 1 gm, then the energy absorbed per roentgen unit is about 90 ergs per gram. At the Seventh International Congress of Radiology (1953), a new unit of absorbed dose called the Rad was adopted. It was defined as the dosage that will impart 100 ergs to each gram of matter through which the radiation passes.

QUESTIONS AND PROBLEMS *Due, Sept. 29*

1. The atomic weight of lead (chem.) as found in galena is 207.216 and from Great Bear Lake ore it has an atomic weight of 206.083. Assuming only the uranium-radium family to be responsible, what percentage of the lead is derived from uranium? If 5 gm of lead are recovered from a certain specimen, how much helium should be in the same source? In this same specimen how many gm of uranium would you expect if the age of the rock is 2000×10^6 years?

Answer: 93.5%, 4.675 gm lead, 0.726 gm helium, 15 gm uranium.

2. A certain hospital has 4 gm of radium valued at $160,000. Radon is pumped off every 48 hrs. How many millicuries are obtained each time? What should be the charge for a 10 millicurie seed of radon, allowing a service charge of $2.00 per seed, a 5% interest rate, and a satisfactory depletion charge?

Answer: 1216 millicuries, $2.365.

3. How many beta particles are emitted per second by the above-mentioned radium in equilibrium with its daughter products?

Answer: 59.36×10^{10} beta particles per sec.

4. How many neutrinos will pass in 1 sec through the body of a man which presents a normal area of 6 sq ft, at a distance of 1000 miles from the above radium?

Answer: 0.01017 per sec.

5. The packing fraction for plutonium 239 is $+4.0$, and for barium 142 and strontium 94 the values are -6.1 and -8.1, all in 10^{-4}. If a plutonium atom undergoes binary fission, producing the above two atoms, what additional particles are set free and how much mass disappears? What is the total release of energy in electron volts and in ergs per atom of plutonium?

Answer: 3 neutrons plus original, 0.2314 mass unit, 214 Mev, 3.43×10^{-4} erg.

6. Potassium is present in the human body to about 0.34% by weight. Express the mass and the number of curies of radioactive potassium 40, in a 180-lb person.

Answer: 0.0306 gm, 4.6×10^{20} atoms (K40); 0.21 microcuries.

7. In a certain feldspar concentrate, rubidium is present to the extent of 530 parts per million (ppm). The total Sr content of the same rock is 440 ppm and Sr 87 is present to 36 ppm. What are the parts per million of Rb 87 in this rock? What percentage of the total Sr is due to Rb decay? If the half-life of Rb 87 is $5 \times 10^{10}Y$, what age is indicated for the rock?

Answer: 147.3 ppm; $[\frac{36}{440} - 0.0702] \times 100 = 1.16\%$; $t = 2.5 \times 10^9 Y$.

CHAPTER 2

THE NUCLEUS

2.1. Early Theories. Evidence that the mass of the atom is largely concentrated in a minute volume, known as the nucleus, was first derived from emperiments dealing with the scattering of alpha particles by various metals (see Chapter 5). The nucleus actually occupies only about 10^{-13} per cent of the total atomic volume. Until 1932 it was generally assumed that the nucleus was made up of protons together with as many electrons as were needed to give the proper charge and mass.

Following the discovery of the neutron it became possible to envisage a more satisfactory method of construction. By combining Z protons with a sufficient number of neutrons N, any isotopic nuclear structure could be created. How such an assemblage of positively charged and uncharged particles could be held together so firmly in the compact nuclear volume is one of the major unanswered current physical problems. The attractive forces must be short range and act independently of charge. Some information regarding the nature of nuclear forces may be derived from experimental studies, particularly those having to do with scattering, such as proton-proton and proton-neutron interactions, at various energies.

2.2. Nuclear Spin. In the Bohr theory of atomic structure the orbital angular momentum of the electron was expressed as an integral multiple l of $\dfrac{h}{2\pi}$ $(\hbar)$ where h is the Planck constant 6.62517×10^{-27} erg seconds. In order to account for the quantum numbers found necessary in the classification of atomic energy levels, the electron was assumed to have a spin angular momentum of $\frac{1}{2}\hbar$. It has accordingly become common practice to say that it has a spin of one half. The spins of many other elementary particles, namely, protons, neutrons, neutrinos, mu mesons, and positrons, are likewise all one half. Other elementary particles such as pi and K-mesons and photons have spins either of zero or an integral number. The former particles as a class are called fermions, and the latter are termed bosons. These names are derived from the type of statistics applicable to the particles, namely, that due to Fermi-Dirac or in the latter case to Einstein-Bose.

The assemblage of particles within the nucleus may be regarded as dynamically similar to the electrons in the orbital structure of the atom. It would then follow that the total angular momentum of a nucleus is the vector sum of the orbital angular momenta l and the spins s of its component nucleons. The total resultant spin is denoted by the symbol I. This quantity for nuclei was first determined from an analysis of its spectrum.[1] A number of rules regarding the spin seemed to follow from these observations. These are, namely:

(a) nuclei of odd atomic mass numbers have an odd number of half-units of spin,

(b) nuclei of even atomic mass numbers have either zero or small integral spins,

(c) nuclei containing an even number of both protons and neutrons have a spin of zero,

(d) with the exception of La^{176}, the spins of all nuclei in the ground state lie between $\frac{9}{2}$ and zero.

2.3. Magnetic Moment. All nuclei for which I is not zero have a magnetic dipole moment. In addition, if the charge distribution in the nucleus is not spherically symmetrical, magnetic moments of higher even orders may occur. Most measurements of nuclear magnetic moments actually yield a nuclear "g" factor which is defined as the ratio of the magnetic dipole

[1] E. Wick, *Acad. Lencei Atti.*, **21**, 170 (1935).

moment to the nuclear spin. The atomic hyperfine structure [2] is intimately related to the magnetic dipole moment of the nucleus.

Evidence for the existence of the nuclear magnetic moment for hydrogen was first offered by O. Stern [3] and his co-workers. A beam of hydrogen molecules was projected perpendicularly through a strong magnetic field having a steep gradient at right angles to the beam. As a result, the beam is separated into a number of components interpretable as due to the magnetic sub-states, from which the magnetic moment is evaluated.

An improved method for measuring magnetic moments using an atomic beam has been developed by Rabi and his associates.[4] In this method it also is possible to say whether the magnetic moment is positive or negative. The expression for the magnetic moment of the electron, μ_e, is

$$\mu_e = \frac{e\hbar}{2mc} \tag{2.1}$$

This magnetic moment is usually referred to as a "Bohr magneton." For a proton, the mass is larger by the factor 1836, so the magnetic moment might be expected to be smaller by the same factor. This quantity may be designated μ_0, and is called a "nuclear" magneton. It has the value 5.05×10^{-24} ergs per gauss. The value of the magnetic moment μ_p actually observed for the proton is found to be $+2.793\mu_0$. A satisfactory theoretical explanation of this quantity currently suffers from the inadequacy of the meson theory in its present form to make exact predictions, although it can suggest the proper order of magnitude.

The magnetic moment of the deuteron, μ_D has been experimentally determined to be $0.8576\mu_0$, and that of the neutron,

[2] H. B. Casimir, *Physica*, **7**, 169 (1940).

[3] I. Estermann and O. Stern, *Z. Physik*, **85**, 17 (1933); O. Frisch and O. Stern, *Z. Physik*, **85**, 4 (1933).

[4] I. Rabi, J. M. Kellogg, and J. Zacharias, *Phys. Rev.*, **46**, 157, 163 (1934); **49**, 421 (1936); **56**, 738 (1939); W. Nierenberg and N. Ramsey, *Phys. Rev.*, **72**, 1075 (1947).

μ_n, is $-1.9135\mu_0$. The negative sign indicates that a negative charge is rotating in the normal spin direction. It can be observed that the magnetic moments are not exactly additive as $\mu_p + \mu_n$ is greater than μ_D by about $0.023\mu_0$. This has been interpreted as evidence for noncentral (tensor) forces existing between the nucleons within the nucleus.

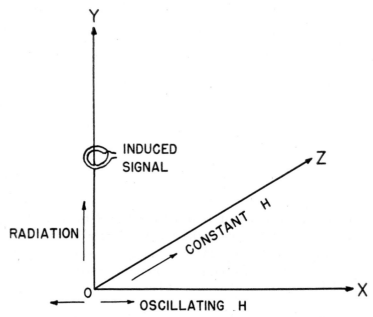

Fig. 2.1. Relative directions of fields in magnetic resonance method of determining magnetic moments (Bloch, Hansen, and Packard).

More recently methods of determining nuclear magnetic moments utilizing radio techniques have been developed.[5,6] In one of these methods a mass of the substance being investigated is placed in a constant magnetic field. By virtue of its nuclear magnetic moment a small magnetic polarization should result. Now by superposing a perpendicular oscillating mag-

[5] F. Bloch, W. Hansen, and M. Packard, *Phys. Rev.*, **70**, 460, 474 (1946).

[6] M. Bloembergen, E. Purcell, and R. Pound, *Phys. Rev.*, **73**, 679 (1948); G. Pake and E. Purcell, *Phys. Rev.*, **74**, 1184 (1948).

netic field the polarization originally parallel to the constant
magnetic field will precess about that field. As the frequency of
the oscillating field is varied, a resonance will occur at the
Larmor frequency. For frequencies near this magnetic resonance an oscillating voltage will be set up in a pickup coil
placed with its axis mutually perpendicular to the two magnetic
fields. The voltage pattern is displayed on the screen of an
oscillograph. This arrangement is represented in Figure 2.1,
except that the pickup coil is placed directly over the specimen
situated at the origin (O).

In addition to a magnetic moment a nucleus may, by virtue
of its charge distribution, possess an electric moment. Such a
moment will produce an energy dependence of a given atomic
or molecular state on the orientation of the nucleus with respect to the rest of the structure. It will therefore also mani-
fest itself in the hyperfine structure of atomic and molecular
spectra. The present knowledge of these moments is derived
from such studies and only electric quadrupole moments have
been observed. A nucleus with a positive quadrupole moment
is elongated along its spin axis, while a negative sign implies a
flattening along the spin axis.

2.4. The Alpha Particle Model. Since the most common
mode of decay of natural radioactive nuclei is by the emission
of alpha particles, it seemed reasonable to conjecture that these
particles exist as stable substructures within the nucleus. The
total binding energy within a nucleus would then consist of a
multiple of that represented by a single alpha particle, namely,
28.7 Mev, plus a quantity due to the bonds acting between the
alpha particles. For example, if the oxygen 16 nucleus be regarded as composed of four loosely bound alpha particles, its
atomic mass should be four times the mass of the He atom
4.003873 or 16.015492. Since the mass is exactly 16, the difference of 0.015492 mass units or 14.4 Mev represents the bondal
binding energy. This energy is small compared to the total
intra-alpha binding energy. If a tetrahedral arrangement be

assumed for the four alpha particles, then the binding energy represented by each of the six equal bonds would be 2.4 Mev. Equivalent bondal energies are observed for many other light stable nuclei with an even Z and the same number of neutrons N. This observation, that the total binding energy per alpha particle seems to be a constant, does not constitute a valid argument in favor of the alpha particle model. It could simply be a special case of the more general approximation that the binding energy per nucleon is approximately a constant over a wide range of nuclear masses.

Experimental results on the scattering of energetic alpha particles by helium atoms can be explained [7] only by assuming that the alpha particles lose their identity effectively in the collisions. It might reasonably be expected, therefore, that in the presence of extremely dense nuclear matter a particular particle would not retain its identity for an appreciably long time. From the remains of dissolved alpha particles new alpha structures might be recreated and destroyed [8] after a time t, believed to be long, when compared to the periods of vibration and rotation of the temporary alpha arrangement. It has so far been impossible to explain many of the observed nuclear characteristics, particularly such items as the observed energy states, by the older alpha particle model.

2.5. The Liquid Drop Model. The discovery of nuclear fission as induced in the very heavy elements by neutron capture and the systematic distribution with mass of the fission fragments gave a new impetus to the consideration of nuclear structure. Bohr and Wheeler proposed [9] a model in which the nucleus was treated as a liquid drop. The nucleons within the nucleus were imagined to behave something like the molecules within a drop of liquid. The evaporation energy of the drop would compare with the total binding energy of the nucleus. In both cases the magnitude is proportional to the number of particles.

[7] J. A. Wheeler, *Phys. Rev.*, **59**, 27 (1941).
[8] H. Margenau, *Phys. Rev.*, **59**, 37 (1941).
[9] N. Bohr and J. Wheeler, *Phys. Rev.*, **56**, 426 (1939).

A highly excited compound nucleus resulting from neutron capture disintegrates to a lower energy state either by the emission of radiation or by an alternate mode of decay in which a portion of the energy is used to produce a deformation leading to a division of the entity. The excitation energy may give rise to modes of motion of nuclear matter similar to the oscillations of a liquid sphere under the influence of surface tension. It was thus possible to arrive at conclusions that were in agreement with observation regarding the variation of the critical energy required for fission in nuclei of various mass numbers. It was also possible to predict the dependence of the cross section for fission of a particular nucleus on the energy of excitation. The distribution of the fission fragments with respect to mass could to some extent be estimated. It was not possible, however, to predict accurately regarding many detailed quantities, such as the density and properties of nuclear levels. The dynamical motions within the nucleus which are responsible for the excited states are apparently more complicated than can be dealt with successfully by this model.

2.6. The Nuclear Shell Model. In the hope that at least some of the simpler properties of nuclei might be satisfactorily described, a model has been envisioned [10] which makes essentially the same assumptions for nuclear particles as was done for electrons in the Bohr-Pauli explanation of atomic structure. Each nucleon is assumed to move in a spherically symmetric field of force due to the combined effect of the other nucleons. Similar to the electronic case, nuclear orbits may be characterized by a set of quantum numbers, n, l, j, m_j, and the corresponding levels filled independently with either neutrons or with protons. The radial quantum number, n, has integral values, with a minimum of $n = 1$ for the lowest level. The orbital angular momentum is represented by l and can assume positive integral values, including zero. Just as it is common practice

[10] M. Mayer, *Phys. Rev.*, **75**, 1969 (1949); **78**, 16 (1950); O. Haxel, J. Jensen, and H. Suess, *ibid.*, **75**, 1766 (1949); M. Mayer, S. Moszkowski, and L. Nordheim, *Rev. Mod. Phys.*, **23**, 315 (1951).

in optical spectroscopy to denote the angular momentum magnitude by letters, the same notation is employed here, namely,

$$l = 0 \quad 1 \quad 2 \quad 3 \quad 4 \quad 5 \quad \text{etc.}$$

$$\text{name} = s \quad p \quad d \quad f \quad g \quad h \quad \text{etc.}$$

Thus a 1 s designation would mean the first level with orbital angular momentum zero and similarly 2 p would represent the second level with an orbital momentum value of unity. The angular momentum j represents the sum of the orbital and spin angular momentum vectors for a single particle. The vectors may be either parallel, for which case $j = l + \frac{1}{2}$, or anti-parallel giving $j = l - \frac{1}{2}$. For an s state with $l = 0$, there exists only one level, namely, $j = \frac{1}{2}$. To complete the designation of a level the total angular momentum j is added. Thus the symbol $2d_{3/2}$ represents the second level with orbital angular momentum 2 and anti-parallel spin one half. The quantity m_j arises from the quantization of direction and can take all positive and negative values that are less than j. The number of states for a level of given l by virtue of the addition of the spin is $2(l + \frac{1}{2}) + 1$ and $2(l - \frac{1}{2}) + 1$.

Proton and neutron levels characterized by the same quantum numbers would not exactly coincide because of the Coulomb forces acting only on the protons and shifting these levels to higher energy. The sequence of levels for nuclear particles may differ greatly from that found for the atomic case due to the different potential distribution. The shell closures which occurred for electron numbers of 2, 10, 18, 36, 54, 86, etc., corresponding to the noble gases would now be different. By a proper choice of the potential distribution and a consideration of the strong spin-orbit coupling existing in nuclear reactions, it becomes possible to obtain shell closures corresponding to the recognized "magic" nuclear numbers 2, 8, 20, 50, 82, 126, etc.

For two specific potential distributions, calculations may be made of the relative energies for successive shells. For the isotropic harmonic oscillator of frequency $\dfrac{\omega}{2\pi}$ the potential V at any radial distance r is assumed to be:

$$V(r) = -V_0 \left[1 - \left(\frac{r}{R} \right)^2 \right] \quad \text{for } r < R$$
$$= 0 \qquad\qquad\quad \text{for } r > R \tag{2.2}$$

where R is an arbitrary nuclear radius. The energy levels are calculable [11] from the expression

$$E = \hbar\omega \left[2(n - 1) + l \right] \tag{2.3}$$

and give for successive shells progressive multiples of $\hbar\omega$ as shown in column 1, of Figure 2.1. For a "square-well" potential distribution,

$$V(r) = -V_0 \text{ (const.)} \quad \text{for } r < R$$
$$= 0 \qquad\qquad\quad \text{for } r > R \tag{2.4}$$

the degeneracy of the harmonic oscillator is removed and each shell is split into levels. The energies of the separated levels are calculable [12] and are usually expressed in multiples of an energy $\tilde{E}$, where $\tilde{E} = \dfrac{2\hbar^2}{m_n R^2}$. The shape of the actual nuclear well is probably intermediate between these two models. By modifying [13] the square well or by combining [10] with it a strong spin-orbit coupling the desired result can be obtained.

In order to obtain the higher magic numbers, the spin-orbit coupling is supposed to split the terms of $j = l \pm \frac{1}{2}$, by reducing the energy of the term $l + \frac{1}{2}$ by an amount that is assumed to increase with increasing values of l. For $l = 2$, the decrease in energy is of the order of the unmodified energy difference and it becomes larger for $l \geq 3$. The depression in energy of the term of higher j may be so strong that it should rightfully be in-

[11] M. Mayer and J. Jensen, *Nuclear Shell Structure*, John Wiley and Sons (1955).
[12] I. Schiff, *Quantum Mechanics*, McGraw-Hill Book Co., Inc. (1949).
[13] E. Feenberg, *Phys. Rev.*, **77**, 721 (1950).

corporated into the previous shell. Thus the term $g_{9/2}$ with its 10 particles is depressed as shown in column 2, Figure 2.2, so that instead of being included in shell V, it is more logically a part of shell IV. Its 10 particles then included with the former 40, yield a completed shell with the magic number 50. Similarly the $h_{11/2}$ term with its 12 particles normally in shell VI is depressed in energy so as to be included with the 70 particles existing in shells up to and including shell V, making in all, the magic number 82. Similar considerations can account for the other magic numbers.

Certain predictions may also be made regarding the expected spins of nuclei. If it is assumed that an even number of nucleons of the same type in a state of given j will arrange themselves to have a spin of zero, then $I = 0$ is expected and is found to exist for the ground state of all even-even nuclei. The angular momentum of an odd-numbered nucleus must equal the angular momentum of the single unpaired particle. For N even, Z odd, or vice-versa, the spin depends upon the number of odd particles and which of the nuclear shells is partially filled and receives the last particle. The spin of the nucleus can assume only the values I of the terms belonging to this shell. Thus if Z is even and N odd, then for $N < 2$, $I = \frac{1}{2}$; $2 < N < 8$, $I = \frac{3}{2}$ or $\frac{1}{2}$; $8 < N < 14$, $I = \frac{5}{2}$; etc. It has been possible [14] in this way to predict the spins for odd-even nuclei up to a high value of Z or of N.

The order of filling the levels does not necessarily follow the exact order indicated in the level scheme of Figure 2.2. If two nucleons of the same kind are "paired" so as to have zero angular momentum, the binding energy of the nucleus is increased by an amount P above the sum of all individual particle binding energies. The magnitude of this pairing energy P increases with the angular momentum j of the single particle level in which the pairing takes place. Where two levels are closely spaced and the upper one is of larger l then after a single

[14] P. Klinkenberg, *Rev. Mod. Phys.*, **24**, 63 (1952).

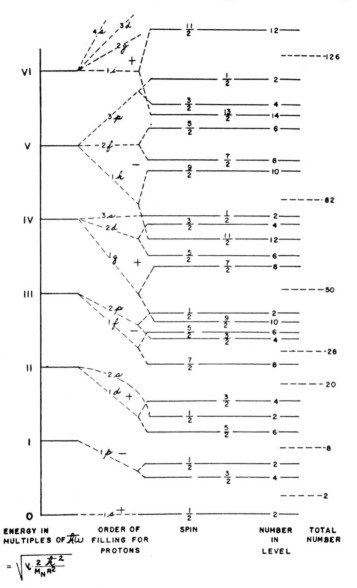

FIG. 2.2. Nuclear levels for "square well" potential with spin-orbit coupling.

particle is added to the lower level it is possible that the paired particles will next occupy the higher l, higher energy level, thus making the spin that of the lower level. As an illustration the expected spins of the ground states of a few nuclei are shown in Table 2.1, together with the observed spin.

TABLE 2.1. EXPECTED AND OBSERVED SPIN FOR CERTAIN NUCLEI

Z	Nucleus	Expected Spin from		Observed Spin
		Shell Model	Pairing	
19	K 41	$d_{3/2}$	$d_{3/2}$	$+\frac{3}{2}$
33	As 75	$f_{5/2}$	$p_{3/2}$	$-\frac{3}{2}$
35	Br 81	$f_{5/2}$	$p_{3/2}$	$-\frac{3}{2}$
63	Eu 153	$d_{5/2}$	$d_{5/2}$	$+\frac{5}{2}$
53	I 127	$g_{7/2}$	$d_{5/2}$	$+\frac{5}{2}$
67	Ho 165	$h_{11/2}$	$d_{5/2}$	$+\frac{7}{2}$
75	Re 185	$h_{11/2}$	$d_{5/2}$	$+\frac{5}{2}$

If the pairing energy is less than twice the difference in energy between the two states, the pairs will first form in the lower energy level. Then by breaking up one pair in the lower level, energy is gained and a pair may be formed in the higher level.

2.7. Parity. In wave-mechanics a system may be described by a function $\psi(x, y, z)$ of the coordinates $x, y,$ and z. The state so described is said to have either even or odd parity according to its behavior when the signs of all its space coordinates are changed and the potential energy function $V(x, y, z)$ is left unchanged. This is equivalent to reflecting the wave function through the origin of coordinates and if on so doing ψ is left unchanged, the parity of the state is said to be even and is designated by a $+$ sign. In the other case, the reversal of coordinate signs changes the sign of ψ and the state is described as having odd or minus parity. In nuclear transformations, parity has been believed to be conserved. This leads to certain selection rules in which the parity of a state may be regarded empirically as an additional quantum number.* The parities of the alphabetically designated states are as follows:

State Designation	s	p	d	f	g	h	etc.
Parity	$+$	$-$	$+$	$-$	$+$	$-$	etc.

In a nuclear disintegration in which electromagnetic radiation is emitted, a knowledge of yes or no for the parity change and the value of the spin change ΔI suffices to identify the multipolarity of the transition.

2.8. The Unified or Collective Nuclear Model. In spite of the successes of the shell or independent particle model, it appears to be inadequate to explain certain observed phenomena, such as the values or the variation with nucleonic number of the nuclear electric quadrupole moment. The experimentally determined values as reported [15] by Townes et al. are shown in Figure 2.3. The ordinates are the quadrupole moment Q divided by the square of the nuclear radius. For nuclear shells less than half complete the sign appears to be negative and for those more than half filled it is positive. For completed shells (i.e., magic numbers) the curve descends through zero from positive to negative values.

Bohr and Mottelson have suggested [16] a nuclear model in which both individual and several particles collectively play a part. The individual nucleons move in orbits in a potential

---

* Note added in proof. Following a theoretical prediction [T. D. Lee and C. N. Yang, *Phys. Rev.*, **104**, 254 (1956)] that in weak interactions parity might not be conserved, certain crucial confirming experiments have been carried out. The beta decay from cobalt 60 at 0.01° K in a strong magnetic field showed electrons emitted with a strong asymmetry [C. S. Wu, E. Ambler, R. Hayword, D. Hoppes, and R. Hudson, Private Communication]. Similarly the decay of positive mu mesons within a magnetic field, into electrons and neutrinos shows a strong positron asymmetry with the magnetic field [R. Garwin, L. Lederman, and M. Weinrich, Private Communication]. These results are interpreted as refuting the principle of the "conservation of parity".

[15] C. Townes, H. Foley, and W. Law, *Phys. Rev.*, **76**, 1415 (1949).

[16] A. Bohr and B. R. Mottelson, *Dan. Mat. Fys. Medd.*, **27**, 4016 (1953).

distribution established by the remaining nucleons and super-imposed upon this are imagined to exist collective periodic oscillations due to groups of nucleons. For almost closed shells the collective motion vanishes because of the stability of the

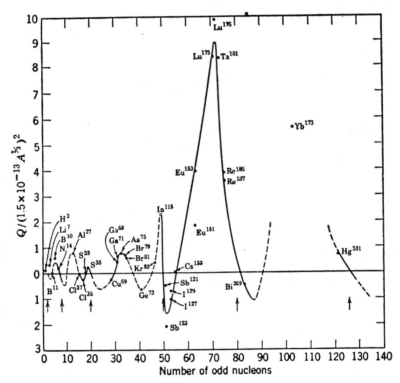

FIG. 2.3. Nuclear quadrupole moment versus nucleon number.

core and the independent particle model is sufficient. For nuclei whose proton numbers Z or neutron numbers N are somewhat distant from the magic numbers, the collective motion becomes significant and can account [17] for the large quadrupole moments. The most important collective motions are imagined to be those associated with oscillations in shape of a constant volume nu-

[17] J. Rainwater, *Phys. Rev.*, **79**, 432 (1950).

cleus. These oscillations would have the character of surface waves.

It is also possible to make predictions regarding the energies of nuclear levels and hence the energies of the gamma transitions in these same nuclei. For a nucleus with axial symmetry, the energy E_{rot} of a state with total angular momentum I and ground state spin of I_0 is shown to be

$$E_{rot} = \frac{\hbar^2}{2\mathcal{J}}[I(I+1) - I_0(I_0+1)] \tag{2.5}$$

where $\mathcal{J}$ is the moment of inertia of the spheroidal deformation and does not include the spherical core. For the ground state of even-even nuclei, $I_0 = 0$, and odd values of I are excluded, so that for successive excited levels, $I = 2, 4, 6, 8$, etc., all of even parity. If in some particular nucleus a known gamma energy represents the transition between first excited level and the ground state, then the quantity $\frac{\hbar^2}{2\mathcal{J}}$ can be empirically evaluated and the energies of succeeding higher excited levels calculated. The agreement between such calculated and observed values for a nucleus of this type, namely $_{72}Hf^{180}$, following K capture in Ta^{180} is shown [18] in Figure 2.4. The divergence in values gets increasingly bad at the higher levels. It is possible to correct for this by introducing a term due to vibration-rotation interaction. The correction in energy, ΔE_I, is expressed as

$$\Delta E_I = - \text{Const } I^2(I+1)^2 \tag{2.6}$$

and the constant can be chosen so that a reasonable over-all agreement is obtained.

For even-odd nuclei in which the ground state is known to have a spin of $\frac{1}{2}$, a special form of the expression for the

[18] J. Mihelich, G. Scharff-Goldhaber, and M. McKeown, *Phys. Rev.*, **94**, 794A (1954).

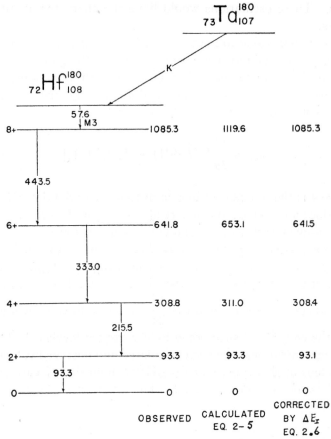

FIG. 2.4.   Nuclear levels in Hf[180], rotational.

energy, E_{rot}, of the rotational levels has been shown to be

$$E_{\text{rot}} = \frac{\hbar^2}{2\mathscr{I}}[I(I+1) + a(-1)^{I+\frac{1}{2}}(I+\tfrac{1}{2})] \qquad \textbf{(2.7)}$$

The constant a is difficult to calculate, but together with $\dfrac{\hbar^2}{2\mathscr{I}}$ it is experimentally determinable in some particular cases.   For successive excited levels I takes values $\frac{1}{2}$, $\frac{3}{2}$, $\frac{5}{2}$, etc.   An ex-

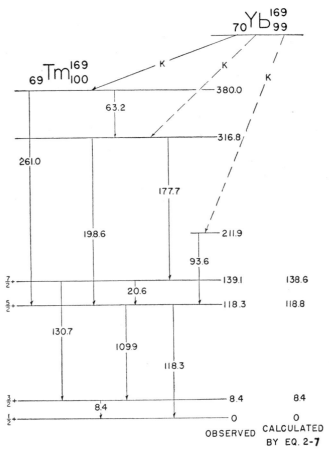

FIG. 2.5.   Nuclear level scheme for Tm[169].

ample of this procedure is shown in Figure 2.5, which represents the nuclear level scheme for $_{69}$Tm^{169} following the decay of Yb^{169}.   By assuming the observed gamma energies 8.4 and 109.9 kev to be transitions as shown, leading to the ground state, the constant a is computed to have a value of $-0\ 775$.   Now by using higher values of I such as $\frac{5}{2}$, $\frac{7}{2}$, etc., with a and g assumed to be constant, the energies of the succeeding levels are computed as shown in the numbers at the right in Figure 2.4. The good agreement at the lower levels does not continue to hold for the higher values indicating that these are not rotational levels. All rotational levels are of the same parity, so short lived transitions between them can be only M1 or E2 in nature.

2.9. Mirror Nuclei. There exist many light unstable nuclei in which Z differs from N by unity. For those nuclei in which $Z - N$ equals one, such as $_4Be^7$, $_6C^{11}$, etc., up to $_{21}Sc^{41}$, positive electron emission or K capture will occur. If $N - Z$ is unity then negative electron emission will take place, as illustrated by $_1H^3$. Such isobaric pairs are termed mirror nuclei and their study allows a comparison of the P,P and N,N bonds existing within the nucleus. If the odd nucleon changes from a proton to a neutron by positron emission then the total number of P,N bonds remains unchanged, but a certain number of P,P bonds are replaced by an equal number of N,N bonds, Thus when $_{21}Sc_{20}^{41}$ changes to $_{20}Ca_{21}^{41}$ by the emission of a positron of maximum energy 4.94 Mev, $Z - 1$ or 20 P,P bonds are replaced by N or 20 N,N bonds. The Coulomb interaction energy between a spherical charge e^+ of radius r and an overlapping equivalent charge e^+ has been shown to be $\dfrac{6}{5}\dfrac{e^2}{r}$. If this arbitrary geometry be extended to apply to all of the protons within the nucleus then on positron emission, the total Coulomb energy decreases by $(Z - 1)\dfrac{6}{5}\dfrac{e^2}{r}$. At the same time a neutron mass m_N replaces the mass of the hydrogen atom m_H with an expected energy increase due to its larger mass. The total energy change, ΔE, is then expressible as

$$\Delta E = E_{\beta+} + 2m_0C^2 = 5.96 \text{ Mev} = 20\left(\frac{6}{5}\right)\frac{e^2}{r} - (m_N - m_H)C^2$$

$$= \frac{24e^2}{r} - 0.781 \text{ Mev} \quad \textbf{(2.8)}$$

This equation may be used to evaluate the nuclear radius, r, as arbitrarily defined above, namely,

$$r = r_0 \sqrt[3]{z + N} = 5.13 \times 10^{-13} \text{ cm} \qquad (2.9)$$

The quantity r_0 appears then from this expression to be

$$r_0 = 1.48 \times 10^{-13} \text{ cm}$$

This value is large compared to the results obtained for the same quantity by other methods. It may be reduced by added assumptions of changes occurring during emission.

QUESTIONS AND PROBLEMS

1. The proton, neutron, and electron have spins of one half. All odd-A nuclei have spins of $n/2$, where n is an odd integer. Show from this that such nuclei cannot be made of protons and electrons but can be formed from protons and neutrons.

2. From Figure 2.2, what prediction would you make for the description of the ground states of the following: $_{23}V^{51}$, $_{31}Ga^{71}$, and $_{51}Sb^{123}$?

   Answer: $f_{7/2}$, $p_{3/2}$, and $g_{7/2}$.

3. Assuming "pairing" to occur, what might be expected for the spin of the ground states of Rb^{85} and Re^{185}?

   Answer: $f_{5/2}$, $d_{5/2}$.

4. Chlorine 33 decays by positron emission with a maximum energy of 4.3 Mev. Calculate from this the radius of the nucleus. What is the value of r_0 as determined from this?

   Answer: 4.54×10^{-13} cm; $r: = 1.41 \times 10^{-13}$ cm.

5. The first two excited levels of $_{65}Tb^{159}_{94}$ are observed by Coulomb excitation to lie at 57 and 136 kev. What nuclear model would be expected best to describe this nucleus? On the basis of such a model, and using equation 2.5, what is the expected ground state spin? What are the energies and multipolarities of the gamma rays occurring in the de-excitation of the above levels? From the above data, at what energy might a third excited level be expected? What would be the spin of this level?

   Answer: $I_0 = \frac{3}{2}$; 57 kev (M1), 79 kev (M1), 136 kev (E2); 239.8 kev; $\frac{9}{2}$.

CHAPTER 3

THE DETECTION OF RADIATION

3.1. The Fluorescent Method. Many substances when exposed even to invisible radiation like ultraviolet or X-rays become copious emitters of visible light. In some of these substances the emission of light persists long after the exposure to radiation. In many other substances the glowing lasts only a fraction of a second after the excitation has vanished. The former phenomenon is called phosphorescence and the latter is termed fluorescence. This, then, allows the detection of radiation by noting the luminosity of a prepared screen, exposed to the radiation. Such materials as platinobarium cyanide, calcium tungstate, or zinc sulfide were first used for such screens.

It was the fluorescing of the glass walls of an X-ray tube that led Becquerel to look for what he regarded as invisible fluorescence. That is, a photographic plate was protected from various fluorescing substances by black paper. On using the double sulfate of uranium and potassium, he found that the wrapped photographic plate became activated whether the salt was illuminated or not.

A device known as the spinthariscope, attributed to Sir William Crookes [1] in 1903, was used in early studies of alpha radiation. Figure 4.1 shows a form of the apparatus as used later by Rutherford in studying the first induced nuclear disintegrations. The individual alpha particles from the source S, or the recoil protons from the gas, will on striking the screen appear as momentarily illuminated spots when viewed through the microscope, so that if not too numerous they can be counted.

[1] W. Crookes, *Proc. Roy. Soc. (London),* **71,** 405 (1903).

By knowing the solid angle subtended at the source the total emission can be found.

The device was used for beta radiation by Regener.[2] In this case each scintillation is probably due to the simultaneous impact of several beta particles, as it is doubtful if a single electron could produce an observable effect.

3.2. The Photographic Method. It has been shown that any ionizing radiation or particle will, on absorption in the emulsion of a photographic plate, produce activation. In the case of gamma radiation the action on the silver bromide crystals is undoubtedly cumulative. Heavily ionizing particles like alpha particles, protons, or deuterons are sufficiently energetic to activate some individual crystal grains through which they pass, although not necessarily all. As a consequence, on development, the actual track of the particle is revealed.

A technique making use of such emulsion tracks to measure the energy of the incident particles was first developed by Wilkins.[3] The average number of electron volts per grain may be determined and then it is necessary only to count the number of activated grains. The method is tedious, and is most successful when used under dark-field illumination. In studying induced disintegration the emulsion may be impregnated with the material to be bombarded. The recoiling particles are thus observed in the developed layer. Figure 5.2C shows one of these tracks with a magnification of 900. This track represents the two oppositely directed alpha particles arising from a lithium 7 nucleus, struck by a neutron.

The photographic-emulsion technique has been particularly successful in recent cosmic ray and heavy-particle studies. Improved emulsions with many more silver grains per unit volume have been developed by the Ilford Company in England and by the Eastman Kodak Company. The latter, known as NTB plates, may be had in thicknesses up to 600 microns or

[2] W. Regener, *Verhandl. deut. physik. Ges.*, **19**, 78 (1908).
[3] T. R. Wilkins and H. St. Helens, *Phys. Rev.*, **54**, 783 (1938); L. C. Martin and T. R. Wilkins, *J. Optical Soc. Am.*, **27**, 340 (1937).

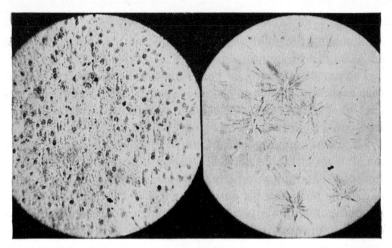

Fig. 3.1*A*. Magnified microscopic section (left) and autoradiograph (right) of liver tissue with intravenous UO_2, showing starlike pattern due to alpha emission from single Kupffer cells. (Courtesy of Dr. John Lawrence.)

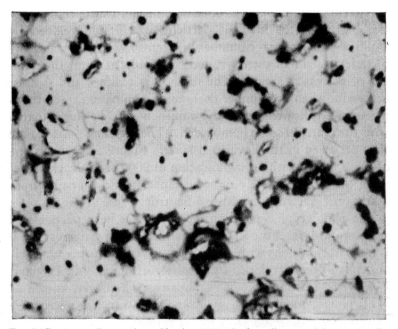

Fig. 3.1*B*. Autoradiogram (magnification 4000 ×) of an alloy containing aged radioactive cobalt crystals obtained by a process of depositing the silver emulsion directly on the polished activated surface. Note the remarkable clarity of detail due to the intimate contact between silver emulsion and radioactive surface. (Courtesy of Henry Gomberg.)

more and are insensitive to visible light. They are particularly suitable for high-altitude studies since they can be carried by free balloons as desired, to elevations previously unattainable, or they may be put within the cyclotron to record meson tracks during a bombardment. Certain emulsions have been perfected that are sensitive not only to heavy particles, but will even show electron tracks. The development and fixing of these emulsions must be carried out more slowly than with ordinary photographic plates and with special chemicals. Figure 11.11 shows the track of a meson producing a star with the resultant proton and alpha tracks, and Figure 10.3 shows the tracks of a pi meson, a mu meson, and the final decay electron.

A photographic technique particularly applicable to studies involving radioactive materials as tracers in biological work, was reported by Lacassagne and Lattés in 1924.[4] A section of the tissue with the absorbed radioactive material is placed in close contact with the photographic plate for a suitable time. The plate will be activated in areas contiguous to the radioactivity but not in those areas close to tissue carrying no radioactive material. Such photographs are termed "autoradiograms" and show directly the distribution of the tracer element. Examples of this technique are shown in Figure 13.2 and Figure 13.4B.

By depositing the unactivated silver emulsion out of solution directly upon the section to be studied considerable improvement in detail is obtained. It is, in fact, possible in many cases to observe the radioactive condition of individual cells as shown in Figure 3.1A. Such an autoradiogram magnified 4000 times is presented in Figure 3.1B showing the microscopic structure of an alloy containing radioactive cobalt.

3.3. Ionization Chambers. Becquerel observed that a charged electroscope would be discharged if uranium was brought near its terminal. Such a device as shown in Figure 3.2A was one of the first simple instruments used to compare

[4] Mme. J. Lattés and A. Lacassagne, *Compt. rend.*, **178**, 630 (1924).

radioactivities. By placing the specimens in order on the terminal plate, their activities are inversely proportional to the times required for the leaves of the electroscope to collapse over a certain definite portion of the angular scale.

Another arrangement, shown in Figure 3.2*B*, was used by Madame Curie in a general investigation of the radioactivity of a wide variety of substances. The specimen is placed on

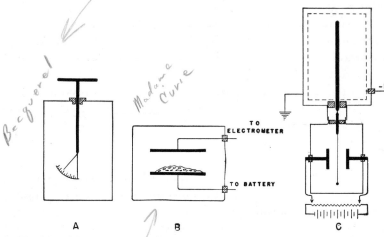

Fig. 3.2. (*A*) Electroscope; (*B*) ionization electrometer; (*C*) ionization chamber with string electrometer.

the bottom plate, and any ionization produced results in an ionization current which is measured by a sensitive electrometer. The conductance between the plates may be affected by other factors, such as temperature and humidity, and sometimes false conclusions can be formed.

An ionization chamber connected to a string electrometer is shown in Figure 3.2*C*. This is a very satisfactory arrangement for detecting and measuring the activity. The outer case of the chamber is capable of holding gases at pressures up to several atmospheres and is electrically grounded. Inside, and insulated from the outer case, is a cylinder of screen wire maintained at a high electric potential. A central insulated rod is connected through a sulfur bushing to a very fine wire, or quartz fiber which has been made electrically conducting by a thin sputtered metallic coating. The fiber is held under a slight tension between two oppositely charged plates and is viewed through a microscope provided with an etched scale in its eyepiece. The charging of the fiber causes it to drift toward the plate of opposite sign. To restore the fiber to its initial position it is momentarily grounded. The sensitivity of the instrument can be varied at will, by changing the potential difference between the plates. The over-all sensitivity can be increased by using in the chamber a heavy gas, such as freon (CCl_2F_2), whose molecular weight is about 129.

3.4. The Vacuum-tube Electrometer. The ions produced in the ionization chamber by the incident radiation give rise to an ionization current. The charge associated with the 100,000 ion pairs which would be produced by a single alpha particle traveling approximately a centimeter in normal air would amount to about 3×10^{-14} coulomb. If this average charge should pass through a high resistance of, say, 3×10^{10} ohms in 1 second, then a difference of potential of approximately 1 millivolt would exist across the high resistance.

Any change in the rate of ionization in the chamber would result in a corresponding change in this voltage. By allowing this small voltage change to swing the grid potential of a special three-electrode vacuum tube, correspondingly large variations would occur in the plate circuit of the vacuum tube.[5] These changes in plate current can be indicated by a direct-reading galvanometer. An arrangement of this type is shown in Figure 3.3. Since the plate current, even with no ionization, may be appreciable, it is desirable to use a potentiometer circuit to offset the steady initial current through the galvanometer.

Since it is desired that the circuit be stable in order to make reliable quantitative measurements, and since the amplifica-

---

[5] L. A. DuBridge and H. Brown, *Rev. Sci. Instruments*, **4**, 532 (1933); D. Penick, *Rev. Sci. Instruments*, **6**, 115 (1935).

tion of the vacuum tube is being pushed to the limit, great care must be taken to guard against such disturbing factors as temperature changes, humidity changes, and fluctuations in supply voltages. It is usually found desirable to enclose the entire system in an electrically shielded chamber and the vacuum tube and associated high resistors in an evacuated volume.

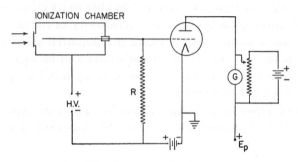

FIG. 3.3.   A vacuum tube electrometer.

With this care,[6] the device is an accurate, quick-acting detector even for very weak radiation.

3.5. Point Counters.   Many other electrical systems have been devised to study the radiation from radioactive bodies. Some of the devices will indicate and record the transit of a single particle.   Most of these developments have been based upon the pioneer work of Gorton in 1905.[7]   He observed that the applied voltage necessary to produce a breakdown discharge from a charged conducting point could be greatly varied by irradiating the gas in the neighborhood of the point.   On using the light from an arc, X-rays, or radioactivity, breakdown was found to occur at 1000 or more volts less than when no radiation was present.

A single 7-Mev alpha ray will produce about 200,000 pairs of ions in its traversal of the gas of an ionization cell.   This would amount to one ten-thousandth electrostatic unit each of

---

[6] J. M. Lafferty and K. H. Kingdon, *J. Applied Phys.*, **17**, 894 (1946).
[7] F. R. Gorton, *Verhandl. deut. physik. Ges.*, **7.2**, 42 (1905).

positive and of negative electricity. This quantity might be further increased by secondary ionization in the strong electric field so as to give an indication of the single alpha particle. In 1908, Rutherford and Geiger [8] described a system in which a high voltage was applied to a point-shaped conductor so as to bring it to a potential just less than breakdown. In this strong electric field any ions formed will be accelerated and in turn they will produce new ions by collision with neutral molecules. As a result a single ionizing particle may, by multiple ionization, be sufficient to cause a discharge. If a condenser is across the gap, and if a high resistance is in series with the source of potential, then the discharge results in a lowering of the voltage at the point so that the current ceases or is "quenched." Without any further ionization, the high potential is again established and ready for the next firing. Such a circuit is rather slow.

By reducing the pressure in the chamber and using a fine wire at the axis of a cylinder instead of a point, and noting the discharge on a string electrometer as in Figure 3.2C, it became possible to count individual pulses occurring at a rate up to five per minute. Improvements in the string electrometer were made, and a photographic arrangement was added so that the continuous motion of the string could be recorded on a moving film. With this apparatus counts were recorded up to 1000 per minute.

3.6. Tube Counters. Numerous papers have appeared dealing with the tube originally introduced by E. Rutherford and H. Geiger. It is now usually called a "Geiger," or a "G-M," tube because of applications and technical improvements introduced by H. Geiger and W. Muller many years later.[9] The most commonly used tube takes the form shown in Figure 3.4A or 3.4B, although they may be made in many other shapes for special applications. A fine wire, usually tungsten, lies at the

---

[8] E. Rutherford and H. Geiger, *Proc. Roy. Soc. A*, **81**, 141 (1908).
[9] H. Geiger and W. Muller, *Phys. Z.*, **29**, 839 (1928); **30**, 489 (1929); S. A. Korff, *Electron and Nuclear Counters*, D. Van Nostrand Co., Inc. (1955).

axis of a metal cylinder. The metal cylinder may be enclosed in a concentric cylindrical sheath of glass or it may serve as the outer tube wall. The cylinder may be provided with a very thin window (at its end) so that easily absorbed radiations may be studied.

The tube is first thoroughly cleaned so that all contamination is removed from the inner surfaces. The volume is evacuated

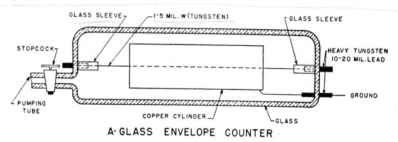

A- GLASS ENVELOPE COUNTER

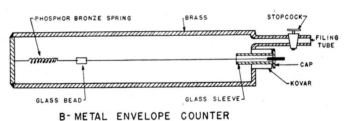

B- METAL ENVELOPE COUNTER

FIG. 3.4. G-M tubes.

as completely as possible and then connected by stopcocks as shown in Figure 3.5 to the suitable gas reservoir for filling. If a quenching vapor, such as alcohol, is to be used, this is admitted first up to the desired pressure of perhaps 1 cm of mercury, by diffusion. The main stable gas is now allowed to enter to build up a predetermined pressure. Monatomic gases, such as helium, neon, and argon, have been used extensively, although diatomic gases, hydrogen, nitrogen, and oxygen also work satisfactorily. The starting potentials for the former are considerably lower than those for the diatomic gases.

The action within a counter tube whose central wire is at a high positive potential may be somewhat as follows. A single ion pair formed between the electrodes will be followed by a drift of each ion, the electron toward the positive central wire and the heavy positive ion toward the cylindrical cathode. The mobility of the electron (defined as its acquired velocity in centimeters per second under an accelerating field of 1 volt per centimeter) may be 1000 times that of the positive ion so that

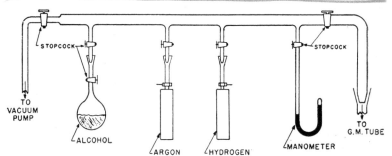

FIG. 3.5. Filling system for G-M tube.

it soon acquires sufficient velocity to produce a new pair of ions on collision. This new electron will travel along toward the anode and may in turn produce another pair of ions. This cumulating drift of electrons may be termed an "electron avalanche." Some electrons will recombine with positive ions, a process which may be accompanied by the emission of photons. In turn, if sufficiently energetic, the photons may eject photoelectrons from atoms in other regions of the tube, thus aiding in the avalanche. At sufficiently high voltages for good operation, the photon ionization is found to spread along the wire at a speed of about 10^7 cm per second.

The positive ions left behind by the fast-moving electrons appear as a positive space charge around the wire which in turn reduces the electric field. This whole process may take place in one millionth of a second in which time a billion or more electrons may have reached the wire. The current established within the tube must be quickly quenched in order that the device is ready for the next incoming signal. This is accomplished by the small amount of heavy vapor in the gas or by the use of a special auxiliary circuit. The action of the heavy vapor molecule is probably to prevent the arrival of the positive ion at the outer cylinder where it might dislodge an electron and recycle the counter. In performing this function

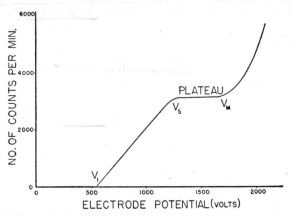

FIG. 3.6.   Variation of counting rate with increasing voltage.

the polyatomic molecule is dissociated by positive ion impact so that eventually the supply remaining is insufficient and must be replaced. A single filling is usually good for about 10^9 counts.

The performance of the tube can be found by using some standard source and noting the number of output counts per second as the applied voltage is increased. A typical performance curve for a hydrogen-filled tube is shown in Figure 3.6. No counts will occur until a certain minimum voltage, V_1, is applied. The number of counts per second increases as the voltage is stepped up until some value, V_s, not sharply defined, is attained, beyond which little or no increase in the counting rate occurs. Finally, at voltages greater than V_M the counting rate again increases. It is essential that the plateau V_s to V_M exist if accurate quantitative results are desired. Without such a plateau any observed change in the number of pulses per second might be due to a change in voltage and not to a change in the intensity of the source.

3.7. Proportional Counters. In the usual G-M tube by virtue of the cylindrical symmetry the radial electric field, ε_r, at a distance r from the center of the anode, will vary as $1/r$. If R_1 is the outer radius of the central wire and R_2 is the inner radius of the outer cylinder, then the electric field ε_r at any radius r is

$$\varepsilon_r = \frac{V_2 - V_1}{r \log_e R_2/R_1} \text{ volts/cm} \tag{3.1}$$

where $V_2 - V_1$ is the potential difference in volts. Hence the field will be very strong immediately outside the central wire and will fall off rapidly as the radius increases. If the potential difference applied to the electrodes is very low, the primary ions will not be accelerated so as to produce additional electrons. At a slightly higher voltage, in a tube such as that represented [10] in Figure 3.4, in the region from about 600 to 900 volts, the primary electrons will be accelerated in the region of high field near the central wire, so as to yield a multiplication of electrons by a factor of 10^3 or 10^4, yet not enough to produce a large electron avalanche. In this condition the height of the output pulse will be proportional to the number of primary ions and hence to the energy of the ionizing primary particle. The tube so used with a suitable recording circuit is termed a "proportional" counter. It is possible to bias the recorder so that only those pulses of height greater than any desired minimum will be recorded. For example, alpha particles or recoil protons with large specific ionization may be counted to the exclusion of gamma rays or beta particles, even though the latter are present in great abundance. It is highly important that the voltage be well regulated, usually to about 0.1%. For the region of the plateau, V_s to V_M, in Figure 3.6, no discrimination

[10] H. Geiger and O. Klemperer, *Z. Physik*, **49**, 753 (1928); B. Zipprich, *Z. Physik*, **85**, 592 (1933); and G. Brubaker and E. Pollard, *Rev. Sci. Instruments*, **8**, 254 (1937).

between primary particles would exist, as any single ion pair would lead to an electron avalanche and be recorded.

In the region of voltages greater than V_M a peculiar phenomenon occurs. There is [11] evidence that the apparently continuous discharge that occurs here is really a succession of pulses initiated by delayed electron emission from the metal surface of the cathode due to its previous bombardment. The metal surface acts much as a pure radioactive emitter in that it has a half-life dependent upon the metal. For example, for brass, lead, and aluminum the half-lives are about 1, 7, and 16 seconds, respectively. If the electron emission is allowed to die out completely, then the voltage necessary to initiate the continuous discharge becomes greater.

3.8. Counter Circuits.

The development of the multielectrode vacuum tube has made possible electrical circuits which,

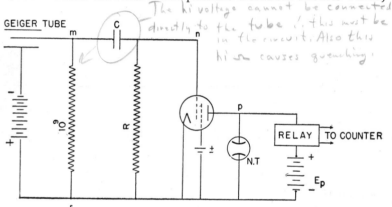

The hi voltage cannot be connected directly to the tube .: this must be in the circuit. Also this hi ~ causes quenching.

FIG. 3.7. Vacuum-tube circuit for recording pulses in Geiger tube.

when used with the Geiger tube, can resolve and count the individual pulses even though they occur in extremely rapid succession. The elementary use of the vacuum tube in this connection is simply illustrated by Figure 3.7. The plate current

[11] M. Wiedenbeck and H. R. Crane, *Phys. Rev.*, **75**, 985, 1268 (1949); M. Tanaka, *Phys. Rev.*, **48**, 916 (1938).

in the vacuum tube depends upon the potential of the control grid, represented by point n. With no ionization in the Geiger tube, no current flows through the high resistance and s and m are at the same positive potential which is communicated through the coupling condenser C to the grid, so that the plate current is sufficiently large to energize the relay. An incident particle produces ionization in the Geiger tube which is accompanied by a current through the high resistance and hence a lowering of the potential of point m and also of the control grid. This results in a decrease in the plate current sufficient to cause the relay contact to be released, and operate any indicating or registering device. At the same time, the decrease in the plate current results in an increase in the voltage across the neon glow tube (N.T.), causing it to flash momentarily. The combination of decreased voltage across the Geiger tube and the nature of the discharge act to quench the current and establish the original conditions. The maximum number of counts per minute that can be recorded by this circuit without loss is not great.

a. *Efficiency*. Immediately following the triggering of the G-M tube, there will occur an inactive time (τ) of about 10^{-4} second, during which it is insensitive to any other particle. Hence if there are actually N particles per second traversing the tube and n of them are counted, then in every second the tube is inactive $n\tau$ seconds. An efficiency E, with respect to time, is then

$$E = \frac{n}{N} = \frac{1 - \tau n}{1} = 1 - \tau n \qquad (3.2)$$

so that for $N = 5000$ particles per second, the efficiency will be only 50%, or if $n = 1000$ counts per second, it must be recognized that about 10% of the particles are not being counted.

A further loss in counting rate may result from the finite probability that an incident particle will not produce a single pair of ions. If, on the average, P ion pairs are produced by a single primary particle, then the chance that zero ion pairs will be made is e^{-P}. An efficiency due to this lack of sensitivity is then expressible as

$$E = 1 - e^{-P} = 1 - \frac{1}{e^P} \qquad (3.3)$$

For alpha or beta particles, P is large and the efficiency is close to 100%. For high energy gamma radiation, if P is unity or less, the efficiency may be very low. The over-all efficiency is then the product of these two efficiencies, multiplied by a third factor relating to the probability of avalanche formation from the original ionization.

    b. Coincidence Circuit. Frequently it is desired to record only those events which occur simultaneously in two detectors. A

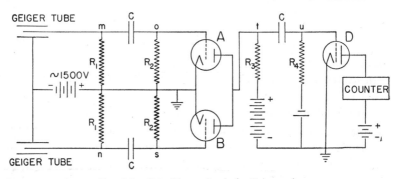

Fig. 3.8. Coincidence circuit for Geiger tubes.

circuit capable of serving in this manner as first used by Rossi [12] is shown in Figure 3.8. The potentials of the grids of both tubes are adjusted to values sufficiently positive to establish the plate currents through both tubes A and B to a certain normal value. At the same time the grid potential of tube D, which may be a gas-filled triode, is made sufficiently negative to reduce its plate current to zero. Any ionizing particle enter-

[12] B. Rossi, *Nature*, 125, 636 (1930).

ing the upper Geiger tube results in the potential of point m and hence that of the control grid of tube A becoming less positive, so that its plate current is reduced to zero. This raises the potential of point t and hence of the control grid of tube D, but not enough to cause it to fire. If, however, particles enter both Geiger tubes simultaneously, then the potential of t increases sufficiently to fire the triode D, and give a simple impulse to the counter. In cosmic-ray studies and in the determination of nuclear level schemes these coincidence circuits have played an important role. In investigations on the behavior of mesons many Geiger tubes are often employed in a single circuit so that they can be arranged in different 3-, 4-, or morefold coincidence sets if desired.

   c. Scaling Circuits. Mechanical registering devices can usually not operate at a frequency greater than 3000 or 4000 per minute. For a speed of this order or greater it is common practice to arrange [13] a circuit of vacuum tubes so that the mechanical register records a single count for each 2, 4, 8, or 16 incident particles, yet by a system of glow lamps or a direct-reading meter the additional single particles can be numbered.

   These circuits are made up of a succession of "scale of two" counters so that the over-all scaling factor is 2^n, where n is the number of times the simple unit of two is repeated. Various types of tubes and arrangements of components in the circuit have been used. A simple two-tube unit using thyratrons is shown in Figure 3.9. Successive incoming pulses fire the two tubes A and B alternately, but only the firing of B passes the impulse on to the next set of thyratrons. A glow lamp in the circuit of A tells when it has fired. The mechanical counter is connected in the output circuit of the last tube. For exceedingly high rates of counting, scaling circuits may be connected together; thus two scale-of-sixteen counters in series can be used

---

[13] See, for example: W. G. Shepherd and R. O. Haxby, *Rev. Sci. Instruments,* **7,** 425 (1936); E. C. Stevenson and I. Getting, *Rev. Sci. Instruments,* **8,** 414 (1937); J. Lawson and H. Lifshutz, *Rev. Sci. Instruments,* **9,** 83 (1938); V. H. Regener, *Rev. Sci. Instruments,* **17,** 180 (1946); G. T. Baker, *J. Sci. Instruments,* **25,** 127 (1948).

to give a scaling factor of 256, or two 64 scalers together give a scale of 4096. For more convenient and rapid reading the output may be made to appear as multiples of ten on decade indicators.

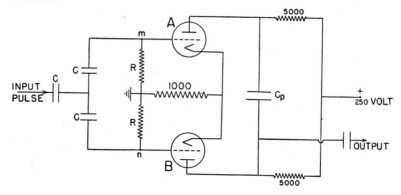

FIG. 3.9. "Scale of two" circuit for recording pulses.

3.9. The Electron Multiplier Tube.

On bombarding certain surfaces by electrons it may happen that each impinging electron expels several electrons from the struck surface. If these electrons are caught in an electric field and driven against another similar surface, each of them may again give rise to several electrons. This process may be repeated several times so that the original electron finally is represented by a^n electrons, where a is the multiplying factor at each surface which may be as much as eight, and n is the number of stages. Such an arrangement as originally used by the Western Electric Company is shown in Figure 3.10. Care must be taken in arranging successive surfaces [14] both as to shape and placement so that each surface is effective in contributing to the electron multiplication. The initial impulse may be from electrons as beta radiation or it may be instigated by photons which photoelectrically

[14] See V. K. Zworykin and J. A. Rajchman, *Proc. I.R.E.*, **27**, 558 (1939); J. R. Pierce, *Bell Lab. Record*, **16**, 305 (1938); J. R. Pierce and R. Winans, *Rev. Sci. Instruments*, **12**, 269 (1941); J. S. Allen, *Phys. Rev.*, **55**, 966 (1939); *Nucleonics*, **3**, No. 1, 34 (1948); and R. W. Engstrom, *Rev. Sci. Instruments*, **18**, 587 (1947).

eject electrons from the first surface. These initial electrons are accelerated here in seven steps, each potential fall being about 100 volts. The secondary emission of each surface is found to be a maximum for a potential of about 400 volts, but

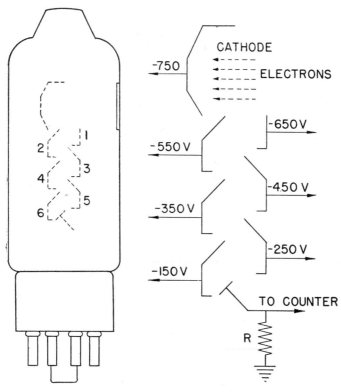

FIG. 3.10. Electron multiplier, assembly and electrode arrangement.

this is not attained in practice. Surfaces of pure beryllium have been successfully used, but the most commonly employed coating consists of caesium oxide or some similar material. To reduce the background level due to random fluctuations it is sometimes desirable to lower the temperature of the entire tube. It is preferable in most work to have the entrance window on the end of the tube, so that an efficient light coupling can be made with the accompanying crystal detector. Such tubes in varied designs with many more stages of amplification are obtainable from the Radio Corporation of America or the DuMont Laboratories. A sketch of the usual coupling is shown in Figure 3.11.

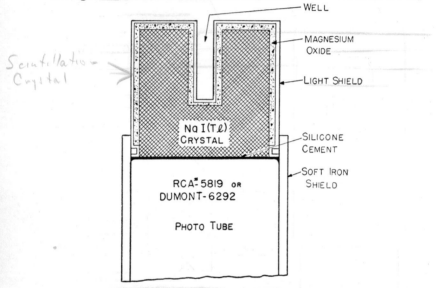

FIG. 3.11. Phototube and scintillation crystal with well.

3.10. Scintillation Counters. When an ionizing particle is absorbed in any one of several transparent phosphors a flash of light of exceedingly short duration may be emitted. Some phosphors [15] in common use are zinc sulfide, calcium tungstate, anthracene,[16] naphthalene,[17] or thallium-activated [18] sodium iodide. The emitted light may be directed upon the input of a photomultiplier tube as shown in Figure 3.11, and a single pulse

[15] R. Frerichs and R. Warminsky, *Naturwissenschaften*, **33**, 251 (1946); H. A. Klasens, *Trans. Faraday Soc.*, **42**, 66 (1946).

[16] L. F. Wouters, *Phys. Rev.*, **74**, 489 (1948); P. R. Bell, *Phys. Rev.*, **73**, 1405 (1948).

[17] R. R. Taschek and H. T. Getting, *Phys. Rev.*, **74**, 1553 (1948).

[18] R. Hofstadter, *Phys. Rev.*, **75**, 796 (1949); G. B. Collins, *Phys. Rev.*, **74**, 1543 (1948).

recorded for each particle absorbed. The magnitude of the pulse is directly proportional to the total energy of the absorbed particle or photon.

Two distinct advantages are apparent in this type of counter over the conventional Geiger tube. The resolving time may be as short as 10^{-8} or 10^{-9} second compared to 10^{-5} or 10^{-6} second for the usual Geiger counter, and hence it is capable of correspondingly faster counting rates. Whereas most Geiger tubes have a low efficiency, the scintillation phosphor may be made large in size so that its increased absorption leads to a very high efficiency.

One prime difficulty must be overcome in the successful use of the scintillation counter. Even in darkness the multiplier circuit will emit a copious output of pulses due to spontaneous

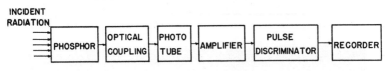

FIG. 3.12. Scheme for connecting scintillation counter.

emission. It is essential that the pulses due to radiation be made larger than the dark pulses, so that they alone are recorded. To accomplish this as far as possible an amplifier and a pulse height discriminator are employed as shown in Figure 3.12. This discriminator may be arranged to admit only pulses between arbitrary energy limits. By successively changing these limits the intensity distribution with respect to energy may be mapped. To speed up this process, multichannel circuits may be arranged so that several adjacent energy intervals are recorded simultaneously. A recently developed 256 channel analyzer as used at the Argonne National Laboratory is shown in Figure 3.13. By using two discriminator circuits, each with its own crystal and tube, coincidences may be observed between a fixed band in one tube and all other energies in the other. If one of the components is beta radiation an anthracene crystal is preferable but for gamma energies NaI(Tl) crystals are generally employed.

By putting the specimen at the bottom of the well-hole shown in Figure 3.11 a summation of all energies occurring in rapid

Fig. 3.13.   A 256 multichannel pulse height analyzer.   (Argonne National Laboratory, Courtesy of S. B. Burson.)

sequence is obtained.   By comparing this summed curve with that obtained with the specimen outside the crystal, a valuable check is given of any proposed nuclear level scheme.

3.11. Crystal Counters.   As early as 1913 it was noted by Roentgen and Jaffé [19] that certain crystals upon exposure to ionizing radiation became electrically conducting.   The appli-

[19] W. Roentgen and A. Jaffé, *Ann. Physik,* **41,** 449 (1913), **64,** 1 (1921); see also Jaffé, *Physik,* **33,** 393 (1932); H. Frolich and N. Mott, *Proc. Roy. Soc. (London),* **171,** 496A (1939); G. Stetter, *Verhandl. deut. physik. Ges.,* **22,** 13 (1941).

cation of this phenomenon to the detection of single ionizing particles was first carried out by Van Heerden [20] and has since been extended by many investigators. An arrangement suitable for this purpose is shown in Figure 3.14. The crystal, which for best results is usually AgCl, LiF, TlBr, or diamond, is mounted lightly between electrodes of silver, platinum, or gold and maintained in darkness at liquid-air temperatures.

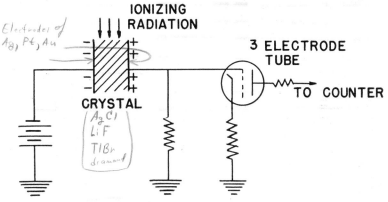

FIG. 3.14. Crystal counter circuit.

The electrons that are set free by the primary ionizing particle will be accelerated toward the positive electrode by the electric field. The lattice point from which the electron came is immobile and will be left positively charged so it might be regarded as a hole or trapping center in its ability to capture wandering electrons. There is evidence that electron multiplication occurs by impact, but not to the extent observed in gases. The average distance that an electron can travel in the crystal before being captured is a measure of the effectiveness of the crystal as a detector. For AgCl and LiF at 78° K. this mean path length is of the order of 10 centimeters, whereas at room temperature it is only about 0.1 centimeter. The diamond crystal may be used satisfactorily at room temperature.

[20] P. F. Van Heerden, Dissertation, Utrecht (1945).

Some of the advantages of the solid crystal counter are as follows: (a) By virtue of its greater stopping power it has a high efficiency in detecting gamma rays and high-energy electrons. (b) Being small in size it offers better geometry in many experiments. (c) The resolving time is shorter than for most G-M tubes, thus allowing a higher counting rate.

These favorable characteristics are counterbalanced by the troublesome annealing procedure and the low-temperature operational requirements. Stability and reproducibility are good only when considerable care is exercised. Only a relatively few of the natural diamond crystals behave satisfactorily. Clear white gem stones seem [21] to be preferred, although there is no certain criterion of successful performance.

3.12. Cerenkov (pronounced sher-en'kof) Counter. In a transparent medium whose index of refraction η is considerably greater than unity, an unusual velocity relationship may exist. If a charged particle of high-energy traverses the medium, its velocity may be very close to that for light in free space ($C = 3 \times 10^{10}$ centimeters per second). On the other hand, the phase velocity of light and hence the electric and magnetic disturbances associated with the moving charge can travel outward in the refracting medium with a velocity V equal only to C/η. It was predicted by Cerenkov [22] in 1934 and substantiated theoretically by Frank [23] and Tamm that the moving charge would on this account coherently emit some of its energy as visual radiation. The angle θ that the emitted radiation will make with the incident particle is as shown in Figure 3.15, and is such that

$$\cos \theta = \frac{1}{\beta\eta} \qquad (3.4)$$

where β is the ratio V/C and η is the index of refraction. The emitted wave front is much like the shock wave in an elastic

[21] D. R. Corson and R. R. Wilson, *Rev. Sci. Instruments*, **19**, 207 (1948).
[22] P. A. Cerenkov, *Compt. rend. U.R.S.S.*, **8**, 451 (1934); *Phys. Rev.*, **52**, 378 (1937).
[23] I. Frank and I. Tamm, *Compt. rend. U.R.S.S.*, **14**, 109 (1937).

medium traversed by a projectile moving with a velocity greater than that of sound.

The effect depends only on the charge of the particle and its velocity and not upon its momentum or energy. Thus, for an electron of 200 Mev energy moving in lucite, $\beta \cong 1$ and $\eta = 1.5$ so that θ is 48 degrees 14 minutes. For a 200-Mev meson, however, $\beta = 0.864$ and θ is only 39 degrees 30 minutes. By shaping the conducting medium with an outer inclined surface

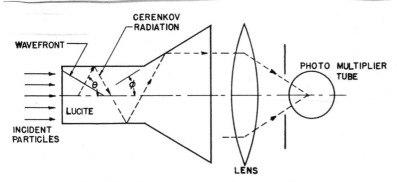

FIG. 3.15. Circuit for detecting Cerenkov radiation.

as shown in Figure 3.15 such that the angle $\phi = \frac{1}{2}\theta$, it is possible to direct by reflections and a converging lens the entire radiation upon the sensitive input surface of a photomultiplier tube. A single count would then be recorded for the complete transit of one charged particle.

For an electron of energy greater than 100 Mev in lucite the Cerenkov radiation amounts to only about 1 Kev per centimeter, while in the same length of path the same electron will lose about 2 Mev by the usual collision phenomena. It might be expected that the Cerenkov radiation would thus be completely masked by the radiation due to recombination, following ionization. Thanks to its directional characteristics, however, it may be uniquely identified.

It has been suggested [24] that the device might well be used

[24] I. Getting, *Phys. Rev.*, **71**, 123 (1947); R. H. Dieke, *Phys. Rev.*, **71**, 737 (1947).

to take advantage of the different angles θ for meson and electron and thus distinguish between them. In addition to several transparent organic materials, such as lucite and styrene, a medium like lithium fluoride, which conducts in the ultraviolet, would serve especially well to demonstrate the effect. The blue glow observed in the water of a reactor, close to the active fuel elements, is radiation of this kind.

3.13. Parallel Plate Counter.

In the measurement of extremely short half-lives such as 10^{-7} second or less, the conventional G-M tube is unsatisfactory. This is due to the inherent delay in the formation of the electron avalanche because of the weak electric field in regions slightly distant from the central wire. By using parallel plates having an area of several square centimeters and spaced a few millimeters apart in an atmosphere of argon plus additional organic vapor, an interesting counter [25] results. The threshold voltage may be from 2000 to 3000 volts with a plateau of 1000 volts. Upon discharge the rise time may be less than 10^{-8} second, and it will yield a pulse 600 volts in amplitude, so that no amplification is necessary. A disadvantage is that the recovery time, approximately 0.01 second, is exceptionally long and even for electrons the efficiency of approximately 10% is not good.

3.14. High-efficiency Gamma Counters.

The ionization produced by gamma radiation within the gas contained in a chamber is dependent largely upon the charged particles which are ejected by the chamber walls. Chambers have been designed [26] with enormously increased gamma sensitivity by increasing the relative ratio of wall area to gas volume. A chamber of this type made up of as many pancake sections as desired with a common anode and cathode is shown in Figure 3.16. Each pancake section has its individual anode as a circular ring of fine wire supported by quartz mountings.

[25] J. W. Keuffel, *Phys. Rev.*, **73**, 531 (1948); L. Madansky and R. W. Pidd, *Phys. Rev.*, **73**, 1215 (1948).
[26] M. Wiedenbeck, *Rev. Sci. Instruments*, **19**, 819 (1948).

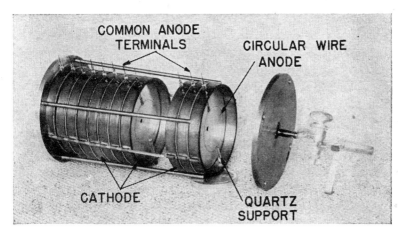

FIG. 3.16. A multicell counter for gamma rays (Wiedenbeck).

3.15. Wilson Cloud Chambers. In 1911, a device was demonstrated by C. T. R. Wilson [27] which made it possible for the first time to see and photograph the "track" of an individual particle. This apparatus functions because of the fact that in a supersaturated vapor, condensing droplets will form, if possible, on any electrically charged particles that are present. For vapors that have a negative specific heat under the condition of saturation, a supersaturated condition can be attained by producing a sudden increase in the volume containing the saturated vapor. For saturated vapors with a positive specific heat, supersaturation can be produced by suddenly reducing the volume. Water vapor and many of the alcohols have negative specific heats and serve well in chambers of the first kind.

Wilson observed that as supersaturation increases, the negative ions first serve as centers of condensation. This will occur when the volume occupied by the saturated vapor is increased about 25%. For an increase in volume of 31% both negative and positive ions serve as nuclei of droplets. For expansions

[27] C. T. R. Wilson, *Proc. Roy. Soc. A*, **85**, 285 (1911).

greater than 38% a dense cloud will form even without the presence of ions. An alpha particle traversing the gas of the chamber may produce on the average 100,000 ions per centimeter of path, whereas an electron or beta particle will produce only about one one hundredth as many. Consequently it is relatively easy to observe the tracks of alpha particles.

A measurable magnetic field is applied perpendicular to the floor of the chamber and hence perpendicular to the velocity of the particles to be photographed, so that their paths are circular. By noting the radii of curvature of the tracks their momenta and hence their energies can be determined. For best results it is important that the particle undergo no scattering collision during its path, for in that event its radius of curvature cannot be determined accurately. To reduce this scattering, hydrogen is used instead of air in the chamber along with the saturated water or alcohol vapor.

For alpha particles the source is usually placed directly in the chamber. Beta rays may be sent into the chamber through a thin window with little loss in energy. Gamma rays are studied by observing the electrons originating in the chamber because of the Compton effect, the photoelectric effect, or by electron pair formation. For the Compton effect, a thin sheet of light material, such as carbon, is placed within the chamber and irradiated with the gamma radiation. For the latter two effects a thin layer of lead is put in the chamber in a similar manner. Neutrons are studied by observing the recoil protons arising because of the impact of the neutrons on any hydrogenous material within the chamber. The hydrogen gas and water vapor serve very satisfactorily in that capacity.

Qualitatively, the value of cloud chamber observations cannot be challenged. In many instances, however, because of the failure to observe proper criteria in the selection of tracks for measurement and the failure to recognize the effects due to scattering and convection, the quantitative results have been lacking in exactness, and misleading in their interpretation.

3.16. The Bubble Chamber. It has been found possible to produce tracks in transparent liquids due to energetic ionizing particles. The liquid first so used [28] was diethyl ether, but many others, such as hydrogen, benzene, pentane, sulfur dioxide, and ethyl alcohol have been found to be satisfactory. The liquid should have a low surface tension and high vapor pressure. The procedure is to heat the liquid under a high pressure to a temperature well above its normal boiling point.

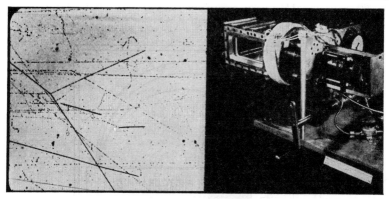

Fig. 3.17.   Pentane-filled bubble chamber and photogram showing carbon disintegration.

A sudden release in pressure leaves the liquid in a highly superheated state, in which condition it is ready to begin violent boiling. The string of ions left by an energetic particle at this instant serve as nuclei for bubble formation. This line of bubbles may be photographed within a few microseconds, and thus yield a record of the event. Figure 3.17 shows a pentane-filled chamber 6 inches long, 2 inches wide, and 3 inches high. The figure includes a typical photogram taken with the chamber receiving the 2 Bev beam of the Brookhaven accelerator. The tracks are probably largely pi mesons and protons. The star shown is probably the disruption of a carbon nucleus.

[28] D. A. Glaser, *Phys. Rev.,* **87**, 665 (1952); *Phys. Rev.,* **91**, 762 (1953); J. G. Wood, *Phys. Rev.,* **94**, 731 (1954).

This small chamber, due to the relative density of the liquid, is equivalent in stopping power to a cloud chamber some 140 feet long. By using liquids of light atoms scattering is minimized and thus magnetic field measurements may be made. The operation cycle may be as short as 3 or 4 seconds.

3.17. The Beta Ray Spectrometer.
The beta rays from excited nuclei consist of electrons varying in energy from a certain maximum value down to zero. The distribution of the

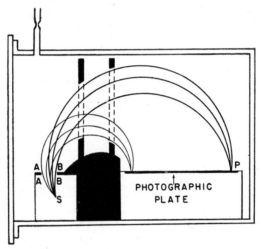

Fig. 3.18. Magnetic semicircular focusing beta ray spectrometer.

number of particles in each energy group seems to follow a certain natural law of probability. To observe this distribution beta spectrometers of various designs have been developed.

a. Magnetic Semicircular Focusing Spectrometer. Figure 3.18 represents a very useful and practical form of spectrometer as devised by Danysz [29] in 1912. It was later improved by Robinson and Rutherford [30] and has been subsequently used in many investigations.

The source of radiation is placed at S and a photographic

[29] J. Danysz, *Le Radium*, **9**, 1 (1912); **10**, 4 (1913).
[30] H. Robinson and E. Rutherford, *Phil. Mag.*, **26**, 717 (1913).

plate is situated as shown perpendicular to the plane of the figure. The source at S sends out a bundle of particles through the aperture AB. A uniform magnetic field is directed perpendicularly into the figure. Those particles having the same velocity will describe circles of the same diameter. If AB is located in the plane of the photographic plate and is not too wide, then all electrons of the same energy will converge almost at the same point P on the photographic plate. Actually the greatest range is attained by the particles through a point C at the center of the slit, situated on a perpendicular from S. Those rays on either side of C strike the plate at a point slightly less distant from the slit than P, thus giving a diffuse image with a sharp outside edge. The total line width w for a source S of negligible width may be expressed as

$$w = SP(1 - \cos \theta) \frac{SP}{CP} \qquad (3.5)$$

where 2θ is the angle ASB.

Beta rays of different energies would result in images P at different distances from the slit. Instead of the photographic plate it is possible to place a slit at P through which the electrons pass into a Geiger tube, connected to a counting circuit. In this case the particles received, travel on circles of the same diameter and different energies are brought to the Geiger tube by varying the deflecting magnetic field.

When natural radioactive substances were first examined in this device it was found that they exhibited certain "lines" representing definite energy groups superimposed on a continuous background. These lines of discrete energies are not true beta rays but are really due to gamma rays that have been internally converted. In this process the gamma ray, in getting out of its parent atom, gives up its complete energy to an orbital electron of the same atom, such as a K, L, or M electron. Monoenergetic gamma rays from an assembly of such atoms will thus be represented by a few groups of electrons each differing from the discrete gamma energy by the binding energy characteristic of the K, L, M, etc., levels.

It is customary to express the performance of the instrument in terms of the solid angle subtended by the image at the source, and by the resolving power, which is defined as the

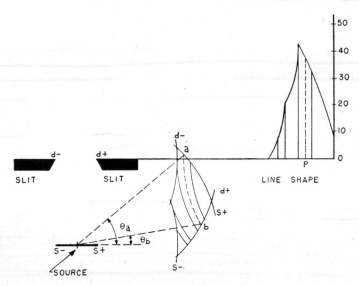

FIG. 3.19.   Graphical determination of electron line shape in semicircular magnetic spectrometer.

ratio of the half width of a spectral line $w/2$, divided by the distance between the source and the spectral line (2ρ). For a relative solid angle of 0.15%, the resolving power of this instrument as usually used is about 0.4%.

The shape of the spectral line may be determined by a simple graphical construction as shown in Figure 3.19. Considering electrons of a single energy in a uniform magnetic field B, all will travel in circular paths of radius ρ. Now by drawing four arcs of radius ρ, one from each edge of the slit and one from each edge of the source, a four-sided area as shown is described. This area contains the centers of all trajectories of radius ρ that can originate in the source, get through the slit, and arrive at the photographic plate. Now using any point in the image such as P as a center with the radius ρ, the intensity at this point is proportional to the number of centers or the length of arc ab within the curved area.

To keep the electron line width as narrow as possible, the mass per unit length in the source must be kept as small as pos-

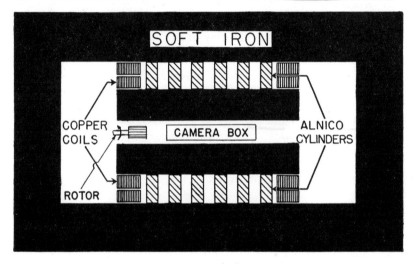

FIG. 3.20.   Alnico magnet for beta spectrometer.

sible, to avoid the slowing down of the electrons in getting out of the material. This may greatly increase the required exposure time and will require that the magnetic field be kept constant for long periods. This can best be accomplished by the use of a permanent magnet as shown in Figure 3.20. Special magnetic alloys known as "Alnico" with remarkably large coercive force and remanence are available. The magnet need have only short Alnico members as indicated and may be magnetized by a momentary current through the exciting coils, after which the remanence maintains the magnetic field unchanging as long as desired.

The relationship between the energy of a beta particle and the radius of its path may be computed. For the circular motion of the electron e, the force toward the center due to a magnetic induction B and velocity v is

$$Bev = \frac{mv^2}{\rho} \tag{3.6}$$

in which ρ is the radius of the path. The mass m is the relativity mass, equal to $m_0(1 - \beta^2)^{-\frac{1}{2}}$, where m_0 is the rest mass and β is the ratio of the velocity of the electron v to the velocity of light c. The momentum P of the particle is then

$$P = mv = \frac{m_0 v}{\sqrt{1 - \beta^2}} = Be\rho \tag{3.7}$$

The energy W of the particle in relativity theory is

$$W = mc^2 - m_0 c^2 = \frac{m_0 c^2}{\sqrt{1 - \beta^2}} - m_0 c^2 \tag{3.8}$$

On expansion this becomes

$$W = \frac{1}{2} m_0 v^2 \left[1 + \frac{3}{4} \frac{v^2}{c^2} + \frac{15}{24} \frac{v^4}{c^4} + \cdots \right] \tag{3.9}$$

or replacing m_0 by m and again expanding

$$W = \tfrac{1}{2} m v^2 [1 + \tfrac{1}{4}\beta^2 + \tfrac{1}{8}\beta^4 - \tfrac{5}{160}\beta^6 \cdots] \tag{3.10}$$

which shows how the classical value for the kinetic energy of high-speed beta particles must be corrected, as β increases in value toward unity. An explicit solution combining equations 3.7 and 3.8 gives

$$P = \frac{1}{c} [W^2 + 2m_0 c^2 W]^{\frac{1}{2}} \tag{3.11}$$

and the observed product $B\rho$ is

$$B\rho = \frac{1}{ce} [W^2 + 2m_0 c^2 W]^{\frac{1}{2}} \tag{3.12}$$

or

$$W = c\sqrt{m_0^2 c^2 + B^2 \rho^2 e^2} - m_0 c^2 \tag{3.13}$$

This relationship is shown graphically in Figure 3.21, so that in practice the observed $B\rho$ can be fitted to the curve and the value of W in Kev read off directly. It is apparent that at high energies the value of $B\rho$ increases linearly with energy W.

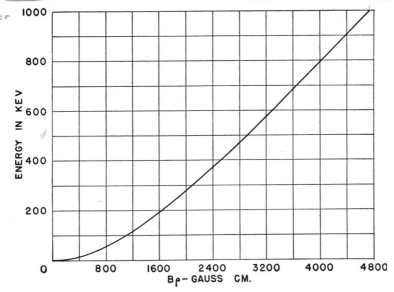

Fig. 3.21. Energy-momentum relationship for beta particles.

In the Appendix, data are given for electron energies up to 15 or more Mev.

b. The Electron Lens. A type of beta spectrometer known as the electron lens is shown in Figure 3.22. A radioactive source S is placed on the axis at one end of an evacuated cylinder. The

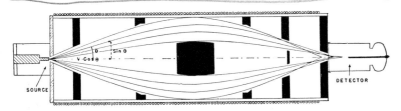

Fig. 3.22. Solenoidal wound electron lens spectrometer.

cylinder is surrounded by a solenoidal wound conductor. At the other end of the cylinder is placed a detecting tube. Between the detecting tube and the source is a heavy absorber of lead, as shown, so that no radiation can be received directly. An arrangement of this sort was first suggested by Kapitza and

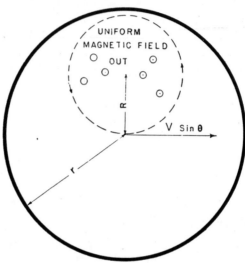

Fig. 3.23. End view of electron lens spectrometer showing projected motion of electron.

was constructed and used by Tricker [31] in 1924. For any current through the solenoidal winding an almost uniform magnetic field will be set up through the coil parallel to its axis, whose value is given by the expression $0.4\pi nI$, where n is the number of turns per centimeter and I is the electric current in amperes.

Any electron e starting out from the source s, with a velocity v, making an angle θ with the axis, will experience a force causing it to execute a helical path. The component of the velocity v along the axis is $v \cos \theta$ and this component carries the electron from left to right with a uniform speed. The radial component

[31] R. A. Tricker, *Proc. Cambridge Phil. Soc.*, **22**, 454 (1924); see also C. M. Witcher, *Phys. Rev.*, **60**, 32 (1941).

of velocity $v \sin \theta$ is at right angles to the magnetic induction B and hence the electron experiences a force $Bev \sin \theta$. As a result of this force the electron will trace out a circular path as viewed along the axis, at the same time that it is being transported. Some electrons will have precisely the right velocity for a particular magnetic field so that they just traverse a complete circle of radius R, as shown in Figure 3.23, while they are carried along the tube from the source to the detector a distance L. At the midpoint they are at their maxiumum displacement $2R$ from the axis. They then arrive back again at the axis tangentially just at the detector. In order that this will happen, the time of transit in the circle, traversing the distance $2\pi R$ at the speed $v \sin \theta$, must just equal the time of transport through the distance L by the speed $v \cos \theta$. This can be expressed as

$$\frac{2\pi R}{v \sin \theta} = \frac{L}{v \cos \theta}, \quad \text{or} \quad \cotan \theta = \frac{L}{2\pi R} \qquad (3.14)$$

Only those particles starting at this angle θ can be successfully received.

From equation 3.6 it follows that $Bev = \frac{mv^2}{\rho}$

$$\rho = R = \frac{mv \sin \theta}{Be} = \frac{L \tan \theta}{2\pi} \qquad (3.15)$$

$BeR = mv \sin \theta$

Hence the momentum of the collected particles mv, which started out from the source S along the surface of a cone, is

$$mv = \frac{BeL}{2\pi \cos \theta} = CB = kI \qquad (3.16)$$

Be $\hookrightarrow$ magnetic induction

where C and k are constants. That is, the momentum of the collected particles varies linearly with the electric current in the solenoid. It is evident that the instrument can be calibrated for all energies by observing the electric current required for the transmission of electrons of any single known energy. An additional advantage of this type of spectrometer is that fairly weak radioactive sources can be studied since, in effect, the detector subtends a large solid angle at the source.

This same principle, except that the electrical conductors are bunched in a short coil, is used in focusing the beam in electron microscopes. Spectrometers for beta rays have been [32] similarly constructed. By changing the current through the winding the magnetic induction B is changed and a different energy group of electrons will negotiate the baffle system and arrive at the detector.

For a relative solid angle of about 0.9% the usual resolving power is approximately 2%. Great care must be taken in the dimensions and the proper placement of the source as a slight variation produces a large distortion at the image.

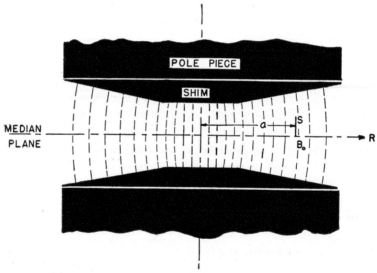

FIG. 3.24. Magnetic field shape for double-focusing spectrometer.

c. *The Double-focusing Magnetic Spectrometer*. While it is true that a focusing exists in the semicircular magnetic spectrometer for those electrons whose paths lie in the median mag-

[32] See O. Klemperer, *Phil. Mag.*, **20**, 545 (1935); and M. Deutsch, *Phys. Rev.*, **59**, 684 (1941).

netic plane, no such effect is apparent for the particles whose velocities have a component upward or downward with respect to this plane. However, by properly shaping the magnetic field it is possible to obtain [33] a simultaneous focusing of monoenergetic electrons within a sizable solid angle. It will be seen that the problem here is much the same as occurs in the operation of the synchrotron. When correctly applied, the time for any radial vibration of the particle must just equal the time for its perpendicular vibration. Then all electrons within a certain solid angle from a point in the source will ideally converge to form a single point in the image.

A form of the magnetic field that has been found [34] satisfactory in practice is shown in Figure 3.24. The magnetic induction B decreases as the radius R increases and it is expressed by the equation

$$B = B_0 \left[1 - \frac{R - a}{2a} + \frac{(R - a)^2}{8a^2} \right] \qquad (3.17)$$

where B_0 is the magnetic induction at a predetermined constant radius a. The oscillations in the two perpendicular directions bring the electrons together after an angular transit of $\sqrt{2}\pi$ or 253.8 degrees, instead of 180 degrees as in the conventional spectrometer. The advantage of the instrument is that a much larger relative solid angle, of the order of 0.4%, may be used and yet a good resolving power of about 0.33% obtained.

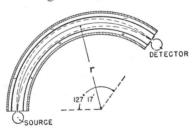

FIG. 3.25. Beta spectrometer with electrostatic focusing.

d. *Beta Ray Spectrometer with Electrostatic Focusing.* It was shown [35] by Hughes and Rojansky that by the use of a radial, inverse first-power, electro-

[33] K. Siegbahn and N. Svartholm, *Nature*, **157**, 872 (1946); *Arkiv Mat., Astron., Fysik*, **33A**, No. 21, 1 (1947).
[34] F. B. Shull and D. M. Dennison, *Phys. Rev.*, **71**, 681 (1947); **72**, 256 (1947).
[35] A. L. Hughes and V. Rojansky, *Phys. Rev.*, **34**, 284 (1925).

static field a bundle of electrons of the same energy could be focused in a manner similar to that accomplished by a magnetic field. It was calculated that for an angle of deviation equal to 127 degrees 17 minutes two electrons starting through the entrance slit as shown in Figure 3.25 will refocus and pass through a receiving slit into the detector. A beta spectrometer operating on this principle has been used [36] successfully by Backus. It is particularly adaptable to the measurement of low-energy particles. The inverse first-power, radial field is provided by the two concentric electrodes made as grids rather than solid plates to avoid scattering. The electrodes are spaced about 1 inch apart with a mean radius of 6 inches and the chamber is evacuated. A linear relationship exists between the energy of the particles and the voltage difference between the electrodes.

If the mean radius is r and the outer and inner electrodes have radii r_2 and r_1, respectively, then it may be calculated for the geometry shown that the energy W of the particles undergoing focusing as shown is approximately

$$W = \frac{V_2 - V_1}{2 \log_e \left(\frac{r_2}{r_1}\right)} = 3.0(V_2 - V_1) \qquad (3.18)$$

In this equation, W is the energy of the particles in electron volts focused by applying to the plates as shown, a potential difference $(V_2 - V_1)$ in volts.

3.18. Calorimetric Methods. When the radiation from radioactive bodies of any kind is absorbed by matter, the temperature of the absorber is increased. This phenomenon was first demonstrated [37] by P. Curie and A. Laborde in 1903. By arranging the junctions of iron-constantan thermocouples, one in a specimen of pure barium chloride and the other in an identical specimen of "radiferous" barium chloride, a steady dif-

[36] J. Backus, *Phys. Rev.*, **68**, 59 (1945).
[37] P. Curie and A. Laborde, *Compt. rend.*, **136**, 673 (1903).

ference in temperature of 1.5° C. was observed. On putting 1 gram of the "radiferous" barium chloride in a Bunsen calorimeter they found that about 14 calories of heat were released per hour.

The amount of heat observed depends upon how completely the varous radiations are absorbed. Many subsequent investigations [38] to ascribe the proper heating effect to each type of radiation have been carried out. Experimental determinations [39] lead to reported values of about 139.6 calories from 1 gram of radium in 1 hour. This value is evidently too low since a summation of the known alpha and beta energies yields a value of 176 calories per gram per hour. It indicates that the radium used was not sufficiently aged to be in equilibrium with its products.

The energy of the particles derived from the fission of uranium was measured by the use of a sensitive calorimeter. It was determined in this way by Henderson [40] that the average energy per atom on fission was about 186 million electron volts.

3.19. The Mass Spectrometer. In determining the properties of "positive" rays, in a discharge tube, J. J. Thomson really constructed the first "mass" spectrograph. The collimated beam of particles was allowed to pass first through a magnetic field in which they received a horizontal deflection and then through an electric field giving a vertical deflection. The deflection of the particles was noted on a fluorescent screen. A beam of positive particles all with the same mass but with different velocities would spread out so as to form a parabola on the screen. Other particles with the same charge but of larger mass would appear as another parabola with smaller displacement.

If the singly charged particles all are accelerated by the same potential, then they will have a common energy. In this case

[38] S. Meyer and V. Hess, *Wien. Ber.*, **121**, 603 (1912); V. Hess, *Wien. Ber.*, **121**, 1 (1912); E. Rutherford and Robinson, *Phil. Mag.*, **25**, 312 (1913).
[39] S. W. Watson and M. Henderson, *Proc. Roy. Soc. A*, **118**, 318 (1928); I. Zlotowski, *J. Phys. radium*, **6**, 242 (1935).
[40] M. Henderson, *Phys. Rev.*, **58**, 774 (1940).

the magnetic field alone will suffice to resolve the particles with respect to mass. An apparatus of this type in which the moving ions traced out semicircular paths was arranged and extensively used by Dempster.[41]

Beams of charged particles that are homogeneous electrically $\left(\dfrac{mv^2}{e} \text{ constant}\right)$ or homogeneous magnetically $\left(\dfrac{mv}{e} \text{ constant}\right)$

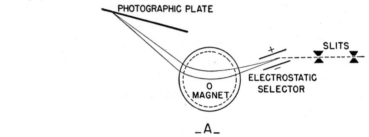

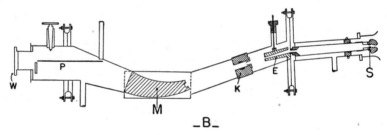

FIG. 3.26. (A) Schematic and (B) detailed sketch of mass spectrograph (Aston).

may be focused like a beam of light. A mathematical analysis demonstrating the possibility was carried through [42] by Fowler, and an apparatus was constructed and used by Aston. The arrangement employed is shown schematically in Figure 3.26A and in somewhat more detail in Figure 3.26B. The narrow beam of rays emerging from the cathode canal is spread into a spectrum by the electric field. After the spreading in the elec-

[41] A. J. Dempster, *Phys. Rev.*, **11**, 316 (1918).
[42] F. W. Aston, *Phil. Mag.*, **38**, 709 (1919); F. W. Aston and R. H. Fowler, *Phil. Mag.*, **43**, 514 (1922); F. W. Aston, *Nature*, **137**, 357, 613 (1936).

tric field, the rays may be regarded as emanating from a virtual
point source within the plates. Now just as it is possible to
take advantage of the dispersive power of glass to form an
achromatic image, so may those singly charged particles of the
same mass be brought together by the magnetic field M to a
common point on the photographic plate P. Those particles
having a slightly different mass will arrive at a different point.

The accurate comparison of two masses in a mass spectrum
depends on the determination of two quantities, the distance
between the lines and the dispersion constant. The latter
quantity is determined by a measurement of the interval between two lines due to masses differing by a small known
amount. The hydrides of the varous elements are useful to
this end. It then becomes possible to investigate an unknown
element by bracketing it with another known element perhaps
in a different state of ionization so as to form doublets. Such
doublets as (O^+, Ti^{3+}), (N^+, Fe^{4+}), (Pd^+, Bi^{2+}), etc., have
been successfully used.

Since the excellent initial work of Aston a great number of
modifications in mass spectrographs have been introduced.
Among the important con-
tributors in this field are
Dempster,[43] Bainbridge and
Jordan,[44] Bleakney,[45] and
Nier.[46]

A sketch of the simple and
effective apparatus devised by
Nier is shown in Figure 3.27.
It is essential that a line

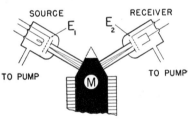

FIG. 3.27. Mass spectrograph (Nier).

through the source slit and the receiving slit pass through the
intersection of the two inclined surfaces limiting the magnetic
field. In this case, a dispersing beam of particles of a given

[43] A. J. Dempster, *Phys. Rev.*, **51**, 67 (1937); **53**, 64 (1938).
[44] K. T. Bainbridge and E. Jordan, *Phys. Rev.*, **49**, 883 (1936); **51**, 384 (1937).
[45] W. Bleakney and J. Hipple, *Phys. Rev.*, **53**, 521 (1938).
[46] A. O. Nier, *Rev. Sci. Instruments*, **11**, 212 (1940).

mass normal at the first surface will leave the second surface
so as to come together at the symmetrically placed receiving
slit.   The angle of refraction is 60 degrees.   To focus different

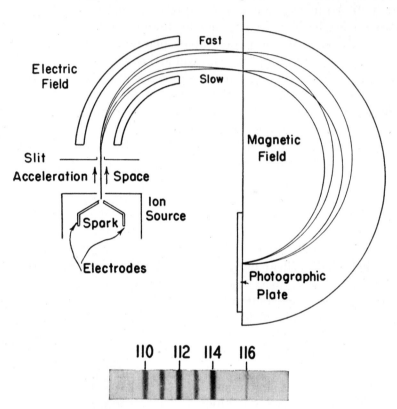

FIG. 3.28. Mass spectrometer (Dr. A. J. Dempster), together with the mass spectrum
of cadmium.

isotopes at the collector, the accelerating voltage at E_1 is
varied.   The ions are again slowed down by a potential at E_2
so that no disturbing influence will arise by secondary ions at
impact.

Figure 3.28 is a sketch of the refracting system of the very
effective mass spectrometer used by Dr. Dempster.   A photo-

gram of the isotopic spectrum of cadmium, showing the six stable isotopes differing from each other by 1 mass unit, is included.

3.20. Time of Flight—Mass Spectrometer. If ions are accelerated so as to have a velocity v perpendicular to a magnetic field of B gauss they will describe circular or helical paths. The time t for one circular transit, from equation 3.6, is

$$t = \frac{\text{distance}}{\text{velocity}} = \frac{2\pi r \cdot m}{Ber} = \frac{2\pi}{Be} m \qquad (3.19)$$

so that its measurement serves to evaluate the mass of the ion. For singly charged ions this time [47] is approximately $670m/B$ microseconds. It is thus possible to pulse an accelerating source and observe the delayed arrival of the ions on a synchroscope which has been triggered by the source. For a uniform magnetic induction of 100 gausses and a singly charged ion of 150 mass units the time is thus about 1000 microseconds. By allowing the ion to make several revolutions the times are correspondingly increased and the resolution improved. The method seems to have particular promise for ions of large atomic mass.

Due 2 weeks from 29 Sept.

QUESTIONS AND PROBLEMS

1. The average energy of formation per pair of ions is 35 ev. A beta ray of energy 1 Mev or more produces about 25 ion pairs per cm. at 50 kev or less about 200 ion pairs are produced per cm. Estimate the range of a 1 Mev beta particle in normal air by assuming the average ion production to be that of the mean. How will it be different in practice?

Answer: 253 cm, much larger.

2. An alpha particle whose energy is 5 Mev has a range in standard air of 3.51 cm. About how many ion pairs are produced during its absorption, assuming the above energy per pair? Express the total

[47] S. A. Goudsmit, *Phys. Rev.*, **74**, 622 (1948); P. Richards, E. Hays, and S. Goudsmit, *Bull. Am. Phys. Soc.*, **24**, R3 (1949); J. Hipple and H. Thomas, *Phys. Rev.*, **75**, 1616 (1949).

charge of one kind produced by the alpha particle in electrostatic units and in coulombs.

Answer: 1.425×10^5, 6.88×10^{-5} electrostatic units, 2.29×10^{-14} coulombs.

3. A beta ray of energy 1 Mev is projected normally to a magnetic field of 800 gausses. Compute the expected radius of curvature on using the relativistic mass.

Answer: 5.93 cm.

4. The capacity of the detecting element in an ionization chamber and electrometer is only 0.4 micromicrofarad. The voltage sensitivity of the electrometer is 5 divisions per volt. How many ions will be required to give a deflection of one division? If the average length of alpha paths in the chamber is 3 cm, what is the effect of a single alpha particle?

Answer: 5×10^5 particles, 0.26 division per particle.

5. What mass of radium in equilibrium with its products would supply energy at the steady rate of 100 watts? What mass of normally disintegrating uranium would supply the same power?

Answer: 488 gm, $\sim$ 1160 tons.

6. If every gamma photon produces 2 ion pairs per cm along its path, how many photons must pass per cm^2 to be represented by an intensity of 2 roentgen units? How will this be affected by the presence of neighboring material?

Answer: 2.08×10^9.

7. In a certain G-M tube the central wire has a diameter of 0.18 mm and is 1200 volts positive with respect to the cylindrical cathode whose inner radius is 1.8 cm. Express the maximum and the minimum values of the electric field along a radius.

Answer: $25{,}200 \dfrac{\text{volts}}{\text{cm}}$, $126 \dfrac{\text{volts}}{\text{cm}}$.

8. The tube in problem 7 is certified by its maker as having a lifetime of 10^9 counts. If used at an average counting rate of 2000 counts per min for a 40-hr week, when should it be replaced?

Answer: At the end of 4 years of service.

9. Every worker in an Atomic Energy Commission production plant carries a condenser badge dosimeter, to assure safe working conditions. If the capacity of the condenser is 5 electrostatic units with an effective volume of 6 cm^3 and it is charged to a potential of 200 volts, what should be its danger potential at the end of a 7-day week if a tolerance dosage of 0.04 r per day is enforced.

Answer: 99.2 volts.

CHAPTER 4

INDUCED RADIOACTIVITY—APPARATUS

4.1. Early Experiments. Shortly after the discovery of radioactivity it was noticed that any material in close contact with a radioactive substance became radioactive. This phenomenon was described in many published papers and the subject was termed "Induced Radioactivity." It was observed that the nature of the induced radioactivity in any body depended solely upon the nature of the original radioactive source and not at all upon the material receiving the activity.

With the discovery of the radioactive families, it became clear that the "induced radioactivity" was due to the arrival of a disintegration product which was itself radioactive. Thus a parent atom on disintegration might by chance result in the heavy daughter atomic residue being projected out of the original radioactive body into the contiguous material. For example, a radium atom of mass 226 will on disintegration yield a helium nucleus of mass 4 and a radon atom of mass 222. To satisfy the conservation of momentum, the velocity of the radon atom will be $\frac{2}{111}$ that of the alpha particle and hence its energy will also be $\frac{2}{111}$ as large. The energy of the alpha particle is 4.744 million electron volts, so the recoiling radon atom has an energy of 85,000 electron volts. This energy is amply sufficient if properly directed to carry the radon atom out of the parent material and into the neighboring substance.

A crystal, such as diamond, will, if packed in radium for some time, undergo an important change in color. The crystal will in turn be found to be radioactive and will emit the same type of radiation that characterizes radon. No physical agent will remove the radon products from the surface, showing that they have been driven in with great energy.

4.2. Disintegration by Alpha Particles—Rutherford.

In 1914, Marsden [1] demonstrated that when hydrogen gas was bombarded by the alpha particles from radium C some of the hydrogen molecules were converted into protons and driven forward. For an elastic collision, conserving momentum and energy, it follows that a single proton would proceed forward with a velocity v_p equal to $\frac{8}{5}$ the velocity of the incident alpha

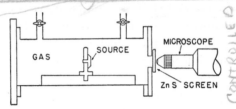

FIG. 4.1.   Apparatus to detect disintegrations produced by alpha particles (Rutherford).

particle v_a. Its energy would therefore be $\frac{16}{25}$ that of the alpha particle. The alpha particle has a range in air of 6.97 centimeters or an energy of 7.75 Mev, so that the proton receives an energy of 4.96 Mev and should travel forward about 32 centimeters in air or 128 centimeters in hydrogen. Marsden found scintillations on a zinc sulfide screen placed more than 100 centimeters from the source of alpha particles.

This investigation made use of an arrangement as shown in Figure 4.1. When the hydrogen gas in the chamber was replaced by pure nitrogen, scintillations were observed through the microscope on the screen at distances as remote as if the scintillations were made by recoil protons. On replacing the nitrogen with oxygen, under similar conditions, no scintillations whatever were observed. Observations of this sort led Rutherford [2] to suspect that the nitrogen nucleus might be disrupted by the impinging alpha particle, and might in its disintegration emit a proton. The protons were found to be

[1] E. Marsden, *Phil. Mag.*, **27**, 824 (1914).
[2] E. Rutherford, *Phil. Mag.*, **37**, 537 (1919).

emitted in all directions from the bombarded element. Such evidence confirmed the conclusions that, with this simple apparatus, controlled transmutation of an element was for the first time accomplished.

This success with nitrogen [3] was followed by an extended investigation of all of the light elements of the periodic table. Rutherford and Chadwick [4] found evidence for the disintegration of all elements from boron to potassium with the exception of carbon and oxygen.

4.3. Nuclear Cross Section. In any interaction between a nucleus and another incident particle, it is frequently instructive to evaluate a "cross section" (σ) for the process concerned. This can be very simply visualized as follows:

Each incident particle will sweep out a cylindrical volume whose area is σ and whose length is equal to its depth of penetration. Imagine N incident particles passing completely through a thin layer of thickness t containing Q particles per square centimeter. Suppose there result n interactions of the type considered. The effective volume swept out by the N incident particles in traversing the layer t is $N\sigma t$ cubic centimeters, and the average volume per nucleus in the material is $\dfrac{1 \times t}{Q}$ cubic centimeters. Hence the number of collisions is $N\sigma t$ divided by $\dfrac{t}{Q}$ or

$$n = N\sigma Q \tag{4.1}$$

and

$$\sigma = \frac{n}{NQ} \text{ square centimeters} \tag{4.2}$$

For a thick target in which t' is the depth of penetration of the N projectile particles, the volume swept out is $N\sigma t'$ and

$$\sigma = \frac{n}{Nt'} \times \frac{A}{\rho \times 6.023 \times 10^{23}} \tag{4.3}$$

[3] E. Rutherford and J. Chadwick, *Phil. Mag.*, **42**, 809 (1921).
[4] E. Rutherford and J. Chadwick, *Nature*, **113**, 457 (1924).

where A is the atomic weight, ρ is the density, and 6.023×10^{23} is the Avogadro number.

It will be found in the various nuclear processes, to be considered later, that this quantity may have values ranging from 10^{-20} to 10^{-32} square centimeter. It is not inherently determined by the dimensions of the bodies and for two given particles may have different values depending upon the particular process considered. This may be used to indicate the probability of a nuclear reaction. Thus a reaction for which σ is 10^{-24} is 100 times more probable than one for which σ is 10^{-26} square centimeter. The cross section 10^{-24} square centimeter is commonly termed a "barn."

4.4. Disintegration by Protons—Cockcroft and Walton Experiment. With the certainty that nuclear disintegrations could be produced by alpha particles, numerous attempts were made to accelerate other ions to sufficiently high speeds to produce a similar effect. Success was first attained at Cambridge by Cockcroft and Walton [5] with the use of accelerated protons. They used a voltage multiplying circuit similar to an arrangement that had been used by T. E. Allibone to accelerate electrons. The principle of operation of the apparatus is illustrated in Figure 4.2A. Condensers of equal capacity are represented by C_1, C_2, C_3, etc. If the switch blades are in the down position, then the battery B is connected across the condensers C_1 and C_5. On moving the blades to the up position, condenser C_5 transfers a proportional part of its charge to condenser C_2. On the next downward movement of the switch blades, C_2 transfers half of its charge to C_6 which in turn passes half of its charge on to C_3. A continuous up and down motion of the switch blades results in a movement of charge upward until every condenser is charged to the potential of the battery. The total over-all potential is the sum of that of the series condensers, and is applied to the discharge tube.

[5] J. D. Cockcroft and E. Walton, *Proc. Roy. Soc. (London)*, **129**, 477 (1930).

In the actual apparatus, as shown in Figure 4.2*B*, an alternating voltage is applied and the switching action is accomplished by the use of rectifying vacuum tubes. The first apparatus attained an output of 300,000 volts. A subsequent apparatus was designed [6] to yield energies up to 800,000 elec-

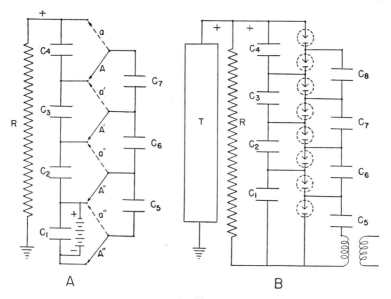

FIG. 4.2. Voltage multiplying circuit; (*A*) mechanical switching, (*B*) vacuum tube switching (Cockcroft and Walton).

tron volts. In operation it was able to deliver a beam of protons up to 10 microamperes at 700 kv. On impact with lithium or beryllium targets, an appreciable yield of alpha particles was observed in all directions, indicating nuclear disintegration. In fact, with lithium, it was found that protons having energies as small as 20,000 electron volts could produce occasional disruptions.

The reaction involved was interpreted as the formation of two alpha particles from the combining of the proton and the

[6] J. D. Cockcroft and E. Walton, *Proc. Roy. Soc. A*, **136**, 619 (1932).

lithium isotope of mass 7. This can be represented by an equation as

$$_1H^1 + {}_3Li^7 \rightarrow {}_4Be^8 \rightarrow 2{}_2He^4 + Q \tag{4.4}$$

The term Q represents the kinetic energy of the two alpha particles in excess of the kinetic energy of the incident proton. It arises from the fact that the combined masses of hydrogen and lithium 7 are greater than the combined mass numbers of two helium atoms by 0.01863 mass units. This mass corresponds to an energy of 17.3 Mev. This very large amount of energy can then occasionally be set free by as little as 20,000 electron volts or a thousandfold energy magnification produced. At this low bombarding energy, however, the probability that one incident particle will produce a disintegration is less than one in a million, so that no overall gain in available energy can be anticipated from this source. Oliphant and Rutherford constructed a similar device, capable of delivering a beam of 100 microamperes of deuterons at the relatively low potential of 250,000 volts. At this energy a high yield of neutrons was produced by bombarding ice made of heavy water.

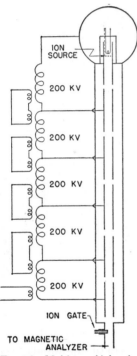

FIG. 4.3. Multistage high voltage transformer.

4.5. Transformers. On account of insulation difficulties it is not feasible to raise the secondary voltage of a transformer to indefinitely high values. By using a Tesla coil arrangement in a tank of oil under pressure, Breit, Tuve, and Dahl [7] reported the production of several million volts but no application was made of the output.

[7] G. Breit, M. Tuve, and O. Dahl, *Phys. Rev.*, **35**, 51 (1930).

By arranging a succession of transformers each of which develops a voltage such as 200 kv and in turn excites another contiguous similar unit, an unlimited output voltage may be derived with no insulation problem greater than that for 200 kv. Figure 4.3 shows a five-stage arrangement of this sort as used by H. R. Crane,[8] with an output of one million volts. The output of each unit is applied to an accelerating cylinder in the discharge tube. Ions are admitted and accelerated only on the positive peak of the potential wave. This arrangement was patterned after a similar installation at Pasadena constructed by Lauritsen and his associates.[9] The multistage transformer was first developed by Sorensen.[10]

4.6. Use of Atmospheric Electricity. It is a well-known fact that at most places on the earth's surface a rather steep normal

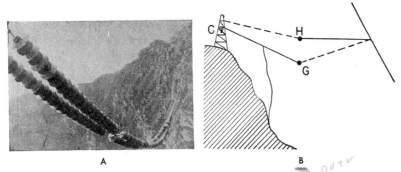

Fig. 4.4. (*A*) View of cable for high potential from atmosphere; (*B*) circuit plan.

potential gradient exists. This gradient is usually of the order of 200 to 400 volts per meter, but in mountainous country, particularly during stormy weather, it may become as large as 100,000 volts per meter. In 1928 an attempt was initiated by Brasch [11] and co-workers at Mount Generoso to utilize this phe-

[8] H. R. Crane, *Phys. Rev.*, **52**, 11 (1937).
[9] C. C. Lauritsen and R. D. Bennett, *Phys. Rev.*, **32**, 850 (1928).
[10] R. W. Sorensen, *J. Am. Inst. Elec. En.*, **44**, 373 (1925).
[11] A. Brasch and F. Lange, *Z. Physik*, **70**, 10 (1931). C. Urban, who conducted the first experiments on atmospheric high potentials, lost his life thereby.

nomenon in the operation of a discharge tube at extremely high potentials. A report on the project was given in 1931. The arrangement used is shown schematically in Figure 4.4*B*. The high potential pickup terminal with its supporting insulated cable stretching form one peak across to a neighboring summit is shown in Figure 4.4*A*. By raising or lowering the grounded terminal *G* with a winch at *C* the gap between *H* and *G* could be varied as desired. For a free height of 100 meters, potential differences up to 15 million volts could be observed [12] between *G* and *H* during and both before and after a severe storm. No successful application of the high voltage was made.

4.7. The Impulse Generator. When charged condensers are connected in series, the over-all potential difference is of course

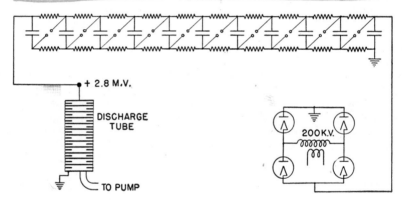

FIG. 4.5.   An impulse generator for high voltage.

the sum of the individual falls of potential. This principle has often been used as a method of voltage multiplication. The condensers can be charged in parallel and then shifted to a series connection. This same procedure has been utilized in high-potential devices known as "impulse" generators. Figure 4.5 shows an arrangement as used by Brasch and Lange [13] capable of developing potentials up to 2.8 million volts. A full wave

[12] A. Brasch, *Naturwissenschaften*, **21**, 82 (1933).
[13] A. Brasch and F. Lange, *Z. Physik*, **70**, 10 (1931).

rectifier supplies EMF to the condensers through the high resistances as shown.

Each spark gap is in parallel with one resistance and one
condenser. When the potential across a spark gap becomes
sufficiently high it breaks down. The breakdown of any one
gap with its consequent lowering of resistance is immediately
followed by the breakdown of all other gaps if they are properly
adjusted. In this condition the circuit may be regarded as if
the high-valued resistances were not present and as if the line
of charged condensers are connected in series by the line of conducting spark gaps. In operation, about two impulses were
produced per second and the output used to accelerate particles
in the discharge tube shown on the left. The wall of this evacuated tube consisted of a stack of alternate conducting and in-
sulating rings of sufficient height to withstand the voltage without external sparking.

4.8. The Van de Graaff Generator. Because of mutual repulsion, any electric charge communicated to a conducting
body will distribute itself over the external surface. The idea
of using this principle as the basis of an electrostatic generator
was proposed as early as 1890 by Lord Kelvin.[14] It was forty
years before a successful working model was produced. By
supplying the charge continuously at the center of an insulated
metal sphere, R. J. Van de Graaff,[15] in 1931, developed a high-
potential generator capable of a steady output. The electric
charge was sprayed onto a moving insulated belt and conveyed
to the center of a large sphere mounted on a cylindrical texto-
lite supporting post. Within the sphere the charge leaked
from the moving belt onto a collector system connected to the
sphere and raised the potential accordingly. The maximum-
limiting potential of the sphere is determined by the breakdown electric field in the gas at the surface of the sphere, or in
the supporting insulator.

[14] John Gray, *Electrical Influence Machines*, Whittaker, London (1890).
[15] R. J. Van de Graaff, *Phys. Rev.*, **38**, 1919 (1931).

Prob. #1

Suppose the radius r of a sphere is, say, 1 meter and the limiting electric field $\mathcal{E}_m$ at the surface is 30,000 volts per centimeter or 100 electrostatic units. It follows that the limiting charge Q_m, the maximum potential E_m, and the capacity C (= 100 electrostatic units) are related as follows:

$$Q_m = CE_m = 100E_m \qquad (4.5)$$

and

$$\mathcal{E}_m = 100 = \frac{Q_m}{r^2} = \frac{100E_m}{(100)^2} = \frac{E_m}{100} \qquad (4.6)$$

Therefore

$$E_m = 100 \times 100 = 10,000 \text{ ESU}$$
$$= 3,000,000 \text{ volts} \qquad (4.7)$$

The first generator consisted of two spheres, each 2 feet in diameter and mounted upon neighboring insulated posts. One sphere was charged positively and the other negatively. A potential difference of 1,500,000 volts was obtained with a continuous current of 25 microamperes. A similar machine with spheres 15 feet in diameter was constructed [16] with the expectation of producing 20 million volts. Due to various difficulties this goal has never been reached.

The maximum electric field that can exist outside of the sphere without breakdown goes to larger values if the pressure of the gas is increased, or, even better, if the space is completely evacuated. This indicated the possibility of higher potentials with apparatus of smaller over-all dimensions, provided a gas-tight housing surrounded the insulated charged conductor. To obtain a satisfactory vacuum, considerable difficulty would be experienced, and this procedure has not been tried. On the other hand, many installations have been put into operation, in which an increased pressure is employed, as shown schematically in Figure 4.6. If air alone is used a definite fire hazard will exist by virtue of the compressed oxygen, so pure nitrogen is usually substituted.

[16] R. J. Van de Graaff, K. T. Compton, and L. C. Van Atta, *Phys. Rev.*, **43**, 149 (1933).

A 2.4-million-volt generator of this sort operating in a tank at a pressure of 100 pounds per square inch was constructed at Wisconsin by Herb and his associates.[17] Two additional features have been introduced allowing still higher output voltages with no increase in dimensions. A relatively small number of heavy gas molecules, such as freon (CCl_2F_2), will, because of their large cross section for electron capture, increase substantially the electric field needed for breakdown.

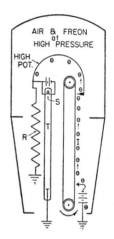

FIG. 4.6. Plan of the Van de Graaff generator.

Under high pressure, air will withstand a greater potential gradient in a short gap than in a long one. Accordingly, Herb converted his generator from one with a single high-potential electrode to an arrangement of three separate concentric electrodes. Each was connected to a respective point distributed along the output resistance, so that in effect there were now three series gaps. In this way the output voltage was raised from 2.5 up to 4.5 million volts.

A compact unit capable of generating up to 4.5 million volts as developed by Dr. Van de Graaff is shown in Figure 4.7. This machine may be used to accelerate either electrons or protons. The discharge tube is usually surrounded by corona rings to distribute the potential uniformly. The accelerated electrons or protons impinge on a target, producing X-rays or nuclear disintegrations.

Many larger installations have now been constructed and put to use for accelerating heavy ions. The dimensions have been chosen so that voltages up to 10 million could be expected. These voltages have not been attained when loaded, usually because of leakage along the surfaces of the insulators. The volt-

[17] R. G. Herb, C. Turner, C. Hudson, and R. Warren, *Phys. Rev.*, **58**, 579 (1940).

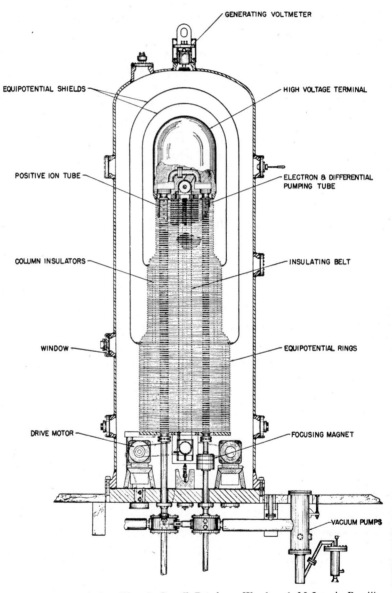

FIG. 4.7.   Skeletal view (Van de Graaff, Buechner, Woodward, McIntosh, Burrill, and Sperduto).

age may be maintained at a constant value by automatic con
trol. A portion of the ion beam deflected in a magnetic field
controls the electric charge sprayed on to the moving belt. If
the voltage drops, the deflected beam increases and hence also
the charge sent up the belt and the potential of the electrode.

4.9. The Linear Accelerator. In 1929, R. Wideroe [18] proposed
an accelerating tube in which the output voltage should be
many times that of the input. The tube should be provided
with a large number of hollow cylindrical electrodes of progressively increasing length all arranged along a common axis. This
was called a "linear accelerator." A schematic diagram of the
device is shown in Figure. 4.8. A working model of the apparatus, provided with 30 accelerating electrodes, was described by Sloan and Lawrence in 1931.[19] A high-frequency
generator operating at an output of 10 megacycles per second
has its terminals connected to the accelerating cylinders arranged in two groups. One terminal is connected to the group
consisting of electrodes numbered 1, 3, 5, etc., and the other
terminal goes to the group of remaining cylinders.

In order that ions beginning at the source S may be carried
continuously along the tube from left to right it is necessary
that the distance from the
center of one cylinder to the
center of the next, including
the gap, be just sufficient so
that the time of transit of
the particle between the two
points is one half the period
of the oscillating current. For

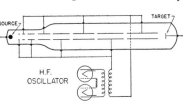

Fig. 4.8. The linear accelerator for high
energy particles.

the early stages this means steps with lengths in the ratio of
the square roots of successive integral numbers, since the ions
gain equal increments of energy at each acceleration. At very
high energies the velocity of the ions approaches the velocity

[18] R. Wideroe, *Arch. Electrotech.*, **21**, 387 (1929).
[19] D. Sloan and E. O. Lawrence, *Phys. Rev.*, **38**, 2021 (1931).

of light as a limit, hence each energy increment is mainly represented by an increase in mass rather than velocity. The cylinders then approach uniformity in size and spacing and the distance between adjacent centers is a half wavelength of the wave emitted by the electric oscillator.

The output of the first arrangement was about one tenth microampere of mercury ions at an effective voltage of 1,260,000. On increasing the input voltage from 42,000 to 79,000 and adding six more accelerating cylinders, the output energy was raised to 2,850,000 electron volts.[20]

A linear accelerator with a somewhat different principle for applying the high-frequency input has been described.[21] In this apparatus a voltage wave was sent along a loaded transmission line, connected to accelerating cylinders so that the voltage surge traveled along the tube at the same velocity as the ions.

A linear accelerator capable of delivering 32 Mev protons has been developed by Alvarez and co-workers.[22] By using 28 radar oscillators coupled to a series of drift tubes an acceleration of slightly less than 1 Mev per foot length of tube has been obtained. Figure 4.9A is a photograph of the exterior assembly showing the many radar transmitters. Figure 4.9B is a view within the 40-foot tank, showing the internal arrangement of drift cylinders. The ions are given an initial acceleration by a high-potential Van de Graaff generator. In many respects the linear accelerator is an ideal source of high-energy particles. It delivers an intense momentary pulse of protons well collimated, free from neutron background, and of uniform energy.

A very successful linear accelerator for electrons, of the traveling-wave type, has been constructed [23] at Stanford University. The cylindrical accelerator tube with properly spaced annular discs constitutes a wave-guide for directing the elec-

[20] D. Sloan and W. Coates, *Phys. Rev.*, **46**, 539 (1934).

[21] L. Snoddy, H. Trotter, W. Ham, and J. W. Beams, *J. Franklin Inst.*, **223**, 55 (1937); see also *Bull. Am. Phys. Soc.*, **21**, 5 (1946).

[22] L. Alvarez, B. Cork, L. Johnston, and C. Richman, *Phys. Rev.*, **75**, 1465 (1949).

[23] M. Chodorow, E. Ginzton, W. Hansen, R. Kyhl, R. Neal, and W. Panofsky, *Rev. Sci. Ins.*, **26**, 134 (1955).

A

B

Fig. 4.9. The 32-Mev linear accelerator at Berkeley (L. Alvarez, W. Panofsky, B. Cork, L. Johnston, C. Richman).

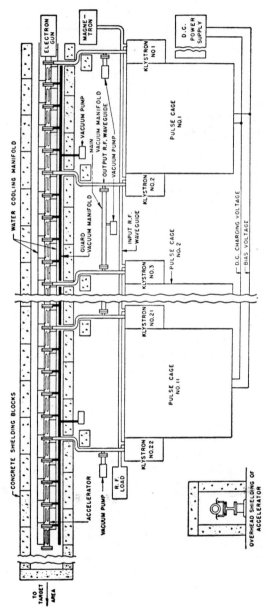

FIG. 4.10.   Linear accelerator for electrons (Stanford University).

trons. As currently operated, the tube is 220 feet long, and power is supplied at 10-foot intervals from powerful klystrons (40 megawatts) operating at a wavelength of 10.5 cm or at a frequency of 2850 megacycles per second. The peak current during each pulse which lasts about 0.3 microsecond is about 50 miliamperes as about 10^{11} electrons are accelerated per pulse and arrive in a beam only about $\frac{1}{4}$ inch in diameter. An output energy of 630 million electron volts has been attained. The electron gun injects electron clusters at a voltage of about 80 kv, sixty times per second. The general arrangement of tube and shielding is shown in Figure 4.10.

4.10. The Focusing of Ions, Electrically. It might be thought that in a long discharge tube, the beam of ions would become dispersed as the distance from the source increased. Figure 4.11 shows that this is not true. This figure shows the gap between two coaxial cylinders when a difference in potential exists

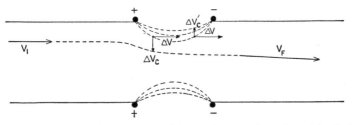

FIG. 4.11. Showing the focusing effect of the gap between charged coaxial cylinders.

between them. Any oncoming ion with a velocity V_1 will receive, in the first half of the gap, an increment of velocity ΔV forward and an increment of velocity toward the axis of the cylinder ΔV_c. During the latter half of the gap it receives an equal increment in its forward motion but now a force acts outward away from the axis. This latter velocity increment $\Delta V_c'$ outward is not as great as that toward the axis, because it is now traveling faster and hence is acted upon by a force for a shorter time. In practice a very real focusing of the ions is accomplished in this way.

When the field at the gap is changing rapidly during the transit of the ions, either a phase focusing or defocusing may be produced. If the potential at the gap is increasing as from A to B in Figure 4.12, the radial force inward during the first half of the gap will be weaker than the outward component during the latter half and defocusing will be produced. Conversely, a decreasing field as from M to N will lead to focusing.

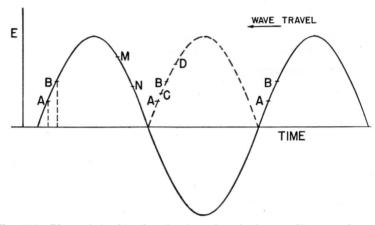

FIG. 4.12. Phase relationship of accelerating voltage in the gap of linear accelerator.

In order to retain phase stability in a linear accelerator, it is necessary to accelerate on the portion of the wave leading to radial defocusing. This may be seen from Figure 4.12. If an ion is for some reason moving too slowly after being accelerated at AB, it will arrive a little later at the next gap, as at CD. It will receive a correspondingly larger acceleration as represented by the ordinate of CD and thus be kept in step along the tube. To avoid defocusing with protons it is possible to cover the entrance to each cylinder with a beryllium foil a few millionths of an inch in thickness or a metal grid to shape the electric field so there is no outward radial component.

4.11. The Cyclotron. At a meeting of the National Academy in 1929, E. O. Lawrence reported on a new principle for the

multiple acceleration of ions. He later supported the theory
with the description of a small working model capable of giving
an output [24] of 80,000 volt protons, using a maximum input of
2000 volts. The device was first called a "resonance magnetic
accelerator" but soon came to be known as the "cyclotron."*

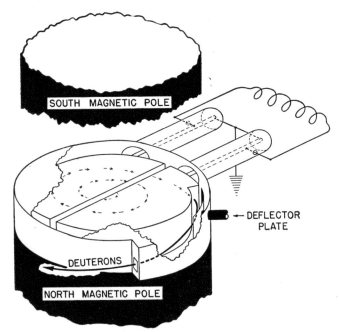

Fig. 4.13. Schematic view, showing action of the cyclotron.

The next development resulted [25] in a current of $\frac{1}{10}$ microampere of 500,000 volt protons, using an input of 5000 volts.
Since that time many cyclotrons have been built throughout
the world. A remarkable development leading to progressively
larger output currents and potentials has been carried out,

[24] E. O. Lawrence and N. Edlefson, *Science*, **72**, 376 (1930).
  * The word *cyclotron*, although rhythmic and pleasing in sound, might be objected to
by scholars of Greek since it comes from "cycle," meaning a circle, and "tron," a
suffix meaning an agent or "that which does." It might be thought that the machine itself was describing circular paths.
[25] E. O. Lawrence and S. Livingston, *Phys. Rev.*, **37**, 1707 (1931).

largely at the University of California. The ultimate in achievement was attained with the successful operation of the "bevatron," yielding protons of energy 6.5 billion electron volts (Bev).

The principle of operation of the cyclotron is shown in Figure 4.13. A large permanent magnet establishes a strong vertical, steady magnetic field, directed upward in the figure. The magnetic induction B between the pole tips may be as high as 16,000 gausses. Between the pole tips is a cheeseboxlike tank whose top and bottom plates are usually made of the same steel as the magnet core. Within the tank are two hollow D-shaped electrodes as shown, supported by long copper arms whose position can be adjusted. These electrodes are called "dees," and they are connected so as to form an oscillating circuit of high frequency, usually about 12 million cycles per second.

The tank is first evacuated to as low a pressure as possible, and then an appropriate gas to become the source of ions is introduced. At the center of the tank on either the floor or the ceiling is a filament maintained at a high negative potential. The column of ejected electrons from the filament will, on striking the gas, yield a column of atomic ions in the space between the dees.

In the presence of the electric field the positive ions are accelerated toward and into the negative dee. On traveling through the magnetic field they will experience a force normal to their velocity, which will result in their describing a circular path of radius r. The centrifugal and centripetal forces are equal. If B is the magnetic induction, e the electronic charge in electromagnetic units, and m the mass of the ion moving at the velocity v, then these forces are

$$Bev = \frac{mv^2}{r} \qquad (4.8)$$

so

$$r = \frac{mv}{Be} \qquad (4.9)$$

Within the hollow dee the electric field is zero and hence the ions will traverse a semicircle which will carry them around and back into the gap. Now if the time of transit for the ion in the semicircular path is equal to the time of one-half cycle of the high-frequency oscillation, then the ion arriving at the gap finds the field reversed and is again accelerated, this time into the other dee. The increased velocity results in the ion describing a new half-circle of larger radius. The success in operation depends on the important fact that the times for all half-circle transits, neglecting relativity corrections, are the same.

The time t for the transit of a half-circle is the distance πr divided by the velocity v. On introducing the value of r from equation 4.9 it follows that

[handwritten: t not a $f(r)$, as long as m is constant.]

$$t = \frac{\pi r}{v} = \frac{\pi m v}{B e v} = \frac{\pi}{B} \frac{m}{e} \quad (4.10)$$

[handwritten: In FM cyclotron m is not constant]

so that the radius r of the orbit does not influence the time.

It is also apparent that the final energy of an ion of definite mass and charge must vary as B^2 and as the square of the maximum radius, because from equation 4.9

$$v^2 = B^2 r^2 \left(\frac{e}{m}\right)^2 \quad \text{and} \quad \frac{1}{2} m v^2 = \frac{m}{2} B^2 r^2 \left(\frac{e}{m}\right)^2 \quad (4.11)$$

It also follows that any change in the frequency n must be compensated by a corresponding change in magnetic induction B to maintain resonance, because from equation 4.10

$$n = \frac{1}{2t} = \frac{1}{2\pi} \frac{e}{m} B \quad (4.12)$$

Hence for protons, $n = 1525B$ and for alpha particles or deuterons, $n = 770B$.

In practice the accelerated ions may have such large energies that their velocity (v) becomes appreciable compared to

the velocity of light (c). In this event their mass is the relativity mass m which is equal to $\dfrac{m_0}{\sqrt{1 - v^2/c^2}}$. It might be expected that this condition would make for a lack of resonance
at high energies and hence place an upper limit on the output
of the device. If the m increases with energy, it is apparent
from equation 4.12 that it is only necessary that B increase
accordingly, in order that t be constant. This can be accomplished by a proper arrangement of the magnetic field so that it
increases slightly at greater distances from the center. Such a
variation would however lead to magnetic defocusing of the
ion beam.

A factor aiding in extending the high-energy upper limit was
the use of a very high oscillating voltage on the dees. In this
way the ions will receive a larger increment of energy each impulse and will acquire their final energy with as few round trips
as possible and all disturbing factors will produce a minimum
effect.

As the ions approach a limiting outer radius they are deviated by a deflecting plate charged to a high negative potential.
This electrode is placed almost tangential to the ion path and
exerts an electrostatic radial force on the ion. This force is
sufficient to bring the ions completely out of the tank if desired.

The particles found to be most effective in nuclear disintegration are deuterons. These atomic ions are produced by the
ionization of heavy hydrogen. Figure 4.14 shows the 10-
million volt beam of deuterons produced by the Michigan
cyclotron and projected into the air through a range of about
64 centimeters. The bluish glow in the path of deuterons is
sufficient to photograph in the dark. Under ideal adjustment
the range of all deuterons will be very nearly the same. In practice it may happen that the beam is not entirely homogeneous.
On using helium gas, alpha particles with a total energy twice
that of the deuterons, for the same geometry, are produced.

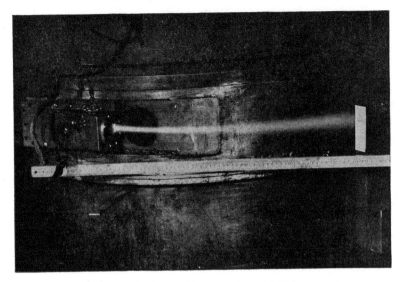

FIG. 4.14. The 10-Mev beam of deuterons from the Michigan cyclotron.

The ions may be kept in a median plane, as they describe their circular paths, by the proper adjustment of the magnetic field resulting in magnetic focusing.   Because of the fringing at the edge, the lines of force will be bowed outward as shown in Figure 4.15. It is apparent, therefore, that an ion either above or below the median plane will experience a force directed toward the center.

Many improvements in technique have been contributed by various workers in the field. One early advance, allowing much higher voltage on the dees, was a mounting and connection so that each dee with its support consti-

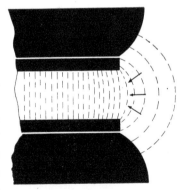

FIG. 4.15.   Illustrating the focusing of ions in the cyclotron by the fringing of the magnetic field.

B

A

Fig. 4.16. (*A*) Cyclotron magnet; (*B*) tank assembly (Mass. Inst. of Tech.).

tutes a quarter-wave line. This eliminated the need of glass
or porcelain supporting insulators for the dees, with all the
difficulties associated with their use, such as puncture or
breakdown. It adds somewhat to the awkwardness of the
apparatus, as the supporting arms must be much more massive, as shown by Figure 4.16B, which is the tank assembly

FIG. 4.17. The 184-inch cyclotron at Berkeley, showing the tank in place with its
30-inch diffusion pump.

of the cyclotron [26] at the Massachusetts Institute of Technology,
with the cover of the chamber removed. The magnet of the
same cyclotron is shown in Figure 4.16A.

The output of a cyclotron is not continuous but consists of
pulses of ions arriving at the target. For each cycle of the alternating current two pulses would be initiated so that for 10
megacycles, 20 million ion groups would arrive at the target per
second. In the largest cyclotrons such as the 184-inch instru-

[26] M. S. Livingston, J. Buck, and R. D. Evans, *Phys. Rev.*, **55**, 1110 (1939).

ment shown in Figure 4.17, only one dee is employed, thus greatly simplifying the adjustments.

4.12. Frequency Modulation. A noteworthy advance, overcoming any hypothetical theoretical limitation on the maximum energy because of the relativistic variation in mass, was the successful introduction of "frequency modulation." If the magnetic field is made to fall off as the radius increases, to achieve magnetic focusing, and if the mass of the particle at the same time increases, then, as indicated by equation 4.10, the time required for the ions to traverse the outer half-circles must obviously become progressively greater. By starting a pulse of ions at the center and slightly modulating the frequency toward lower values, the condition for resonance can be maintained for that group of particles from the center to the outer radius. For 15-Mev protons, this was accomplished [27] by a high-speed rotary vacuum condenser, so that the frequency changed by about 13% with an optimum modulation frequency of 500 cycles per second. For the 184-inch cyclotron yielding 190-Mev deuterons, the frequency is made [28] to change from about 12.6 to 9 megacycles per second in about one one-hundredth of a second, and it then returns to the original value and a new pulse of ions is in turn escorted outward to the target. The instantaneous pulse current may be very large, but the average output current is reduced since the interval between the arrival of ion pulses is appreciable. Since defocusing is overcome, there is no necessity to go to excessively high voltage on the dee and in practice only about 5000 volts are used. A cyclotron provided with frequency modulation is termed a "synchrocyclotron."

Modern circuitry allows the attainment of frequency modulation over a wide range in a relatively simple manner. One property of the many ferrites used is that their permeability

---

[27] J. R. Richardson, K. MacKenzie, E. Lofgren, and B. T. Wright, *Phys. Rev.*, **69**, 669 (1946).

[28] W. Brobeck, E. O. Lawrence, K. MacKenzie, E. McMillan, R. Serber, D. Sewell, K. Simson, and R. L. Thornton, *Phys. Rev.*, **71**, 449 (1947).

decreases at high magnetic fields. Thus, if the frequency of the accelerating voltage is controlled by a resonant circuit containing an inductance with a ferrite core, then on saturating the ferrite the permeability decreases and the frequency increases as desired.

Another method takes advantage of the fact that the super-dielectric constant of barium titanate ($BaTiO_3$) may be reduced by the action of a strong direct electric field. The accelerating voltage is controlled by a resonant circuit as shown in Figure 4.18, in which the condensers are of the titanate type.

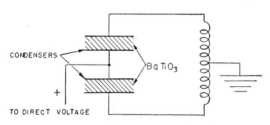

CONDENSERS

$Ba\,TiO_3$

+

TO DIRECT VOLTAGE

Fig. 4.18. Frequency modulation circuit with $BaTiO_3$ capacitance.

The application of a direct voltage at C reduces the dielectric constant and hence increases the natural frequency of the circuit. The voltage may be varied in the proper shape to give the required frequency change. Due to the sufficiently short time of relaxation, the high dielectric constant is restored promptly with the removal of the direct electric field.

A useful nomograph relating the energy, the range, the maximum radius, the magnetic induction, and the wavelength of the oscillator, for alpha particles, protons, or deuterons in the cyclotron, is presented in Figure 4.19.

4.13. The Betatron. A device particularly suited to accelerating electrons to high potentials was first developed by D. W. Kerst in 1940.[29] The apparatus was called a "betatron" and its functioning depended upon well-known physical principles. The initial unit was able to speed up electrons to an energy of

[29] D. W. Kerst, *Phys. Rev.*, **60**, 47 (1941).

Could be compared with Transformer since electrical energy is put in and gotten out.

Good practical use is for studying penetration, etc. of X-rays.

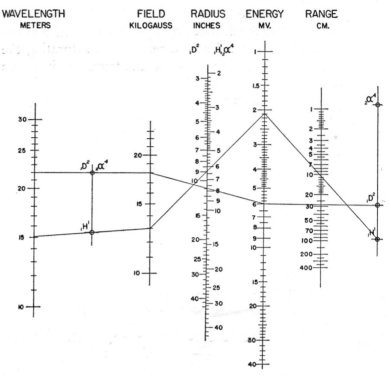

Fig. 4.19. Nomograph relating wavelength, field, and radius of cyclotron to energy
and range of protons, deuterons, or alpha particles.

2.3 Mev. This was soon followed by an enlarged unit [30] with
an output of 20 Mev. Subsequent development of a much
larger instrument at the General Electric Company resulted
in a 100 million volt beam of electrons.

The principle of operation may be readily understood by referring to Figure 4.20. If the magnetic flux within the circle
perpendicular to the page be increased, as by bringing a north
pole toward it, then any turn of wire about the circle will have
an EMF induced in it, whose instantaneous value is the time
rate at which the magnetic flux changes and is represented as

[30] D. W. Kerst, *Phys. Rev.*, **61**, 93 (1942).

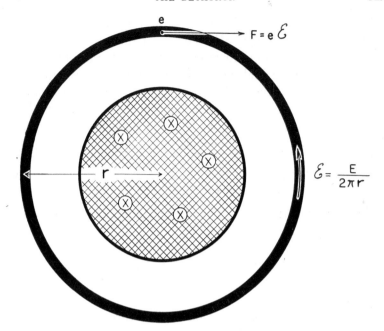

Δ flux causes increase in speed

$d\phi/dt$. This would tend to make positive electricity travel about in a counterclockwise sense, and electrons in a clockwise direction. If the electrons were in free space they would only start their clockwise transit and continue tangentially. However, if they were traveling in a magnetic field also directed into the paper, then from the "motor" rule they would experience a central force perpendicular to their velocity. If this force were precisely the right magnitude, then the electron path would be circular. As long as the flux through the central area is increasing, so long will the EMF continue in the same sense and the faster the electron will go. Now if the magnetic induction B at the electron orbit increases at the same rate as the momentum of the electron, then the path of the electron will be a circle of constant radius r.

The energy acquired by any charge e on falling through a potential difference E is eE. Hence, if the velocity acquired by the electron is sufficient to carry it around many trips while E persists, then the final energy is the energy per turn multiplied by the number of trips. The time derivative of the flux ϕ is the instantaneous electromotive force in the surrounding loop and for some change from ϕ_1 to ϕ_2 in a time t, the average electromotive force E is $\dfrac{\phi_1 - \phi_2}{t}$. For the electron at the path of radius r there exists a tangential electric field $\mathcal{E} = \dfrac{E}{2\pi r}$ and a force F equal to $\mathcal{E}e$. The acceleration a of the electron of charge e and mass m is then

$$a = \frac{F}{m} = \frac{e\mathcal{E}}{m} = \frac{eE}{m2\pi r} = \frac{e}{m}\frac{\phi_2 - \phi_1}{2\pi rt} \qquad (4.13)$$

A typical calculation may be carried through to note the order of magnitude of the various quantities. In the electromagnetic system imagine $\phi_2 - \phi_1 = 1,000,000$ maxwells in $1/1000$ second, then for a radius of 10 centimeters, $E = 10$ volts and $a = 2.8 \times 10^{14}$ centimeters per second per second. If it were not for the increase in the mass of the electron, the velocity of the electron would have practically attained the velocity of light in the interval of $1/10,000$ second. In $1/1000$ second it would have traveled 2.8×10^7 centimeters or 448,000 times around. It would therefore have gained in energy 4,480,000 electron volts.

Actually, due to the increase in mass as the velocity of the electron approaches the speed of light, a condition is attained where the velocity changes only slightly with increased energy. On equating the force toward the center, Bev, to the centrifugal force, mv^2/r, it follows that the momentum

$$mv = Ber \qquad (4.14)$$

Hence to keep r constant, any change in momentum mv must be compensated by a corresponding change in B. Any change in momentum $\Delta(mv)$ may thus be represented as

$$\Delta(mv) = (B_2 - B_1)er \qquad (4.15)$$

The same momentum change of the electron was due to an impulse from the induced electric field $\mathcal{E}$, so that

$$\Delta(mv) = Ft = \mathcal{E}et = \frac{E}{2\pi r}et = \frac{(\phi_2 - \phi_1)e}{2\pi r} \qquad (4.16)$$

On equating the last terms in equations 4.16 and 4.15, it follows that

$$B_2 - B_1 = \frac{\phi_2 - \phi_1}{2\pi r^2} \qquad (4.17)$$

The flux ϕ through the circle may be regarded as the product of the circular area and the average value of the magnetic induction B within the circle. If the magnetic induction at the orbit is zero when the flux is zero, then at any subsequent time the B at the orbit must be just one half the average B within the circle.

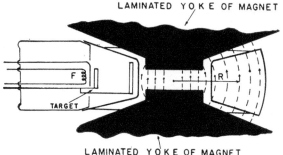

LAMINATED YOKE OF MAGNET

LAMINATED YOKE OF MAGNET

FIG. 4.21. A sectional sketch of betatron.

A sectional view of the accelerator is shown in Figure 4.21. By tapering the pole tips to a smaller clearance at the center, the condition of a larger average B within the orbit is achieved. The electrons are injected from a hot filament and speeded

up by an accelerating field.   In their transit they may spiral
slightly inward or outward, depending upon focusing conditions,
until they reach a stable orbit.   As the flux increases, the iron
at the center will ultimately approach saturation.   When this
condition is attained equation 4.17 is no longer satisfied and the
orbit tends to grow smaller.   When a slightly smaller radius is
reached the particle impinges upon a target, usually consisting
of a thin sheet of tungsten.   At this high energy the efficiency
of X-ray production is very great, so that with beams so far
possible, cooling the target offers no serious difficulty.

The varying magnetic field is usually achieved by applying
to the large magnet, made from assembled sheet steel lamina-
tions, an alternating current whose frequency lies between 60
and 600 cycles per second.   The winding on the iron core is
tuned to resonance at the desired frequency by the use of a
large condenser.   The ions are accelerated only during one
quarter of the cycle.

At the University of Illinois a unit capable of developing 250
Mev is in operation.   It has been shown by Kerst [31] and others
that the amount of iron needed may be greatly reduced if the
magnetic flux is biased to a negative value.   This may be
accomplished by using a relatively small number of back turns
about the soft-iron pole tips, carrying a steady direct current.
The change in flux, accelerating the electron, then begins while
B is negative (and approaching zero) rather than when it is
zero and increasing.

4.14. The Synchrotron.   In the betatron the energy communicated to the electron per turn is very small, so that, in
total, many revolutions must be made to build the energy up to
the desired high value.   Many suggestions [32] have been made
of alternative methods to achieve the same result more easily
by the direct application to the particle of high-voltage impulses.   The particle would still be kept in a circular path by

[31] D. W. Kerst, *Phys. Rev.*, **68**, 233 (1945).
[32] V. Veksler, *Jour. Phys. Chem.*, U.S.S.R., **9**, 153 (1945).

a magnetic field. A proposed device was described by Mc-Millan [33] and called the "synchrotron." The multiple acceleration of the particle in a circular path was first accomplished by the betatron effect together with the application of a high-frequency voltage. This voltage can be applied by allowing the particles to pass repeatedly through a cavity resonator as produced by a "klystron" oscillator or any other equivalent circuit. By varying B as in the betatron, together with the application of frequency modulation, the ion is kept in a semi-stable orbit, increasing only slightly in radius as the energy changes. Several machines of this type, designed to accelerate electrons in the range of 300 Mev, have been constructed.

A design in which the quadrants of the circular magnet are separated by straight sections, known as the "race-track," was proposed.[34] This permits easy injection of high-energy electrons and avoids the necessity of betatron action for the initial acceleration. On this account the amount of iron needed is relatively very small, as there is no central steel core. By injecting electrons at 500 kev, their velocity is already 86% of that of light and consequently the frequency modulation of the accelerating electric input need be only about 15%.

4.15. The Cosmotron. With the successful operation of electron synchrotrons with straight sections, designs were proposed for similarly accelerating protons. At the Brookhaven National Laboratory the machine is called a "cosmotron" and has delivered protons with energies approximating 2.5 Bev. The orbital diameter is 60 feet and the protons are injected at 3.6 Mev by a Van de Graaff generator. The ring-shaped magnet is C type in section with a vertical gap of 9 inches. At 3.6 Mev the mass of the proton is only 0.4% greater than its rest mass, whereas at 3 Bev it is 4.2 times as large. The velocity at injection is only about 0.0862 times that of light, and the equi-

[33] E. M. McMillan, *Phys. Rev.*, **68**, 143 (1945).
[34] D. M. Dennison, T. Berlin, and H. R. Crane, *Phys. Rev.*, **69**, 542 (1946).

librium orbit requires a magnetic field of 300 gausses and radio frequency power at 360 kilocycles per second. At a discharge energy of 3 Bev the magnetic field must have risen to 14,000 gausses and the oscillator frequency to about 4000 kilocycles per second. By increasing the field proportionally with the

FIG. 4.22.   General view of cosmotron with control panel (Brookhaven National Laboratory).

momentum of the particle, the orbital radius will remain constant. The accelerating impulse up to about 2 kilovolts is delivered to the protons each revolution in a gap located at the center of one of the straight sections. By the use of one of the many patented ferrite materials, which have a high permeability at the frequencies employed, yokes may be constructed so that the beam itself constitutes the secondary winding of the accelerating transformer. A general view of the instrument looking through the control room is shown in Figure 4.22.

4.16. The Bevatron. A much larger machine of the same type as the cosmotron has been constructed and successfully operated at the University of California (Berkeley). Protons are first accelerated by a Cockroft-Walton generator up to 460 kev and passed on to a linear accelerator from which they are injected at 9.9 Mev into a straight section of the large accelerat-

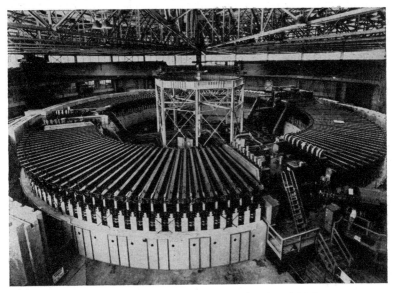

Fig. 4.23. The bevatron. (Radiation Laboratory, University of California, Berkeley.)

ing tube by an electrostatic inflector. While only a fraction of the ions that are introduced survive, pulses consisting of as many as 10^{10} protons, at energies approximating 6.5 Bev have been reported. The radii of the curved tracks vary from slightly less to something more than 600 inches. Figure 4.23 shows an over-all view of the magnet including the linear accelerator. At energies of this magnitude it will be seen that there exists the possibility of making a positive hyperon by nucleon bombardment. Pulses arrive at the target at the rate of about ten per minute.

It has been reported that a larger machine of similar type is projected in the U.S.S.R. but is not yet in operation.

4.17. The Alternating Gradient Strong Focusing Accelerator. In the operation of the synchrotron it was shown that a proper shaping of the magnetic field could result in the establishment of restoring forces on any particle that strayed from the equilibrium orbit. A particle might then execute radial and vertical oscillations. If a quantity n is defined such that

$$n = -\frac{dB/B}{dR/R} = -\frac{R}{B}\frac{dB}{dR} \tag{4.18}$$

then the vertical oscillations will have a frequency f_v such that

$$f_v = \sqrt{n}\cdot f \tag{4.19}$$

where f is the normal accelerating frequency. If the field falls off as R increases, then $\dfrac{dB}{dR}$ is negative and n is positive. For the radial oscillation frequency f_r, it may be shown that

$$f_r = \sqrt{1-n}\cdot f \tag{4.20}$$

In the synchrotron the value of n lies between zero and unity, and for $n = \frac{1}{2}$, f_v equals f_r, and during a half-period, the particle would sweep out an angle equal to $\sqrt{2}$ times π radians or 253 degrees.

In an unpublished paper in 1950 by N. Christophilos and in a later report [35] an accelerator has been proposed leading to the possibility of obtaining protons of very high energy. The original design envisaged an enormously long ring-shaped magnet consisting of a sequence of alternately converging and diverging magnetic lenses of equal strength. The over-all result is converging and the amplitudes of both radial and axial displacements may be kept very small, so that the magnet aperture and hence the magnet size may be greatly reduced. The

[35] E. Courant, M. S. Livingston, and H. Snyder, *Phys. Rev.*, **88**, 1190 (1952).

original calculation for a 30 Bev proton output assumed an orbit radius of 300 feet with 240 magnet sectors each 7.85 feet long. For the strong focusing in each sector the value of n was calculated to be 3600.

The attractive features of this design led to numerous supplementary calculations and considerable modification in the earlier suggested details, before the construction of a machine of this type was actually begun. The focusing magnets may be something of the shape shown in Figure 4.24.

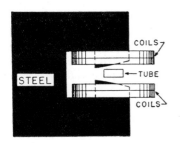
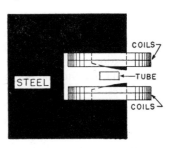

POSITIVE ELEMENT   NEGATIVE ELEMENT

FIG. 4.24.   Focusing and de-focusing elements of an alternating gradient fixed field accelerator.

Perhaps the most significant proposal has been the suggestion [36] to use a shaped magnetic field, unvarying with respect to time. The magnetic field pattern is designed so that stable orbits of all energies from injection up to the output energy are accommodated within the evacuated proton tube. The required momentum compaction is achieved by a strong variation in the field with radius. Phase stability is accomplished by the proper modulation of the frequency of the accelerating voltage.

By arranging two such fixed-field alternating gradient accelerators so that their high frequency beams circulate in

[36] K. Symon, D. Kerst, L. Jones, L. Laslett, and K. Terwilliger, *Phys. Rev.*, **103**, 1837 (1956).

opposite directions, through a straight section, common to both machines, then by particle collision enormously high energies may be obtained.[37]   The successful operation, among other things, would require very large pulses of particles such as 10^{15} in each accelerator in order that an adequate number of collisions such as 10^7 per second could occur.

QUESTIONS AND PROBLEMS

1. The large Van de Graaff generator originally built at Round Hill consisted of two insulated spheres 15 ft in diameter, one to be charged positively and the other negatively.   Assume that the electric field could have been built up to 20,000 volts per cm without serious corona loss or breakdown.   Express the electrical capacity of each sphere, its maximum charge, and the maximum possible potential difference between spheres.   348
     Answer: 228.6 ESU, 271.3 × 10^4 ESU, 9.15 Mv.
2. The cyclotron oscillator operates at a wavelength of 26 m.   What magnetic field would be required for resonance using (*a*) protons, (*b*) deuterons, (*c*) alpha particles, and (*d*) electrons?   If the diameter of the circle of maximum radius is 44 in., what is the energy of the emergent beam in each case?
     Answer: 7570, 15,140, 15,000, 4.123 gausses; 8.5, 17.3, 34, 0.0046 Mev.
3. If the maximum voltage between duants is 40,000 volts, for cases (*a*) and (*b*) above, how far does each proton and each deuteron travel?
     Answer: 252.9 m, 514.6 m—minimum.
4. In the impulse generator shown in Figure 4.5, the capacity of each individual condenser is 0.01 microfarad.   A full-wave rectifier delivers the output of the transformer whose rms value is 80,000 volts at a frequency of 60 cycles per sec to the bank of condensers.   What is the maximum voltage across the discharge tube, and the average discharge current?
     Answer· 1.244 million volts, 135 milliamperes.
5. In a large betatron assume that the average flux density within a circle of diameter 6 ft changes linearly from zero up to 12,000 maxwells per cm^2 in $\frac{1}{500}$ sec.   What is the energy given to an electron each revolution at the 6-ft diameter?   What is the acceleration of the

[37] D. Kerst, F. Cole, H. Crane, L. Jones, L. Laslett, T. Ohkawa, A. Sessler, K. Symon, K. Terwilliger, and N. Nilsen, *Phys. Rev.*, **102**, 590 (1956).

electron? How fast will it be moving at the end of the above interval, how many trips will it make, and what is its final energy?

   Answer: 1578 ev, 48.4 × 10^{14} cm per sec^2, ∼ 3 × 10^{10} cm per sec, 1.042 × 10^5, 164 Mev.

   6. The Brookhaven accelerator has four circular members with an effective radius of 30 ft and four alternate straight sections 17 ft long. The proton groups are injected at an energy of 4 Mev and develop a terminal energy of 3 Bev. Assume an energy increment of 3 kev per revolution and a final pulse of 10^9 protons at 5-sec intervals. Calculate the following:

   a. The number of trips made and total distance traveled per particle.
   b. The frequency at injection and at exit.
   c. The magnetic field at injection and at exit. $n = \frac{1}{2\pi} \frac{e}{m} B$ (4.12)
   d. The average beam current and average power.

   Answer: (*a*) 10^6 trips, 78.5 × 10^6 meters or 48,600 miles, (*b*) 340 kilocycles/sec, 3710 kilocycles/sec, (*c*) 510 gausses, 23,400 gausses, (*d*) 3.2 × 10^{-5} micro-amperes, 0.096 watt.

HOUR TEST 22 Oct.

Prob. Due 20 Oct,

CHAPTER 5

ALPHA RAYS

5.1. Discovery. By 1899 it had been shown by Becquerel and others that a strong perpendicular magnetic field could resolve the radiation from radium into two components. A deflected portion was called beta radiation and the entire undeflected part was originally termed alpha radiation. In 1900 Villard [1] found that the nondeflected component was in large measure absorbed by thin layers of material, but a smaller portion of the radiation was able to penetrate fairly thick layers. In 1903, by the use of a strong magnetic field, Rutherford [2] succeeded in deflecting the easily absorbed portion of the previously nondeflected radiation, but the penetrating component showed no deflection. The deflected component was bent in a direction opposite to that of the beta radiation and hence was positively charged. This beam was termed "alpha" radiation and was later shown to consist of a stream of helium ions, [3] that is, helium atoms each of which was stripped of its two orbital electrons. On collecting alpha radiation the electrons are recaptured and normal helium gas appears.

5.2. The Specific Charge of the Alpha Particle. The application of a field of magnetic induction B to the collimated beam of alpha particles from a radium source will result in any particle of mass m, charge e, and velocity v, describing a circular path of radius r, because of the central force F_c given by

$$F_c = \frac{mv^2}{r} = Bev \tag{5.1}$$

[1] P. Villard, *Compt. rend.*, **130**, 1178 (1900).
[2] E. Rutherford, *Phil. Mag.*, **5**, 177 (1903).
[3] E. Rutherford, *Physik. Z.*, **4**, 235 (1903).

In another observation an electric field $\mathcal{E}$ is applied so as to produce a deviation opposite to that produced by the magnetic field. On applying both fields simultaneously so that the net deflection is zero, then

$$F = Bev = \mathcal{E}e \tag{5.2}$$

Since in the magnetic deviation the charge is expressed in electromagnetic units and in the electric deflection, electrostatic units are employed, it follows that

$$v = \frac{c\mathcal{E}}{B} \tag{5.3}$$

where c is the velocity of light. On substituting this value of v in equation 5.1, the specific charge e/m can be expressed in terms of measurable quantities as

$$\frac{e}{m} = \frac{v}{rB} = \frac{c\mathcal{E}}{rB^2} \tag{5.4}$$

The first reported values, given by Rutherford,[4] were that e/m was 6300 electromagnetic units per gram and v was 2.5 $\times 10^9$ centimeters per second. It was subsequently shown, particularly on using polonium as a source, since its particles have a single velocity, that the value of e/m was about 4300 in the same units. On comparing this with the corresponding value for positive rays in discharge tubes the former was found to be only half as large.

The positive rays had been assumed to be singly charged atomic ions of hydrogen. It was therefore concluded that alpha rays were either singly charged hydrogen ions of mass 2 or doubly charged ions of helium. Since helium was generally found in radioactive ores it was reasonable to accept the latter choice. The best experimental value for e/m for alpha particles ap-

[4] E. Rutherford, *Physik. Z.*, **4**, 235 (1902); T. des Coudrés, *Physik. Z.*, **4**, 483 (1903); A. S. McKenzie, *Phil. Mag.*, **10**, 538 (1905); E. Rutherford and T. Royds, *Phil. Mag.*, **17**, 281 (1909).

pears [5] to be 4813 electromagnetic units of charge per gram. Using the most recent values for the electronic charge and the mass of the helium atom, the specific charge of the alpha particle is calculated to be 4821.5 ± 0.05 in the same units.

5.3. Range of Alpha Particles. Early experiments showed that alpha rays were readily absorbed by thin layers of materials. Even in gases their range was only a few centimeters. Unlike most other radiations their absorption in matter does not follow the exponential law. It was suggested by W. H. Bragg [6] in 1904 that the ionization along the path could be expressed as proportional to $\sqrt{r + c}$, where r is the number of centimeters from the end of the range and c is a constant equal to 1.33. It was later shown that this apparent decrease in ionization along the path was due to the fact that from radium there were several groups of particles, each with a different range. In any one range, theoretically, no particles were lost until the full thickness was traversed. This type of absorption would be expected if the heavy helium ions initially were all of the same energy and in passing through matter produced similar trails of ions. The ions produced consist of electrons detached from the neutral atoms of gas, and an equal number of positive ion residues. Each ion pair formed in air represents about 35 electron volts loss in energy to the alpha particle. The energy lost and the ionization produced are not exactly proportional. This is due to the fact that the ions produced possess varying amounts of kinetic energy, and some electrons are merely lifted to metastable levels producing excited but not ionized atoms. The mass of the alpha particle is about 7440 times that of the electron; hence, in collision of the two, the alpha particle loses little momentum.

The number of ions formed per centimeter of path, often called the "specific ionization," is found to be a function of the

---

[5] E. Rutherford and H. Robinson, *Phil. Mag.*, **28**, 552 (1914); G. H. Briggs, *Proc. Roy. Soc. A*, **118**, 549 (1928).

[6] W. H. Bragg, *Phil. Mag.*, **8**, 719 (1904); **13**, 333 (1907).

velocity. In general, the slower the velocity the greater the specific ionization, as if the longer the time the alpha particle spends in passing a group of atoms the greater is its chance of creating ions. The variation in specific ionization in air under standard conditions, produced by the alpha rays from polonium and from radium C′ is shown [7] in Figure 5.1. By

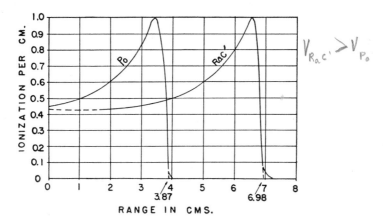

FIG. 5.1. The variation in specific ionization along the path of alpha particles from polonium and from radium C′.

taking the ionization about 5 millimeters from the end of the range as 1.0, then the initial ionization is only about 0.42. Occasionally an alpha particle collides with a nucleus such that it suffers a large refraction. This is an event with a low probability of occurrence.

An alpha particle having spent all its energy comes to the end of its course. Since all particles in a group have initially the same energy and on the average produce the same ionization per centimeter, then their range will be the same. This approximate uniformity in range is demonstrated in Figure 5.2, A and B. These are the photographs of cloud tracks produced by the alpha radiation from a source of Th(C + C′). The two

[7] G. H. Henderson, *Phil. Mag.*, **42**, 538 (1921); I. Curie and F. Behounek, *J. phys.*, **7**, 125 (1926); I. Curie and F. Joliot, *Compt. rend.*, **187**, 43 (1928).

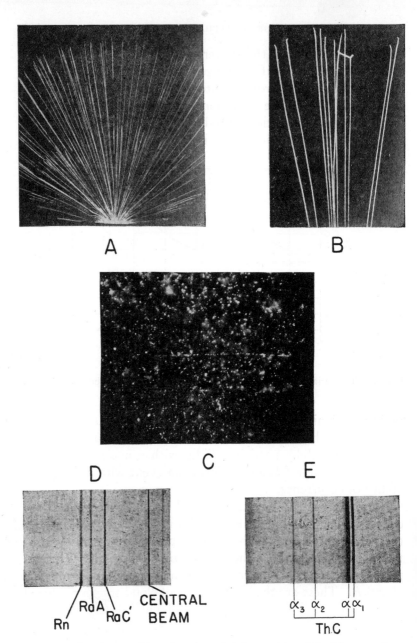

Fig. 5.2. The photographic registration of alpha particles; (*A*) alpha rays from Th(C + C′); (*B*) same, enlarged at end of range; (*C*) emulsion track of alpha; (*D*) spectrum of alpha rays from radium; and (*E*) same, from thorium C.

ranges of the particles from thorium are 4.78 and 8.62 centimeters and the groups are easily distinguished in A. In B the paths of the particles are shown enlarged at the end of their range. The collision of one alpha particle with a nitrogen nucleus is revealed by the tracks of both recoil particles.

The ranges of various alpha groups have been the subject of many investigations. For ranges between 3 centimeters and 8 centimeters a relationship known as Geiger's law states that range R varies directly as the cube of the velocity v. Since the kinetic energy W varies directly as the square of the velocity, then the range varies directly as the $\frac{3}{2}$ power of the energy. This may be represented by an equation as

$$R = av^3 = bW^{3/2} \tag{5.5}$$

where a and b are constants. This is not unexpected since the range is proportional to the energy W divided by the number of ion pairs per centimeter of path. The latter is inversely proportional to the velocity or to $\sqrt{W}$. The numerical value of a is found to be about 9.67×10^{-28}. At greater velocities the range varies more nearly as v^4 and at lower energies the range varies almost directly as $v^{1.5}$. No simple formula satisfies the range velocity relationship for unlimited energies. Figure 5.3 shows graphically the range in centimeters of standard air for alpha particles with energies up to 8 Mev as determined by Mano.[8] These ranges have been calculated by Bethe and Bloch,[9] and the curve has been experimentally verified and extended by Holloway and Livingston.[10] More recent calculations, extending the range to higher energies, are presented in Figure 5.4. The energy loss per centimeter of path is included in the same figure.

Figure 5.2C shows the path of an alpha particle in a photographic emulsion. The energy may be determined by counting the number of activated grains comprising the path. The

[8] G. Mano, *J. phys.*, **5**, 628 (1934).
[9] H. Bethe and F. Bloch, *Ann. Physik*, **16.3**, 285 (1933).
[10] M. Holloway and M. S. Livingston, *Phys. Rev.*, **54**, 18 (1938).

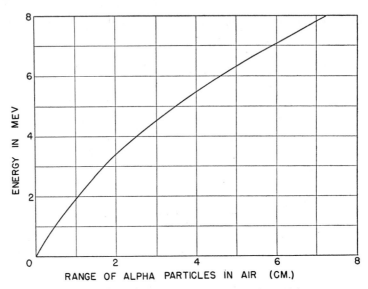

FIG. 5.3. Range-energy relationship for alpha particles.

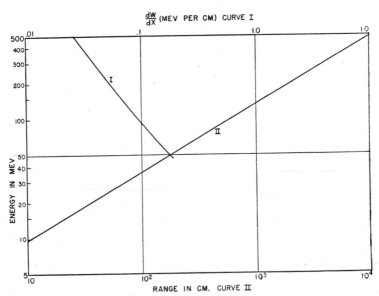

FIG. 5.4. The range-energy relationship for alpha particles in air and the energy loss in Mev per centimeter at high energies.

total range in microns of alpha particles in the newer photo-graphic emulsions as a function of their energy is included in Figure 10.7.

5.4. The Straggling of Alpha Rays.   It at first appeared that the alpha rays from a particular source terminated abruptly after traversing a certain definite thickness of absorber.   On

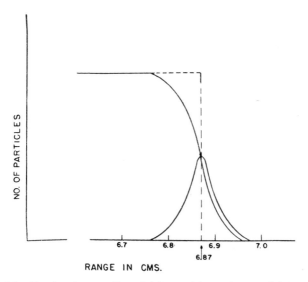

RANGE IN CMS.

FIG. 5.5.   Showing the straggling of alpha particles at the end of their range.

attempting to express this thickness precisely, the true value appeared slightly uncertain.   This is illustrated by Figure 5.5 which represents [11] the end of the range of the particles from radium C′ in air.   This result was obtained by a careful study of the alpha tracks observed in a Wilson cloud chamber.   An explanation of the effect had already been proposed.[12]   The path lengths of the alpha particles in a monoenergetic group will be arranged about a most probable value according to the Gaus-

---

[11] I. Curie and P. Mercier, *J. phys.*, **7**, 289 (1926); L. Meitner and K. Freitag, *Z. Physik*, **37**, 481 (1926).
[12] C. G. Darwin, *Phil. Mag.*, **23**, 901 (1912); N. Bohr, *Phil. Mag.*, **30**, 531 (1915) L. Flamm, *Wien. Ber.*, **124**, 597 (1915).

sian law of errors. The amount of variation or straggling depends upon the process involved in the energy loss. Such calculations were made for radium C′ in air involving all possible transfers and indicated a spread of ±0.09 centimeter in the range as shown. The true range would therefore in this case not be the observed maximum, 6.96 centimeters, but rather the corrected value 6.87 centimeters.

Similarly the number of alpha particles arriving at any detector per second will fluctuate with time. The total number observed in any second may be more or less than the average value by an amount expressed as a fluctuation. To reduce errors due to this fluctuation a large number of observations N are noted. The result, together with the uncertainty, is expressible as $N \pm \sqrt{N}$. Thus if 10,000 particles are counted, the error due to fluctuations is of the order of 1%.

5.5. Stopping Power. The density of air is 0.00129 gram per cubic centimeter and that of aluminum is 2.699. Thus it might be expected that $\frac{1}{2100}$ centimeter of aluminum would be equivalent in stopping power to 1 centimeter of air. Actually it takes a somewhat thicker layer of aluminum, namely $\frac{1}{1700}$ centimeter, to be equivalent to 1 centimeter of air under standard conditions. Thus the stopping power of aluminum is spoken of as 1700. The stopping power is thus defined as the reciprocal of that thickness of substance equivalent to 1 centimeter of air, in its ability to stop alpha radiation. If the stopping power of an element be divided by the number of atoms per cubic centimeter, the quotient is termed the atomic stopping power of the substance.

The stopping is done by electrons, and if each electron functions equally effectively, then it might be expected that the atomic stopping power S divided by the atomic number Z should be a constant. This could be termed the stopping power per electron. Actually this is found to be not the case. In the heavier elements a large share of the electrons are tightly bound in inner orbits so that they play a lesser part in ionization and the consequent slowing down of the alpha rays. It was observed by Bragg [13] that for most elements the atomic stopping power S varied directly as the square root of the atomic weight (A). Glasson found [14] that it equally well could be regarded as varying as $Z^{2/3}$, where Z is the atomic number of the element. These values of the atomic stopping powers and their products with $A^{-1/2}$ and $Z^{-2/3}$ for a few elements are shown in Table 5.1. The atomic stopping power of oxygen is taken as unity. It is remarkable that such simple relationships fit the data so well.

TABLE 5.1. THE ATOMIC STOPPING POWER OF THE ELEMENTS BASED ON S (OXYGEN) = 1

Element	Z	A	Atomic Stopping Power (S)	$SA^{-1/2}$	$SZ^{-2/3}$
H	1	1.00	0.200	0.20	0.20
Li	3	6.94	0.519	0.20	0.25
Be	4	9.02	0.750	0.25	0.29
C	6	12.01	0.814	0.25	0.25
N	7	14.00	0.939	0.25	0.25
O	8	16.01	1.000	0.25	0.25
Mg	12	24.32	1.23	0.25	0.24
Al	13	26.97	1.27	0.24	0.23
Si	14	28.06	1.23	0.23	0.22
Cl	17	35.46	1.76	0.29	0.26
Fe	26	55.85	1.96	0.26	0.23
Ni	28	58.69	1.89	0.25	0.21
Cu	29	63.57	2.00	0.25	0.22
Zn	30	65.38	2.05	0.25	0.22
Ag	47	107.88	2.74	0.26	0.21
Cd	48	112.41	2.75	0.26	0.21
Sn	50	118.70	2.86	0.26	0.21
Pt	78	195.23	3.64	0.26	0.20
Au	79	197.20	3.73	0.27	0.20
Pb	82	207.21	3.86	0.27	0.20

[13] W. H. Bragg and R. Kleeman, *Phil. Mag.*, **10**, 318 (1905).
[14] J. L. Glasson, *Phil. Mag.*, **43**, 477 (1922).

5.6. Range and Half-life.

In 1911, Geiger and Nuttall [15] arrived at an interesting conclusion relating the half-life of an alpha emitter and the energy or range of its alpha particles. The element under study was placed at the center of a hollow glass sphere whose inner surface was silvered with a conducting layer and connected to a high potential. The active substance

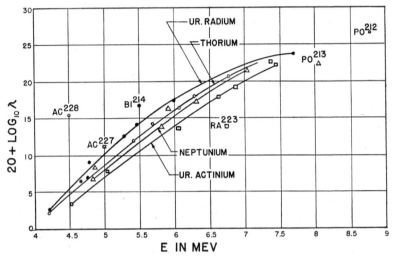

FIG. 5.6.   The Geiger-Nuttall relationship for the radioactive families.

at the center was on a small disk which was connected to an electrometer. The ionization current was observed as a function of the gas pressure. The ionization was found to increase as the pressure increased up to a certain critical value at which the alpha radiation no longer reached the surface. At higher pressures the ionization current remains constant.

It was found that, if the logarithm of the range in centimeters was plotted versus the logarithm of the disintegration constant, λ in reciprocal seconds, then for a particular family, such as the uranium-radium family, the points lie on a straight line. Instead of the logarithm of the range in air, the energy in Mev may equally well be plotted.

[15] H. Geiger and J. M. Nuttall, *Phil. Mag.*, **22**, 613 (1911).

Similar linear relationships are found to represent the thorium, the neptunium, and the actinium radioactive series. The four curves are nearly parallel as shown in Figure 5.6. For the very heavy isotopes with even Z and an even number of neutrons, whose half-lives vary from 0.1 microsecond up to

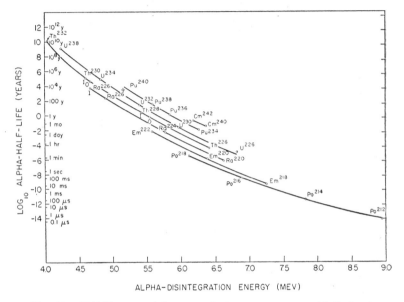

FIG. 5.7. Half-life versus alpha energy for heavy even-even nuclei (Seaborg).

10^{12} years, Seaborg finds [16] seven smooth curves when the logarithm of the half-life is plotted versus the energy. The curves correspond to the seven elements from polonium up to curium and are shown in Figure 5.7.

For samarium, the range in air of 1.16 centimeters has been observed. This is the shortest range for any of the natural emitters and corresponds to the half-life of 1.7×10^{11} years or a disintegration constant λ of 1.29×10^{-19} per second. The half-life of any element emitting alpha particles of range less

[16] I. Perlman, A. Ghiorso, and G. Seaborg, *Phys. Rev.*, **75**, 1096 (1949).

than a centimeter would be so long that it would be regarded as stable.

5.7. Alpha Energy and Neutron Number. If the alpha energies from heavy nuclides having a common Z and varying N are examined, certain regularities appear. The varying values of the alpha energies as N increases progressively are shown

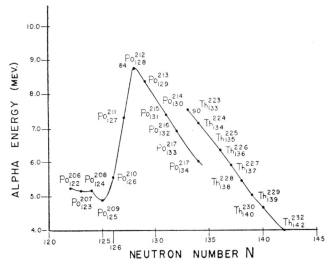

FIG. 5.8. Alpha energy versus neutron number for Po and Th.

graphically for the isotopes polonium ($Z = 84$) and thorium ($Z = 90$) in Figure 5.8. A lower energy indicating a longer lifetime or greater stability is observed in polonium as N approaches the magic number 126 (actually 125). As the neutron number N increases from this value, the energy increases to a maximum and then decreases. In thorium the lower neutron numbers are already much greater than 126 and the energy decreases progressively, presumably toward the next higher magic number.

5.8. Alpha Ray Spectra. W. H. Bragg very early found from ionization measurements that there were four groups of alpha particles emitted by a source of radium. It was not until 1930 that precise measurements were made on these alpha spectra. At that time Rosenblum [17] examined a number of radioactive elements by means of a magnetic spectrometer with semicircular focusing. Several emitters were each found to send out only a single monoenergetic group of alpha particles. Another list of elements had spectra consisting of two or three distinct energies. A few elements, such as radium C′, thorium C, and radioactinium, each emit several discrete energy groups. The resolved spectra obtained with a source of radium are shown in Figure 5.2D and those from a source of Th C are shown in Figure 5.2E. The most energetic ray lies on the right in each case and is the least deflected.

TABLE 5.2.   ALPHA AND GAMMA ENERGIES, Th $C(_{83}Bi^{212})$

Alpha Energy		Gamma Energy
Mev	Per Cent	(Mev)
6.084	27	0.040
6.046	70	0.144
5.760	1.7	0.164
5.618	0.15	0.288
5.600	1.1	0.328
5.481	0.02	0.432
		0.448
		0.472

The accuracy of these measurements has subsequently been improved and more complex structures revealed. For example, Th $C(_{83}Bi^{212})$ is found to emit six alpha groups [18] and at least eight gamma rays as shown in Table 5.2. Only the highest energy alpha group represents a transition to the ground

[17] S. Rosenblum, *J. Phys.*, **1**, 438 (1930).
[18] A. Rytz, *Comptes rendus*, **233**, 790 (1951).

154 ALPHA RAYS

state of the daughter product Th C''($_{81}$Tl^{208})...

154 ALPHA RAYS

state of the daughter product Th C''($_{81}$Tl^{208}). The remaining alpha groups combine with the gamma transitions to allow a determination of the nuclear levels in Tl^{208}. The total energy difference between the two ground states is the maximum energy of the alpha particles, 6.084 Mev, plus the recoil energy of the daughter Tl^{208}, which is 0.117 Mev. As the Tl recoil

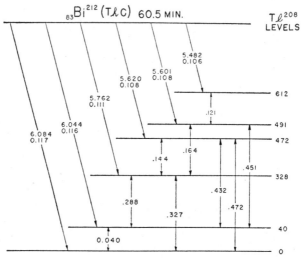

FIG. 5.9. Nuclear levels in Tl^{208} following alpha emission from Bi^{212}

energy is different for each alpha energy, being only 0.1056Mev for the lowest value, the observed gamma energies do not combine with the observed secondary alpha energies to give a good fit unless each is corrected. The nuclear level scheme shown in Figure 5.9 fits very satisfactorily the observed data.

The multi-channel pulse height analyzer may be profitably employed to obtain rapidly both the relative intensities and the energies of close lying alpha peaks. The primary radiation either enters an ion chamber or falls, without absorption, on a phosphor with its photomultiplier tube. The output signal, after passing the amplifier and discriminator, may be selected or rejected by the analyzer circuit according to its energy.   Figure 5.10 shows the resolution obtainable with an instrument of this type.[19]   The entire width of the energy band admitted in this figure is about 1 Mev and the three peaks representing the radiations from the isotopes of astatine of masses 207, 209, and 211, differing from each other by about 0.1 Mev, are well separated.

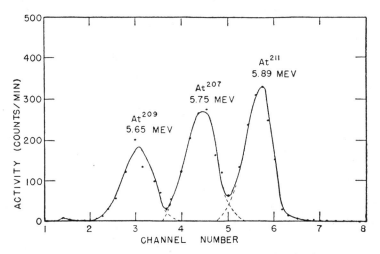

FIG. 5.10.   Resolution of alpha peaks in astatine by the pulse height analyzer.

5.9. Scattering of Alpha Particles.   The alpha particles were at first considered to travel in straight undeviated lines through matter.   More careful observation showed that a portion of the original beam was in general deviated through small angles, depending upon the thickness of the layer of material and its atomic number.   The greater the atomic number of the matter and the less the velocity of the alpha particle, the greater is the average deviation.   In these experiments a few particles are occasionally found whose deflection may be as much as 90 degrees or more.   Thus for Ra C′ about one particle in every 8000 suffers such a large deflection in passing through a very thin layer

[19] G. Barton, A. Ghiorso, and I. Perlman, *Phys. Rev.*, **82**, 13 (1951).

of gold.[20]   These particles have undoubtedly come very close
to an atomic nucleus so that an interaction occurred in which
they suffered a large change in momentum.

From X-ray studies of crystal structure the diameter of
atoms is established as being of the order of 3×10^{-8} centimeter.   The diameter of the nucleus, possessing most of the
mass, is only a very small fraction of this.   An estimate of the
nuclear dimensions could be made from a careful observation of
these scattered particles.   It had initially been considered that
these large deflections must be due to multiple encounters since
it was currently thought that the electric field within the atom
could not be of sufficient intensity to deflect such a heavy body
as the alpha particle in a single encounter.   Rutherford [21]
showed that they must be due to a single encounter, as the
probability of one particle already largely deflected having a
second encounter of the same sort was very small.   Rutherford
was first to postulate that the total positive charge of the atom
was concentrated in a small nuclear volume and that the equal
negative charge was distributed over the much larger domain,
occupied by the atom.   For all deflections greater than about a
degree, only the central positive charge need be considered and
it was assumed to be concentrated in a minute volume as a
point.   The force between the positive nucleus and the positive
alpha particle was considered to be a simple coulomb repulsion.
On considering the heavy nucleus with a charge Ze to remain at
rest during the collision, the path of the alpha particle will be
a hyperbola whose external focus is the scattering nucleus as
shown in Figure 5.11.   The distance of nearest approach b will
be a minimum for an alpha particle striking the nucleus directly, and in this case the alpha particle will be scattered
through an angle of 180 degrees.   By equating the original kinetic energy of the alpha particle to the potential energy, as

[20] H. Geiger and E. Marsden, *Proc. Roy. Soc.*, **82**, 495 (1909); *Phil. Mag.*, **25**, 604
(1913).
[21] E. Rutherford, *Phil. Mag.*, **21**, 699 (1911).

the positive charge $2e$ approaches the nuclear charge Ze, and is brought to a stop at the distance b,

$$\frac{1}{2} m_\alpha v_\alpha{}^2 = \frac{2eZe}{b} \quad \text{or} \quad b = \frac{4Ze^2}{m_\alpha v_\alpha{}^2} \tag{5.6}$$

Rutherford showed that if Q is the total number of incident particles falling normally on a thin scatterer of thickness t, and

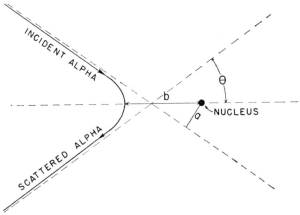

FIG. 5.11. The scattering of an alpha particle by a nucleus.

if n is the number of atoms per cubic centimeter in the scatterer, then the number of particles N arriving at a fixed receiver at a distance r centimeters from the scatterer along an angle ϕ to the original direction would be given by the following equation:

$$N = \frac{Qntb^2 \lceil \mathrm{cosec}^4\, \phi/2 \rfloor}{16r^2} \tag{5.7}$$

This equation could be checked experimentally, term by term, by allowing a single factor to vary at a time. Geiger and Marsden [22] were the first to deal with this problem. Alpha rays from a radon source were allowed to fall normally on a scatterer consisting of an extremely thin foil of gold, placed directly

[22] H. Geiger and E. Marsden, *Phil. Mag.*, **25**, 604 (1913).

on the axis of a spectrometer. The value of N was noted at scattering angles ϕ varying from 150 down to 15 degrees, by rotating an arm carrying a small zinc sulfide screen with accompanying microscope. The quotient $\dfrac{N}{\text{cosec}^4 \phi/2}$ was found to be essentially a constant. It varied only from about 28 to 38, being greater at the smaller angle. Similarly, at a fixed angle it was noted that N varied inversely as the square of the energy of the incident alpha particles, as would be expected from equation 5.7, since b^2 is in the numerator, and b varies inversely with the energy as shown by equation 5.6.

The magnitude of the nuclear charge Ze as well as the numerical value of b were determined from scattering experiments. Van den Broek [23] was the first to suggest that the positive nuclear charge might be equal to the atomic number Z times the electronic charge e. For gold, silver, and copper it appeared [24] that the distances of closest approach of fast alpha particles were less than 3.2, 2.0, and 1.2×10^{-12} centimeter, respectively.

Later evidence [25] indicated that the radii are considerably smaller than first expressed and that the radii of various nuclei should vary as the cube root of the number of constituent particles as given by the atomic weight. This would be expected if the volume required for each neutron and proton within the nucleus is about the same.

The radius r is usually expressed as

$$r = \sqrt[3]{A} \cdot r_0 \tag{5.8}$$

The value of r_0, as reported from different experimental methods, lies between 1.2 and 1.5×10^{-13} cm. This then represents the radius of the proton.

If the energy of the alpha particles is greatly increased it is

[23] A. van den Broek, *Physik. Z.*, **14**, 32 (1913).
[24] J. Chadwick, *Phil. Mag.*, **40**, 734 (1920).
[25] E. Rutherford and J. Chadwick, *Phil. Mag.*, **50**, 889 (1925).

reasonable to expect a deviation from the angular scattering predicted by the Rutherford equation. Even at energies below 9 Mev it was found [26] that alpha particles were scattered by helium through large angles to a much greater extent than expected. An explanation of the observed results was given [27]

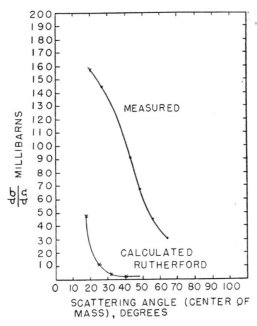

FIG. 5.12.   Differential scattering of protons in helium.

based upon the momentary formation of a compound nucleus $_4Be^8$ which had an excited level about 3 Mev above the ground state. Information on high energy alpha-helium scattering is still to be obtained. By projecting the 32 Mev proton beam from the linear accelerator through a helium scatterer, some interesting results as shown in Figure 5.12 have been reported.[28]

[26] C. Mohr and G. Pringle, *Proc. Roy. Soc. (London)*, **A160**, 193 (1937); S. Devons, *ibid.*, **A172**, 559 (1939).

[27] J. A. Wheeler, *Phys. Rev.*, **59**, 126 (1941).

[28] B. Cork, *Phys. Rev.*, **89**, 78 (1953); J. Benveniste and B. Cork, *ibid.*, **89**, 422 (1953).

This shows the differential cross section as a function of scattering angle expressed in the center of mass system (see topic 8.11) as expected from the Rutherford equation and as observed. A detailed analysis of the scattered particles showed that all of the scattered protons observed had suffered elastic collision. If excited states of He^4 exist, then it might have been expected that a portion of the transitions from the compound Li^5 nucleus would have been to a metastable level in helium and hence give protons of less energy. Their absence is regarded as evidence that no such heavy particle excited level exists in the helium nucleus.

5.10. Transmutation by Alpha Particles. If the alpha particle should penetrate into the nucleus, then the Coulomb law of repulsion would no longer completely regulate its behavior. New forces of an attractive nature would now appear. Scattering experiments indicated for the very heavy elements, a nuclear radius of the order of 0.7×10^{-12} centimeter. To bring an alpha particle to that position would, from the coulomb repulsion, require an energy W of

$$W = \frac{2Ze^2}{r} = Z \times 0.411 \text{ Mev} \tag{5.9}$$

Thus for uranium whose Z is 92, an energy of 37.5 Mev would be expected. An alpha particle should thus be prevented from entering the nucleus by this exceedingly high barrier. On surmounting the barrier the particle would fall forward by virtue of the attractive forces. Such a distribution of the potential is shown in Figure 5.13. It should be equally hard for an alpha particle to leave the nucleus.

It was actually found possible to induce nuclear transmutation by the alpha rays from radium C whose energy is only 5.5 Mev. Similarly alpha particles emitted by many radioactive bodies have energies of only a few million electron volts.

This incompatibility was reconciled by the wave-mechanical

treatment of the process. Wave mechanics concedes [29] a finite probability for a particle with an energy less than that of the peak of the barrier being able to penetrate it. The greater the energy of the alpha particle and the lower the height of the barrier the greater is the probability of its passage. There is thus a close relationship between the energy of the emitted alpha particles and the half-life of the source.

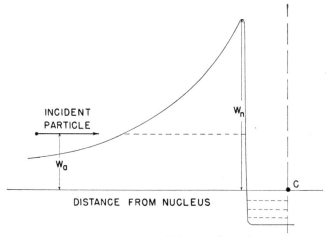

FIG. 5.13.   The potential barrier of a nucleus.

As soon as devices for accelerating particles to high potentials were developed they were utilized to produce controlled alpha rays. Thus a cyclotron that will produce deuterons whose energy is 10 Mev is almost exactly in condition to produce alpha particles of 20 Mev. With sources of this kind most of the elements of the periodic table have been bombarded and the disintegration products observed. The addition of the energetic alpha particle to the nucleus makes an unstable or excited condition. The return to a stable nucleus may take place by any one of several competitive processes each with quite a different probability of occurrence.

[29] G. Gamow, Z. *Physik*, **51**, 204 (1928); R. Gurney and E. Condon, *Nature*, **122**, 439 (1928).

Thus the excited nucleus may emit a gamma ray, a neutron, a proton or, if sufficient energy is available, any combination of the particles. In most cases the yield of disintegrating atoms increases with the energy of the incident particle but this is by no means always true.

a. Alpha-proton Reaction. One of the early reactions studied [30] was the bombardment of aluminum with alpha particles varying in energy up to 10.5 Mev. The range and number of the emitted protons were observed. The protons were found to have several definite ranges for any given energy of the exciting alpha particle, in all about eight groups being observed. As the energy of the alpha particles is increased the yield of protons shows distinct maxima at certain definite values of the energy. These particular alpha energies at which the number of protons was represented by peaks in the yield curve, were interpreted as being resonance channels through the nuclear barrier. For aluminum at least six such resonance energies were found, namely at 4.0, 4.49, 4.86, 5.25, 5.75, and 6.61 Mev. The width of some of the levels was also determined and found to be about 200 Kev.

This reaction could be represented as $_{13}Al^{27}(\alpha, p)_{14}Si^{30}$, or it could be shown by the equation

Transmutation

$$_{13}Al^{27} + _2He^4 \rightarrow _{14}Si^{30} + _1H^1 + Q \qquad (5.10)$$

where Q is the disintegration energy representing any inequality in the sums of the atomic masses on the two sides. From experiments of Chadwick and Constable,[31] Q was found to be 2.07 Mev. Using the latest values of the masses an unbalance of 0.003517 mass units is noted which would correspond to 3.27 Mev.

b. Alpha-neutron Reaction. Another very common transmutation effected by the alpha particle is one in which a neutron leaves the excited nucleus. The resulting nucleus thus has

[30] W. E. Duncanson and H. Miller, *Proc. Roy. Soc. (London),* **146,** 366, 396 (1934).
[31] J. Chadwick and J. E. Constable, *Proc. Roy. Soc. (London),* **135,** 48 (1932).

an atomic number greater by two than the original atom and heavier by three mass units. One of the most widely used reactions of this sort is a mixture of radon and beryllium used as a source of neutrons. The reaction can be abbreviated as $_4Be^9(\alpha, n)_6C^{12}$ or it can be represented by the equation

$$_4Be^9 + _2He^4 \rightarrow _6C^{12} + _0n^1 + Q \qquad (5.11)$$

9.015046   4.003873   12.003804 1.008986 (5.706Mev.)

The disintegration energy Q necessary to account for a deficiency in mass on the right side of 0.006129 mass unit, represents an energy of about 5.706 Mev. It has been found that a mixture of one millicurie of radon with sufficient beryllium [32] to absorb all the alpha radiation will emit about 6700 neutrons per second. Since the radon emits 37.0 million alpha particles in the same time, it would seem that at least one in every 5000 alpha particles is able to get into the beryllium nucleus and send out a neutron. This is a rather high probability for a nuclear reaction.

With polonium alpha particles on beryllium, about 3000 neutrons are observed per second per millicurie of polonium. By noting the energy of the neutron groups emitted by the Be-Po mixture as well as the energy of the accompanying gamma rays it is possible to propose a level scheme for the carbon 12 nucleus. Lower lying levels occur at 4.43 and 7.65 Mev with neutron groups at energies of 11.01, 6.58, and 3.36 Mev. Higher levels, up to 26.4 Mev, may be induced in carbon 12 by other modes of excitation.

Reactions become more complicated when the very-high-energy particles now available are employed. In general, many alternate decay reactions are possible and occur. Enough energy is available in the excited compound nucleus to evaporate or "spallate" many particles, resulting in some cases in the production of isotopes differing by many atomic numbers from

[32] F. Paneth, E. Gluckauf, and H. Loleit, *Proc. Roy. Soc. (London),* **147,** 412 (1936).

that of the target element. Figure 5.14 shows the increase in the cross section for the reaction $Ni^{60}(\alpha, N)Zn^{63}$ as the incident energy of the alpha particle increases.[33] At about 20 Mev a

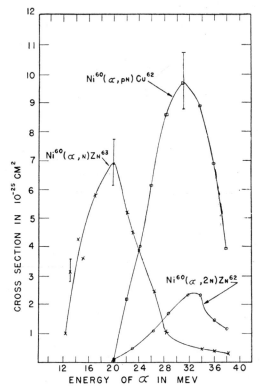

FIG. 5.14. Disintegration of Ni^{60} by alpha particles.

competing reaction, in which two neutrons are emitted, becomes possible. On increasing the energy the cross section for the formation of Zn^{63} decreases while that for Zn^{62} increases. Above about 32 Mev additional processes in which three particles are emitted become possible, thus accounting for the maxima in the Zn^{62} and Cu^{62} curves.

[33] S. H. Ghoshal, *Phys. Rev.*, **80**, 939 (1950).

5.11. Alpha Particle Escape. If the alpha particle retains its identity within the nucleus, then it might be expected to execute harmonic motion in the field of the remainder of the nucleus. For the case of zero orbital momentum the motion would be an oscillation between opposite barriers. The action integral as used in the atomic problem may perhaps be extended to apply within the nucleus, namely,

$$\int P \cdot dQ = nh$$

where P is the momentum, Q is the space coordinate of the particle and h is the Planck constant. Then for the lowest vibrational state $Mv \cdot r = h$ or the radius r is equal to the De-Broglie wavelength $\left(\dfrac{h}{Mv}\right)$ of the particle. The energy of the particle alternates between all kinetic energy at the center and all potential when stopped at the barrier. For such an alpha particle in the oxygen nucleus the bondal energy W was shown to be about 7.5 Mev or 12×10^{-6} ergs per particle. If the radius is 3.8×10^{-13} cm, the maximum velocity is $\dfrac{2Wr}{h}$ and the average velocity $\dfrac{2Wr}{\pi h}$ becomes 4.82×10^8 centimeters per second. It follows that this alpha particle would present itself at a barrier 1.27×10^{28} times per second. If the atom is stable, the disintegration constant λ approaches zero. In general, λ is equal to the product of the frequency of arrival at the barrier, f, and a probability P of break-through. For an alpha emitter such as radium, λ is 1.36×10^{-11} per second; and if f is of the same order as in oxygen, then P must be of the order of 10^{-39}, or only one of every 10^{39} particles that arrive at the barrier can escape.

Ties waves and particles together.

Due Monday 1 Nov

QUESTIONS AND PROBLEMS

1. Alpha rays from thorium C′ (10.536 Mev) bombard nitrogen nuclei and protons are observed in the forward direction. Express their maximum energy.

$$_2He^4 + {_7}N^{14} \rightarrow {_8}O^{17} + {_1}H^1$$

Answer: 8.70 Mev.

2. Alpha particles from radon have an energy of 5.486 Mev. By how much do the masses of radon and radium A differ?

Answer: 4.009851 mass units.

3. Lithium 7 is bombarded with protons whose energy is 1 Mev. Two alpha particles are produced each having the same energy. What is this energy and at what angles do the alpha particles emerge?

Answer: 9.17 Mev, 85 deg 20 min.

4. In an alpha ray spectrograph, the radiation from polonium is to be bent into a circular path 30 cm in diameter. Express the uniform magnetic induction in gausses that would be sufficient. What would be the energy difference for two beams registering on a photographic plate as lines 1 cm apart, for semicircular focusing?

Answer: 22,200 gausses, 0.35 Mev.

5. If the cross section for the disintegration of nitrogen by the alpha particles from thorium C′ is 10^{-25} cm^2, how many disintegrations are produced per second by one microcurie of thorium C′ surrounded by nitrogen gas under standard conditions?

Answer: approx. 2.

6. If N alpha particles are scattered by a thin foil of silver to a certain receiver placed at an angle of 30 deg with the forward direction, how many scattered particles would be expected by the same receiver in the same time placed so as to allow a scattering angle of 60 deg? Also for 90 deg?

Answer: 0.072 N, 0.018 N.

7. Prove that an alpha particle will on elastically colliding with a proton, give up at most $\frac{16}{25}$ of its energy.

$$mv = \sqrt{2mE}$$

AMU   MEV

$$X + Y + \upsilon = Z + R + \upsilon'$$

$$m + m + \frac{E}{c^2} = m + m + \frac{E}{c^2}$$

$$1 esu = 300 v$$
$$1 v = 10^8 emu$$
$$1 emu \ of \ current = 10 amp$$
$$1 amp = 3 \times 10^9 esu$$

Math Simple, Physics HAR

p. 103

No. Rng.

Vol. (cm³)

$$\frac{Number}{cm^3} \ (Range)$$

CHAPTER 6

BETA RAYS

6.1. Historical. That portion of the radiation from a radio-active source that was strongly deflected [1] by a perpendicular magnetic field was termed beta radiation. It was noted that the particles were negative in sign. They were soon identified as electrons emitted from the nuclei of the atoms of the source, some with a very high velocity. They were shown [2] to be in many ways very like the stream of cathode rays in a discharge tube. The energies of the beta particles however may be much greater than those of the usually observed cathode rays. Energies equivalent to those possessed by electrons falling through a potential of several million volts are not uncommon. For such electrons the relativity mass m is the rest mass m_0 multiplied by the factor $(1 - \beta^2)^{-1/2}$, where β is the ratio of the electron velocity v to the velocity of light c, namely 3×10^{10} centimeters per second. Velocities of these high-energy particles may approach very closely that of light.

The electronic charge associated with the beta particles given off by a radioactive body may be observed by placing the emitter on the well-insulated plate of an electrometer and noting the positive charge acquired in a definite interval of time. The beta particles on leaving the nuclei of the emitting atoms, in effect, increase the nuclear positive charge. This is equivalent to increasing the atomic number of the element.

6.2. Absorption and Range of Beta Particles. Beta rays are generally far more penetrating than alpha particles. While

[1] H. Becquerel, *Compt. rend.*, **130**, 206 (1900).
[2] S. Mayer and E. von Schweidler, *Physik. Z.*, **1**, 90 (1899).

the most energetic alpha particles may be completely absorbed
in a few centimeters of air, beta particles may describe paths
in air several hundred centimeters in length, or they may traverse layers of aluminum a few millimeters thick. On passing
through successive layers of absorber the total number of beta
particles in the beam as well as the energy of each particle decrease progressively.

Early investigation of beta spectra by magnetic spectrometers led to a false conclusion [3] regarding their nature. Particles
were observed with energies varying continuously from zero up

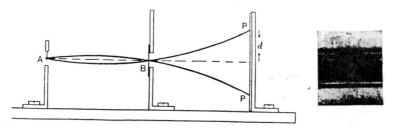

Fig. 6.1. Reproduction of early apparatus of von Baeyer and Hahn to resolve electron
groups.

to some definite maximum value. Superimposed upon the continuous distribution were several groups of particles, each
group having a definite discrete energy. A copy of one of the
early spectrograms with a plan of the apparatus is shown in
Figure 6.1. The source is at A and electrons passing through
the slit B blacken the photographic plate at P. The magnetic
field is first maintained constant at some fixed value perpendicular to the page, outward, and then for the same time reversed. These monoenergetic groups were later found to be
electrons coming not from the nuclei but rather from the electronic orbits of the atoms. They arise from the internal conversion of gamma radiation that is emitted from the radioactive
nuclei along with the beta radiation.

[3] O. von Baeyer, O. Hahn, and L. Meitner, *Physik. Z.*, **12**, 273 (1911); **13**, 264
(1912).

Even if the beta rays were originally all of the same energy, their ranges through matter would have a considerable spread in values. This follows from the fact that the electrons are so easily scattered by the atoms through which they pass.

The loss in energy of a beta particle on passing through matter is due to its production of ion pairs along its path. The number of ion pairs produced per centimeter of path increases as the velocity of the beta particle decreases. This varies from about 25 pairs per centimeter at 2 Mev to about 200 per centimeter at 40 kev. The ionization potential for oxygen and nitrogen is only about 14 volts. Actually the average energy loss per pair of primary ions formed is about 35 electron volts. This additional energy may result in secondary ionization so that the total number of ions per centimeter may be several times that of the number of primary ions. Some of the energy may be used for other purposes such as the excitation of molecules or atoms, that is, the lifting of electrons to unstable levels without actually removing them or producing ions.

Each beta particle in its transit through a collection of atoms, in addition to losing energy to the electrons, may suffer a change in direction due more to its interaction with nuclei than with electrons. The average angle of deflection of the beta particles on traversing thin layers of material is found [4] to be proportional to the square root of the thickness t. For elements of various atomic number the scattering at a particular angle is found [5] to be proportional to the square of the atomic number Z.

At high energies the range of beta particles in matter varies almost linearly with the energy. At low energies the range is more nearly proportional to the square of the energy. This relationship is shown graphically in Figure 6.2, in which the range in aluminum is expressed in terms of the number of grams per square centimeter for complete absorption and the

[4] J. A. Crowther, *Proc. Roy. Soc. A*, **84**, 226 (1910).
[5] J. A. Crowther and B. F. Schonland, *Proc. Roy. Soc. A*, **100**, 526 (1922).

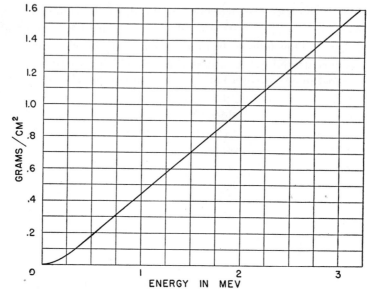

FIG. 6.2.   Range in aluminum for complete absorption.

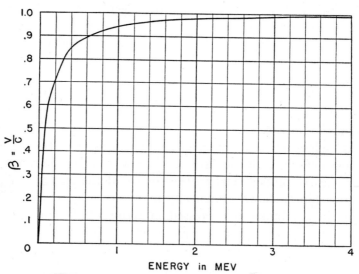

FIG. 6.3.   Relationship between energy and velocity relative to that of light for electrons.

energy in million electron volts. In Table 6.1 a few values are
given in successive horizontal columns for the energy of the
beta particles in thousand electron volts, the ratio of the velocity of the electron to the velocity of light, the range in aluminum expressed in grams per square centimeter, and the
range in centimeters of air. The relationship between velocity
and energy for electrons is shown graphically in Figure 6.3 for
energies up to 4 Mev. A more extensive range is presented in
Table A III in the Appendix.

TABLE 6.1

Energy (Kev)	2.55	10.5	24.7	46.6	79.1	127.8	204.7	341	662	1127	2058	3114
$\beta = v/c$	0.1	0.2	0.3	0.4	0.5	0.6	0.7	0.8	0.9	0.95	0.98	0.99
Grams/cm²	0.00005	0.00027	0.0012	0.0041	0.0087	0.0215	0.045	0.100	0.260	0.525	1.03	1.57
R (cm)	0.04	0.23	1.0	3.4	7.3	17.9	37.5	83	217	437	860	1300

6.3. The Feather Rule for Beta Energies. Feather observed
that the maximum range of beta particles in aluminum could
be used empirically to evaluate the energy of the particles.[6]
Experimentally, the intensity of the radiation is noted as the
thickness of an interposed aluminum absorber is progressively
increased. These data may then be represented as in Figure
6.4, where the ordinate is the intensity plotted on a logarithmic
scale. It is noted that for the radiation under consideration
thicknesses of aluminum greater than 0.36 gram per square
centimeter produce almost no diminution in intensity. At this
point only gamma radiation is transmitted. It is thus possible
to determine with a fair degree of accuracy the amount of absorber needed to just completely absorb the beta radiation.
The relationship deduced by Feather is

$$R \left(\frac{\text{gm}}{\text{cm}^2} \right) = 0.543E \text{ (Mev)} - 0.16 \qquad (6.1)$$

or

$$E \text{ (Mev)} = \frac{R}{0.543} + 0.294 \qquad (6.2)$$

[6] N. Feather, *Proc. Cambridge Phil. Soc.*, **34**, 599 (1938).

For the data shown, which represent the beta radiation from the indium isotope of mass 116, complete absorption seems to be produced by about 0.36 gram per square centimeter. This

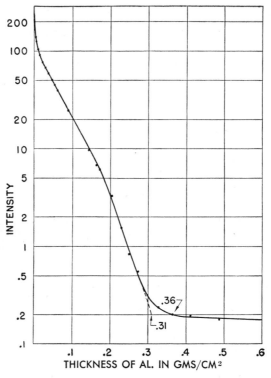

FIG. 6.4. The intensity of beta rays from indium 116 on passage through aluminum.

value, when inserted in equation 6.2, indicates an energy of 0.960 Mev. It is interesting to note that for this same energy the magnetic beta spectrometer as shown in Figure 3.17 indicates a value of 0.86 Mev. Thus in noting the maximum range, attention must be given to the resolution of the observed curve. In the figure shown, it is reasonable by analysis to choose a range of 0.31 gram per square centimeter. This results in a value of energy in complete agreement with the magnetic spectrometer.

6.4. Beta Energy by Aluminum Half-value Thickness. It is empirically possible to approximate the upper energy limit of a beta spectrum by noting the thickness of aluminum required to reduce the beam intensity to half-value. Figure 6.5 shows graphically the amount of aluminum expressed in

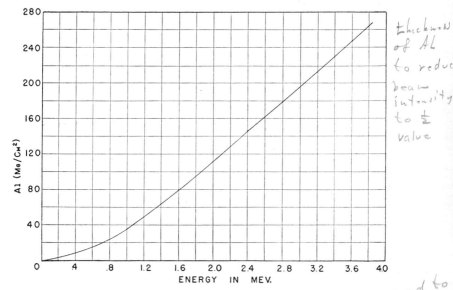

thickness of Al to reduce beam intensity to ½ value

FIG. 6.5.   Beta energies versus half-value thickness of aluminum. *Compared to Fig 6.2 for Complete absorption*

milligrams per square centimeter required for beta energies up to 4 Mev. This is easier to apply than the Feather technique since it is not necessary to determine an exact upper absorption limit.

6.5. The Beta Spectrum. The distribution of energy characteristic of the particles comprising the beta radiation from a radioactive source may be studied by a Wilson cloud chamber. The expansion chamber is provided with a thin window for the particles to enter, and a strong perpendicular magnetic field to produce a curvature in their paths. Such beta ray tracks are shown in Figure 6.6. A measurement of the radius ρ of each circular trace together with the known magnetic induction B allows an evaluation of the energies of the individual beta particles. By counting a sufficiently large number of tracks, the fluctuations are averaged and a histogram as shown in Figure

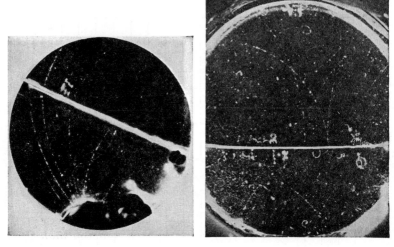

FIG. 6.6. Cloud chamber tracks of electrons moving in a magnetic field directed into the page.

6.7 is obtained. The ordinates represent the number of observed particles in successive equal intervals of $B\rho$. A smooth curve may be drawn so as to average any irregularities. The general form of such contours is that of a probability curve extending from a low value at zero momentum up through a most probable range to a definite limiting maximum value of the energy.

The observed distribution is quite likely to be an incorrect representation of the true number of particles at each energy. Because of their loss in energy and scattering in the gas there will appear to be relatively too many particles of low energy.

By using hydrogen gas in the chamber this error can be greatly reduced.

More exact distribution curves may be obtained by the use of beta ray spectrometers. These are of various types (as pre-

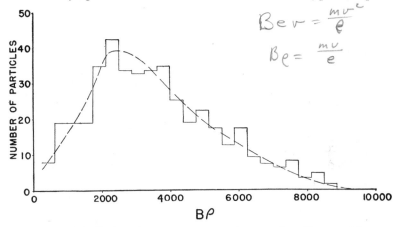

$$Bev = \frac{mv^2}{e}$$

$$Be = \frac{mv}{e}$$

FIG. 6.7. Distribution of momentum among a large number of beta particles.

viously described), and in them the beta particles may go from the source to the receiver with little or no scattering agent intervening. The type of distribution curve and the high precision attainable at the maximum energy cutoff is illustrated in Figure 6.8*A*. These data were obtained with a semicircular

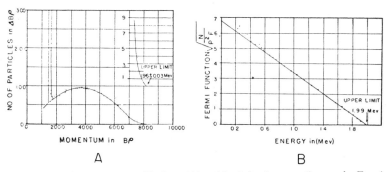

A   B

FIG. 6.8. The beta spectrum of indium 114 and its behavior according to the Fermi theory.

magnetic focusing spectrometer, using as a source the isotope of indium of mass 114.[7]

6.6. The Neutrino. If it be assumed that only discrete energy states can characterize the nucleus, then this observed continuous distribution of beta energies is difficult to explain. Two possibilities might allow a continuous distribution. One of these involves the abandonment of the notion of the conservation of energy in processes occurring within the nucleus. This suggestion was proposed,[8] perhaps not seriously, by Bohr, Kramers, and Slater.

Another possibility would be that in the transition from one definite energy state to another only a portion of the fixed energy difference is carried off by the beta particle. The remaining part of the energy is carried away by some other non-detectable type of radiation. To satisfy this need a new elementary particle was postulated. This particle was called the "neutrino" and is visualized as being a neutral particle whose rest mass is less than that of the electron. Because of the absence of charge it can pass through matter with little or no absorption and cannot be detected directly.

A calorimetric experiment justifying this conclusion was carried out by Ellis and Wooster.[9] Radium E emits electrons with a maximum energy of 1050 kev and with an average energy of about 390 kev. In the thermal measurement of the energy released, an average value of 350 kev was observed. It was accordingly concluded that the remainder of the energy was not released in any form ultimately converted into heat within the heavily shielded calorimeter and hence must have been carried off as an undetectable radiation. More direct experiments to establish with certainty the existence of the neutrino have been carried out. In general they are not completely conclusive.

These experiments showed that momentum is not conserved in beta decay, if only the electron and recoil nucleus are con-

[7] J. L. Lawson and J. M. Cork, *Phys. Rev.*, **57**, 982 (1940).
[8] N. Bohr, H. A. Kramers, and J. C. Slater, *Z. Physik*, **24**, 69 (1924).
[9] C. D. Ellis and W. A. Wooster, *Proc. Roy. Soc. A*, **117**, 109 (1927).

sidered, yet there was no evidence that a single neutrino is emitted. Hamilton showed [10] that there should be a correlation between the electron and neutrino directions, depending upon the "forbiddenness" of the beta transition. The more highly forbidden the transition, the more the neutrino and

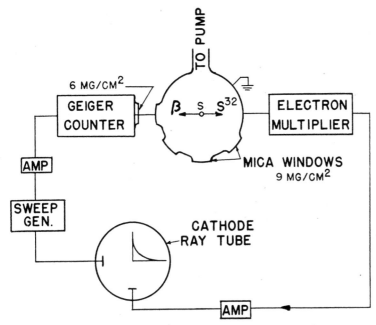

FIG. 6.9. Plan of apparatus to investigate the effect of the neutrino.

electron tend to go in the same direction, particularly when their momenta are equal. This angular correlation was investigated by Sherwin,[11] using an apparatus as shown in Figure 6.9. A source of phosphorus 32, approximately a monolayer in thickness, was deposited by evaporation, and mounted in a vacuum at the center of the chamber, S. For an electron leaving toward the left a recoil S^{32} nucleus should be ejected toward the right. The phosphorus is a pure beta emitter of

[10] D. R. Hamilton, *Phys. Rev.*, **71**, 456 (1947).
[11] C. W. Sherwin, *Phys. Rev.*, **75**, 1799 (1949); **73**, 173 (1948).

14.5-day half-life with an upper energy limit of 1.69 Mev. The emission of a beta particle triggered the cathode ray synchroscope, so that should a recoil nucleus be recorded by the electron multiplier, giving a delayed coincidence, the time of the delay could be determined. From the time of the delay, the velocity and the momentum of the recoil nucleus could be calculated. The momentum of the electron was determined by a magnetic spectrometer. It was concluded that the missing momentum must be in a single package and that its vector is most probably in the same hemisphere as that of the electron, and that its rest-mass is very nearly zero.

Formally it is common practice to distinguish between a neutrino ν, emitted on electron capture or positron emission, and the antineutrino $\bar{\nu}$, emitted in negative beta decay. It has been proposed to observe the latter by a radiochemical method in which Cl^{37} is converted to A^{37} by neutrino capture with the emission of a beta particle, thus

$$_{17}Cl^{37} + \bar{\nu} \rightarrow {}_{18}A^{37} + {}_{-1}e \tag{6.3}$$

The A^{37} decays by K capture back to Cl^{37} with a half-life of 35 days. If neutrinos and antineutrinos differ in their interactions with nucleons, then this capture may not occur. To check this possibility and, if possible, to measure the capture cross section, enormous tanks of carbon tetrachloride (CCl_4) are placed [12] in strong antineutrino (fission product) fields near the pile. The argon produced will be removed from the carbon-tetrachloride by sweeping it with helium and then separating in a liquid nitrogen trap.

Even though the capture cross section of the neutrino is as small as calculations indicate namely of the order of 5×10^{-44} cm^2 there still exists the possibility of its detection directly. In the capture process the proton accepts the neutrino and converts to a neutron and positron, thus

$$P + \nu \rightarrow N + {}^{+}e \tag{6.4}$$

[12] R. Davis, *Phys. Rev.*, **97**, 766 (1955).

The problem is then to observe delayed coincidences between the positron annihilation and the neutron capture, due to this process alone, and no other. This was first attempted [13] at the Los Alamos Laboratory. A large cylindrical tank containing 10.7 cubic feet of liquid scintillator, rich in hydrogen, was employed. The liquid was loaded with sufficient cadmium or boron to reduce the mean neutron capture time to about 5 microseconds. The cosmic ray background was largely eliminated by G-M tubes above and below the cylinder arranged in anticoincidence. Ninety photomultiplier tubes arranged in two banks of 45 each, for the positron and neutron signals respectively, supplied the coincident pulses. The apparatus was set up near a Hanford reactor and the change in delayed coincidence counting rate observed when the pile power was changed from zero to maximum. The reported value of counts attributable to neutrinos alone was of the order of 0.41 ± 0.20 counts per minute.

To carry the work to a more definite conclusion an improved arrangement, employing 330 5-inch phototubes, was set up at the Savannah River site. A reactor dependent signal was now observed such as 0.56 ± 0.06 and 2.88 ± 0.22 counts per hour, for two different runs. These results [14] are compatible with a neutrino capture cross section of $4 \pm 1.5 \times 10^{-44} \times 10^{-44}$ cm^2.

6.7. The Positron. In 1932, in cosmic-ray studies, C. D. Anderson [15] observed, in a vertical Wilson chamber, tracks with a curvature indicating that the particles carried a positive charge. Although they were at first announced as protons, subsequent studies showed these particles to be both as to mass and as to charge identical with electrons except opposite in sign. They were called "positrons."

It was soon found that many of the induced radioactivities, on decaying to normal atoms, emitted positrons. This is particularly true of those radioactive isotopes that are less in

---

[13] F. Reines and C. Cowan, *Phys. Rev.*, **92**, 830 (1953).
[14] F. Reines and C. L. Cowan, private communication.
[15] C. D. Anderson, *Phys. Rev.*, **41**, 405 (1932); **43**, 491 (1933).

mass than the stable isotopes of the same element such as
O^{15}, N^{13}, C^{11}, etc.

The form of the distribution curve for the positrons is very
much like that observed for negative particles. Certain isotopes such as Cu^{64} emit simultaneously both negative and positive particles with a single half-life. The upper limit of the
spectrum for the Cu^{64} positrons is 0.66 Mev compared with
0.58 Mev for the negatives. The stopping power of matter for
positrons has been found [16] to be quite similar to that displayed for negative electrons. The mean lifetime of the positron in a gas at normal pressure is of the order of 10^{-7} sec. In
solids and liquids the lifetime may be of the order of 10^{-9} or
10^{-10} sec. On decay the positron is annihilated by combining
with a negative electron. Both presumably are at low energies
so that two equal and oppositely directed gamma quanta each
of 0.51 Mev are emitted.

6.8. The Specific Charge of the Electron and the Positron.
The ratio of the charge e to the mass m_0 for beta particles from
radium was first determined by Becquerel in 1900, establishing
the fact that these particles were the same as cathode rays or
electrons.[17] He obtained a value 1×10^7 electromagnetic
units per gram. One year later, W. Kaufmann [18] in a more accurate determination found in the same units a value of $1.77 \times$
10^7. Since that time, a great number of investigations dealing
with this quantity have been carried out. The careful investigation by Bucherer [19] was considered to yield the best value
until recently, namely 1.763×10^7 electromagnetic units per
gram. The value of e/m as observed, of course, gets smaller as
the velocity of the beta particle increases, since the mass also
increases.

With the discovery of the positron, it became of interest to
see if its specific charge was exactly that of the negative elec-

[16] B. R. Curtis, *Phys. Rev.*, **53**, 986 (1938).
[17] H. Becquerel, *Compt. rend.*, **130**, 809 (1900).
[18] W. Kaufmann, *Physik. Z.*, **2**, 602 (1901).
[19] A. H. Bucherer, *Ann. Physik*, **37.3**, 592 (1912).

tron. This subject could be advantageously studied by using as a source radioactive copper of mass 64, since it emits both positives and negatives simultaneously. It was shown [20] that e/m_0 is the same for both types of particles, within an accuracy of better than 2%.

The value of the specific electronic charge as now calculated is 1.75768×10^7 electromagnetic units per gram.

6.9. Positronium. The possibility that for a short interval before annihilation the positron and electron exist together as an

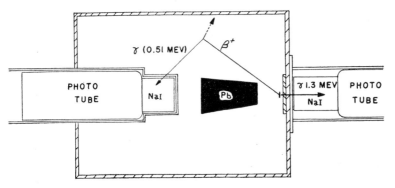

FIG. 6.10.   Arrangement to observe the delayed decay of positrons.

entity similar to an atom was proposed [21] in 1945 by Ruark. He predicted some of the spectral properties of such a structure and suggested for it the name "positronium." Compared with the hydrogen atom the reduced mass of the electron is half as large and hence all energies are less by a factor 2. Experimental evidence for the existence of positronium was reported [22] in 1949. The arrangement of the apparatus was as shown in Figure 6.10. A positron-emitting source, Na^{22}, also emits a prompt gamma ray of energy 1.28 Mev. By means of a multichannel delayed-coincidence circuit the distribution of time

[20] C. T. Zahn and A. H. Spees, *Phys. Rev.*, **53**, 357 (1938); A. H. Spees and C. Zahn, *Phys. Rev.*, **58**, 861 (1940).
[21] A. E. Ruark, *Phys. Rev.*, **68**, 278 (1945).
[22] J. Shearer and M. Deutsch, *Phys. Rev.*, **76**, 642 (1949); **83**, 866 (1951).

intervals between counts in phototubes A and B could be analyzed. The former is due to the prompt gamma ray and the latter to the delayed annihilation radiation.

The results for two gases, namely, oxygen and freon (CCl_2F_2), each at varying pressures, are shown in Figure 6.11. The rate of decay of a collection of positrons in matter had been predicted [23] by Dirac to be expressible as the sum of two terms. The first term represented the state in which the spins of the two combining electrons are anti-parallel (singlet), and for the second term the spins are parallel (triplet state). For free collisions in a gas, λ should be proportional to the pressure as shown in the results for oxygen in Figure 6.11. In freon the results indicated that the decay rate was not proportional to the pressure but that λ remained small, or the mean life relatively long, even at high pressures. The conclusion was drawn that in freon, and also in many other gases, positronium is formed in a time that is short compared to 10^{-7} sec. About one quarter of the particles are in the singlet state and decay in about 10^{-10} sec. The remaining three quarters show a longer period (10^{-7} sec) characteristic of the triplet state. The longer period decay has been shown to be characterized by three-quantum decay, so that its gamma distribution appears to be continuous. Some gases, such as nitrous oxide (NO), seem to have a large cross section for converting the

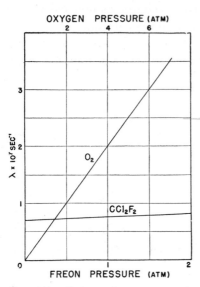

FIG. 6.11.   Positron decay constant in oxygen and freon.

[23] P. Dirac, *Proc. Camb. Phil. Soc.*, **26**, 361 (1930).

triplet ortho-positronium to the singlet para-positronium state. This is perhaps what happens also in oxygen.

6.10. The Fermi Theory of Beta Decay. In 1934, Fermi proposed a theory of beta decay.[24] He assumed that the negative beta particle was emitted by a transition within the nucleus in which a neutron was converted into a proton. Along with the electron, a neutrino escaped from the nucleus. The total energy of the pair from a definite emitter is a constant. A study of the energy distribution of the beta particles reveals the manner in which the energy is shared between the neutrino and the electron. To explain the observed distribution it became necessary to make an assumption regarding the interaction between the electron-neutrino field and that of the heavy particle.

The form of the derived expression for the probability P of the ejection, in unit time, of a beta particle whose energy lies between W and $W + dW$, expressed in units of mc^2, was given as

$$P \, dW = Kf(Z, W)pW(W_m - W)^2 \, dW \qquad (6.5)$$

where p is the momentum of the electron in units of mc and is equal to $(W^2 - 1)^{1/2}$. Fermi showed that the function $f(Z, W)$ could be explicitly evaluated. Kurie[25] rearranged the equation so that it could be readily subjected to test by the observed data. In this form the number of particles in each successive equal interval of momentum was denoted as N and the reduced equation became

$$\left(\frac{N}{f}\right)^{1/2} = A - B(W + 1) \qquad (6.6)$$

in which A and B are constants.

Thus on plotting the square root of $\dfrac{N}{f}$ against $(W + 1)$, a straight line of negative slope should be obtained. The inter-

[24] E. Fermi, Z. *Physik,* **88**, 161 (1934).
[25] F. Kurie, J. Richardson, and H. Paxton, *Phys. Rev.,* **49**, 368 (1936).

cept on the energy axis would be one mc^2 greater than the maximum beta transition energy Wm.

Early data were obtained by the counting of tracks within a cloud chamber. With air in the chamber a large percentage of the low-energy tracks were multiply scattered. More reliable observations were made by using hydrogen in the chamber. On making plots according to the Kurie arrangement of the Fermi equation, a partial test could be made either of the theory or of the data used. If the theory is correct, then good data should give a straight line. Any deviation from a straight line might then be interpreted as an insufficiency in the theory or in the observed results. All early data treated in this way failed to yield linear plots with the Fermi equation.

6.11. The Konopinski-Uhlenbeck Theory. The observed apparent failure of the Fermi theory stimulated further theoretical consideration of beta decay. Following the same procedure as Fermi, but by introducing and including higher-order derivatives of the interaction between the heavy particle and the electron-neutrino field, Konopinski and Uhlenbeck [26] were led to several alternative expressions for the beta distribution. Certain of these expressions could be excluded at once, from energy considerations. The expression offering most promise was, when rearranged to yield a Kurie plot, quite similar to that for the Fermi equation. The only difference was that, instead of the term $\left(\dfrac{N}{f}\right)^{1/2}$, there appeared the term $\left(\dfrac{N}{f}\right)^{1/4}$ in the reduced equation.

The best data were put in proper form to test this relationship and in most cases a straight-line plot resulted. It was thus at first assumed that the Konopinski-Uhlenbeck theory was correct. As the technique of taking data improved it became apparent that the experimental data were not reliable.

At low energies, serious errors due to back scattering and multiple scattering existed. The beta spectra of several emit-

[26] E. J. Konopinski and G. E. Uhlenbeck, *Phys. Rev.*, **48**, 107 (1935).

ters were resurveyed, taking great care to reduce back scattering and multiple scattering. It now appeared that when these data were checked by the Kurie plot, the Fermi equation was more nearly satisfied than the Konopinski-Uhlenbeck relationship. This is shown in Figure 6.12, which represents [27] the positron spectrum from a radioactive copper isotope of mass 64 having a

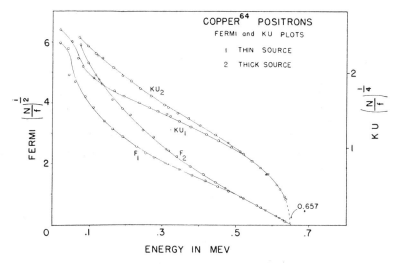

FIG. 6.12. The beta spectrum of copper 64, using a very thin source and a thick source.

half-life of 12.8 hours. In one experiment the thick source consisted of a mass of copper of 50 milligrams per square centimeter, whereas in a second run having an equally strong radioactivity, the mass of the copper was only 2 milligrams per square centimeter. It is apparent that except for low energies the Fermi curve seems most linear. This same result is more strikingly observed in the beta spectrum of the indium isotope of mass 114. This electron distribution as observed in a magnetic spectrometer is shown in Figure 6.8A. On the Kurie plot, following the Fermi equation, shown in Figure 6.8B, the points

[27] A. W. Tyler, *Phys. Rev.*, **56**, 125 (1939).

lie very closely along a straight line whose intercept on the energy axis is at 1.99 Mev.

The spectrum of the beta radiation from phosphorus 32 has been widely studied. The distribution of momentum, as observed by Lawson,[28] is plotted in Figure 6.13, both according to the Fermi theory and the Konopinski-Uhlenbeck modification. The fit with the Fermi theory seems definitely better.

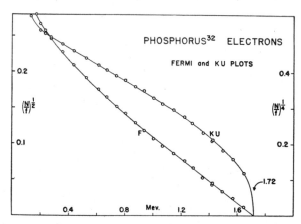

FIG. 6.13. The electron distribution from phosphorus 32, plotted both according to the Fermi and the Konopinski-Uhlenbeck theories.

6.12. The Sargent Rule. It was observed by Sargent[29] in 1933 that for many of the naturally radioactive elements a simple relationship existed between the maximum energy of the beta radiation and the decay constant or half-life, $T_{1/2}$, of the activity. On plotting the logarithm of the disintegration constant λ versus the logarithm of the maximum beta energy, a straight line of slope 5 was found. Thus an equation of the form

$$T_{1/2}W^5 = c \qquad (6.7)$$

seemed valid for the relationship where c is a constant. Several activities seemed to lie off the line in the graph and in fact

[28] J. L. Lawson, *Phys. Rev.*, **55**, 1136 (1939).
[29] B. W. Sargent, *Proc. Roy. Soc. (London)*, **139**, 659 (1933).

another group could be formed represented by another equation with a constant c' different from c by a large factor. This is shown in Figure 6.14.

Of the many induced radioactivities now known to exist, several such groups may be formed. Those emitters for which the

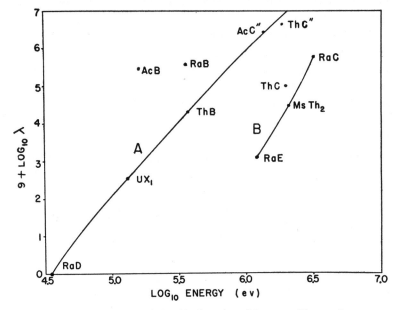

FIG. 6.14. The Sargent relationship for a few of the natural beta emitters.

constant c is a minimum are said to undergo "allowed" transitions. The next group of emitters for which c is about 100 times as large, decay by "first forbidden" transitions, a succeeding group with correspondingly larger c by "second forbidden" transitions, and so on.

In optical spectra it was found desirable to formulate a set of selection rules under which the possibility of a certain transition could be determined. In a similar way criteria can be established so that the probability of a particular nuclear disintegration can be predicted.

On the emission of a particle the nucleus changes from an initial to a final state usually with a change ΔI in spin. At the same time a change may or may not occur in another attribute of the system of particles called "parity." This quantity is either even or odd for a nucleus, depending upon its symmetry characteristics. It may be regarded empirically as an additional quantum number describing the energy level.

To show the degree of "forbiddenness" of a beta ray, Konopinski has developed [30] a function $f(Z, W_m)$ which, while much more complicated, is like the Sargent term in that when multiplied by the half-life $T_{1/2}$ it gives a constant for any similar group of beta emitters. This value is such that for the known beta emitters the $\log_{10} ft_{1/2}$ lies between a low of 3 and a high of about 15. A simple nomograph arranged by Moszkowski [31] as shown in Figure 6.15, allows the approximate determination graphically of the "log ft." Corrections must be added for varying Z and in the case of branching if the mode of decay under consideration is less than 100%.

As the beta spectra of the many newly created radioactive isotopes were obtained, wide variations were observed in the nature of their Kurie plots. No single simple relationship seemed to satisfy all transitions. Within the more general framework of the Fermi theory it has been shown [32] possible to account for the varied beta spectra. The simple idea was that the probability of formation of a particle is proportional to the probability that it can be found at the site of the transforming nucleon. It became necessary to define a coupling energy density, h, such that

$$h = g\psi_N\psi_{+e}\psi_{-e}\psi_\nu \tag{6.8}$$

where g measures the strength of the coupling and the ψ's are the probability amplitudes for the nucleons ready to decay and for each of the product particle states. The ψ's may be multi-

[30] E. J. Konopinski, *Rev. Mod. Phys.*, **15**, 209 (1943).
[31] S. A. Moszkowski, *Phys. Rev.*, **82**, 35 (1951).
[32] E. Konopinski and L. Langer, *An. Rev. Nuc. Sci. II*, **261** (1953).

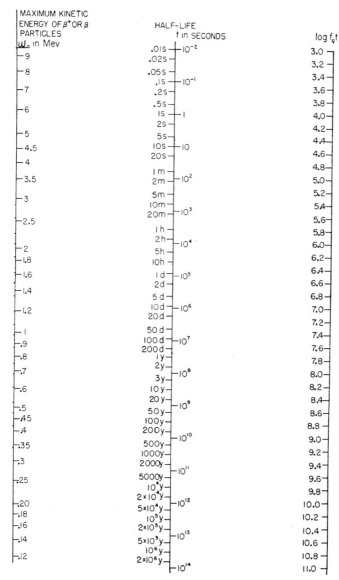

FIG. 6.15. Nomograph for determining log *ft* values (Moszkowski).

TABLE 6.2. TYPES OF BETA SPECTRA

A. Super-Allowed. Mirror Nuclei, $\Delta I = 0$. No Parity Change

Isotope	Half-life	W_{max}	Log ft
C 11	20.4 M	0.98	3.6
O 15	125 S	1.68	3.7
Mg 23	12.2 S	2.99	3.7
Cl 33	2.0 S	4.4	3.7

B. Allowed. $\Delta I = 0, 1$. No Parity Change

Ne 23	40.4 S	4.2	4.9
P 34	12.5 S	5.1	4.7
Ga 73	5.0 H	1.4	5.5
Rh 104	44.0 S	2.6	4.7
In 114	72.0 S	1.98	4.4

C. First Forbidden. $\Delta I = 0, 1$. Yes, Parity Change

Br 87	56.0 S	8.0 (30%)	7.3
Kr 88	2.77 H	2.8 (20%)	6.8
Ba 139	85 M	2.27	6.7
Ce 144	285 D	0.30 (70%)	7.2
Pt 199	31 M	1.8	6.3

D. Unique First Forbidden. $\Delta I = 2$. Yes, Parity Change

Cl 38	37.4 M	4.81 (53%)	8.0
As 76	26.2 H	3.1 (60%)	8.9
Sr 90	19.9 Y	0.54	8.9
Pr 142	19.2 H	2.20	8.0
RaE (Bi 210)	5.0 D	1.17	8.1

E. Second or Higher Forbidden. $\Delta I = 2$ or more. No Parity Change

Be 10	2.7×10^6 Y	0.56	13.7
Na 22	2.7 Y	1.8 (0.06%)	14.0
Rb 87	5.6×10^{10} Y	0.27	16.5
Cs 137	33 Y	1.18 (8%)	12.2
K 40	1.35×10^9 Y	1.36 (90%)	17.6

F. l-Forbidden. $\Delta I = 1$. $\Delta l = 2$. No Parity Change

P 32	14.4 D	1.70	7.9
Ni 63	73 Y	0.065	6.8
Zn 65	247 D	0.32 (2.5%)	7.5
I 126	13 D	1.26 (40%)	7.6

plied together in a variety of ways so that five independent forms of h are obtained. These are symbolized as h_s, h_v, h_t, h_a, and h_p, called, respectively, scalar, vector, tensor, axial vector, and pseudoscalar interactions. The choice between these various forms appears [33] sufficient to satisfy the numerous peculiarities observed in the many cases of beta decay.

Table 6.2 shows only a few of the many beta emitters in each of the several classes. Those transitions are chosen which terminate in the ground state of the final nucleus. There are in all about 20 known mirror nuclei, as represented in Class A for which the number of protons Z, before emission, is equal to the number of neutrons existing after the decay. The value of the log ft in almost every case lies close to 3.6. For these the spin change is zero, excluding $0 \rightarrow 0$, with no change in parity. For each higher order of forbiddenness the log ft increases by a factor of about 2.

6.13. "K" Electron Capture. From theoretical considerations, it was suggested by Yukawa [34] that any long-lived positron-emitting nucleus might also decay by capturing one of its own orbital "K" electrons. The branching ratio for the two modes of disintegration was shown [35] to depend upon the energy available, the density of electrons, and the spin change associated with the positron emission. The probability of capture should increase with the half-life or with the magnitude of the spin change associated with the transition.

A successful search for this phenomenon was made by Alvarez in 1938.[36] On bombarding titanium with deuterons a radioactivity was produced which was identified as due to an isotope of vanadium of mass 49. The half-life was 600 days. The only possibility of recognizing the reaction was to study the X-rays emitted by the atom. If a vanadium ($Z = 23$) nu-

[33] E. Konopinski, *Rev. Mod. Phys.*, **27**, 254 (1955).

[34] H. Yukawa and S. Sakata, *Proc. Phys. Math. Soc. Japan*, **18**, 128 (1936).

[35] G. Uhlenbeck and H. Kuiper, *Physica*, **4**, 601 (1937); C. Moller, *Phys. Rev.*, **51**, 84 (1937).

[36] L. Alvarez, *Phys. Rev.*, **53**, 213 (1938); **54**, 486 (1938).

cleus captures a K electron, the nucleus becomes titanium ($Z =$ 22) and the X-rays emitted as the "K" shell is refilled will be the characteristic X-rays of titanium. These were positively identified by their characteristic absorption. Many cases of "K" electron capture have now been observed.

6.14. Transmutation by Electrons. Several early attempts [37] to induce radioactivity in elements by bombardment with electrons having energies up to a million electron volts were unsuccessful. On considering the problem theoretically, Guth [38] concluded that success might be expected if the energy of the incident electrons exceeded in value the threshold for photoelectric disintegration. Since beryllium had been shown [39] to have a photoelectric threshold of 1.6 Mev it became possible to test the theory with the 1.8-Mev output of the Van de Graaff generator at Notre Dame University. The reaction anticipated [40] would be representable by the symbol $_4Be^9(e, n)_3Li^8$ or by the equation

$$_4Be^9 + _{-1}e^0 \rightarrow _3Li^8 + _0n' \rightarrow _4Be^8 + _0n' + _{-1}e^0 \quad (6.9)$$

In carrying out the experiment, neutron emission was detected by noting the activation induced in foils of silver, rhodium, or indium placed near the target. For incident energies greater than 1.63 Mev, positive evidence of neutron production was observed. It was shown by using different thicknesses of beryllium that the disintegration was not due to gamma or X-rays arising from the decelerated electrons. The cross section at 1.73 Mev for the reaction was found to be only of the order of 10^{-31} square centimeter.

Since this first successful disintegration experiment it has been found possible to excite many radioactivities in heavy elements by electrons. The activities which can be produced

[37] J. Livingood and A. Snell, *Phys. Rev.*, **48**, 851 (1935); G. P. Thomson and J. Saxton, *Phil. Mag.* **23**, 241 (1937).
[38] E. Guth, *Phys. Rev.*, **55**, 411 (1939).
[39] J. Chadwick and M. Goldhaber, *Proc. Roy. Soc.* (*London*), **151**, 479 (1935).
[40] G. B. Collins, B. Waldman, and W. Guth, *Phys. Rev.*, **56**, 876 (1939).

in this manner are those associated with the excited state of a normally stable atom. Such metastable states, representing energy levels up to 1.5 Mev or more, exist in indium, lead, strontium, silver, and many other elements.

6.15. The Scattering of Electrons. The elastic scattering of high-energy electrons by atomic nuclei has been the subject

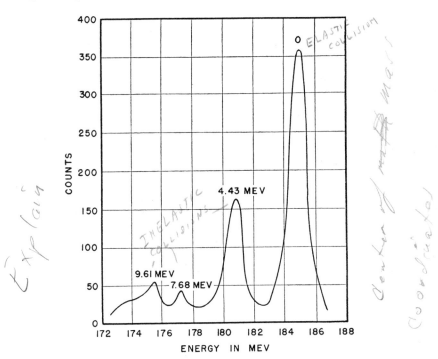

FIG. 6.16. Electron scattering at 80 degrees by 187 Mev electrons on carbon (Stanford University).

of many experimental studies.[41] Using a monoenergetic incident beam, the energy distribution in the scattered beam is observed both as a function of the angle and of the Z of the scattering element. In addition to the elastically scattered electrons

[41] R. Hofstadter, B. Hahn, A. Knudsen, and J. McIntyre, *Phys. Rev.*, **95**, 512 (1954); J. H. Fregeau and R. Hofstadter, *Phys. Rev.*, **99**, 1503 (1955).

there generally appear at any angle other peaks of lesser energy corresponding to inelastic scattering. In this phenomenon the scattering nucleus receives some energy other than that due to

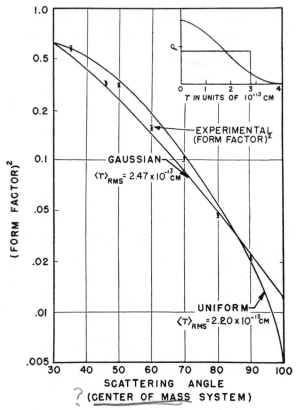

FIG. 6.17. Form factor for the carbon nucleus.

recoil and is left in an excited state. Figure 6.16 shows the results obtained with the 187 Mev electron beam of the Stanford linear accelerator on a carbon target, at a scattering angle of 80 degrees. Several peaks are apparent at energies less than that of the elastically scattered beam, corresponding to as many excited levels of the carbon 12 nucleus, with the energies as shown. Many other light nuclei have been similarly studied.[42]

An approximate expression for the electron scattering cross sections for light nuclei is based upon the Born approximation. The differential cross section may be expressed as that due to a point nuclear charge, multiplied by a "form" factor, due to the actual distribution of the nuclear electric charge. It is possible to introduce certain parameters relative to the charge such that a best fit is obtained between the calculated and experimental curves. Then one measures essentially a radius of the nuclear charge, and its radial density. Figure 6.17 shows the treatment for the carbon nucleus. The points shown are for the form factor as experimentally observed at various angles. Two types of charge density are considered, namely, a Gaussian distribution with maximum at the center and a uniform density. The two computed curves with radii chosen for best fits, as shown in insert, indicate that the actual charge distribution lies halfway between a Gaussian and a uniform model, with a root mean square radius of 2.4×10^{-13} cm.

QUESTIONS AND PROBLEMS

Done in book.

1. Show that the radius of curvature ρ, of an electron whose energy is W Mev, moving at right angles to a field of B gausses is

$$\rho = \frac{10^4}{3B} \sqrt{W(W + 1.02)} \text{ cm}$$

2. What thicknesses of aluminum will effectively absorb the beta rays from (*a*) phosphorus 32, and (*b*) lithium 8, making use of the Feather rule?

Answer: 0.28 cm, 2.3 cm.

3. In a cloud chamber, a high-energy electron describes a track of radius 30 cm in a magnetic field of 9000 gausses. Express its momentum in gauss cm and its energy in Mev.

Answer: 270,000 gauss cm, 80.5 Mev.

[42] R. B. Helm, Stanford University, *HEPL Report No. 40* (1956).

4. A beta spectrometer as shown in Figure 3.22 with a solenoidal winding of 10 turns per cm, carrying a current of 20 amperes, brings particles back to the axis 60 cm from their source on the axis. The circular slit through the baffle at the center has an effective diameter of 20 cm. Express the momentum in gauss cm and the energy of the particles focused at this current. On changing the current to 10 amperes or to 40 amperes, show what happens.

Answer: 2709 gauss cm, 0.447 Mev.

5. An electron of energy 1 Mev is elastically scattered through an angle of 120 deg by a carbon nucleus at rest at the surface (see Figure 6.6). What energy and what momentum transfers take place?

Answer: Carbon nucleus recoils at approximately 30 deg with 271 ev.

6. The radioactive line source in a magnetic spectrometer has an electrical capacity of 0.4 electrostatic units. It has a source strength of 20 microcuries and is completely nonconducting. How many minutes will be required for the potential of the line source to build up to 1000 volts? What will be the effect of this on the observed electron energy? How avoid the effect?

Answer: 62.8 min; observed value too small.

[handwritten in margin: conversion of energy]

[handwritten in margin: electricity]

[handwritten: #5 Use relativity to get same as book. ⮑ in book appendix]

CHAPTER 7

GAMMA RADIATION

7.1. Discovery and Nature of Gamma Radiation. By allowing the collimated radiation from a sample of radium to pass through a perpendicular magnetic field, a certain portion of the radiation appeared to be undeflected. This undeflected beam was originally all called alpha radiation. In 1900, P. Villard [1] allowed this radiation to pass obliquely through a stack of photographic plates. Although much of the radiation was absorbed by the first layer, he found that some of it penetrated the entire stack of plates, tracing its path by activating every emulsion. Rutherford used a much stronger magnetic field and found that the more easily absorbed portion could be slightly deflected, indicating that it consisted of a stream of positively charged particles. There still remained the undeflected penetrating portion of the radiation. This was called gamma radiation and has been shown to consist of electromagnetic waves, identical in nature to very penetrating X-rays.

The wavelength of gamma rays was determined by the same technique used in evaluating the wavelength of X-rays. It was shown by Bragg that a wavelength λ would be reflected by a crystal at a grazing angle of incidence θ if the lattice distance of the crystal d satisfied the equation

$$\lambda = 2d \sin \theta \qquad (7.1)$$

This method can be used for gamma rays with energies up to about 100 kev. An experimental arrangement as used by

[1] P. Villard, *Compt. rend.*, **130**, 1178 (1900).

Rutherford [2] and Andrade is shown in Figure 7.1. The spectrogram reproduced [3] is actually that of the high-energy "K" series lines from a heavy element. For very energetic gamma radiation the wavelength λ becomes so small that no satisfactory crystal lattice exists capable of satisfying the Bragg law with an appreciably large reflecting angle θ. In this energy region gamma rays have been studied either by their absorption in specific elements, such as lead, or by observing the behavior

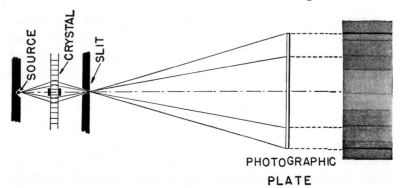

PHOTOGRAPHIC
PLATE

FIG. 7.1.   A crystal spectrometer for gamma rays.

of recoil electrons, produced by the gamma rays, in electric or magnetic fields. Large scintillation crystals with a pulse height analyzer are also useful in evaluating gamma energies.

7.2. The Bent-crystal Focusing Spectrometer. In the Bragg reflection from a single crystal face, no focusing occurs. In 1930, DuMond and Kirkpatrick [4] suggested the use of many small crystals of calcite properly mounted on an arc so that in effect the assembly performed as a curved grating and gave an increased intensity at the image. Many investigators [5] subsequently made use of shaped or bent crystals to obtain increased sensitivity with weak sources. Such spectrometers may

[2] E. Rutherford and P. Andrade, *Phil. Mag.*, **28**, 262 (1914).
[3] J. M. Cork, *Phys. Rev.*, **25**, 197 (1925).
[4] J. W. DuMond and H. A. Kirkpatrick, *Rev. Sci. Instruments*, **1**, 88 (1930).
[5] J. Johann, *Zeit. f. Phys.*, **60**, 185 (1931); Y. Cauchois, *J. phys. radium*, **7**, 3 (1932); B. Hamermesh, *Bull. Amer. Phys. Soc. Series II*, **1**, 220 (1956).

be either transmission or reflection instruments. The geometry for reflection is as shown in Figure 7.2. The atomic crystal planes are bent, with C as center, but the actual reflecting crystal face is shaped with O as center. Radiation of a particular

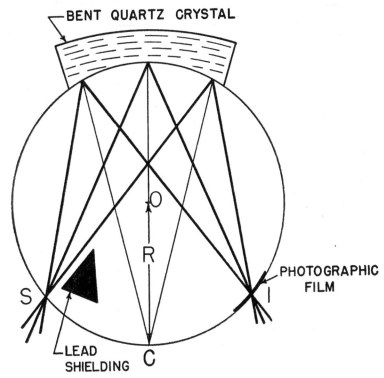

Fig. 7.2.   The bent-crystal focusing spectrometer.

wavelength from a line source S will now be cooperatively reflected by the entire crystal surface to a line in the image I.

Even though the Bragg angle is small for high-energy radiation, the linear dimensions of the mounting may be increased so that a satisfactory resolving power results. A transmission instrument of this type with a 7.7 meter focal length as set up near the Argonne reactor is shown in Figure 7.3. The (310) planes of a large bent quartz crystal reflect the radiation through a collimator to a battery of scintillation crystals. The over-all sensitivity is such that energies may be well resolved through the range of a few Mev. The instrument is currently used in the evaluation of the energies of the gamma rays emitted on neutron capture.

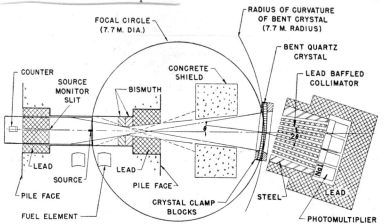

Fig. 7.3. Plan of 7.7 meter quartz transmission spectrograph. (Courtesy of Dr. B. Hamermesh.)

7.3. Origin of Gamma Rays.

Gamma rays originate in the excited nuclei of atoms. They represent the energy difference between an excited state and a lower energy state which may or may not be the ground level. That is, between the highest excited and the ground states there may exist several possible energy levels. In such a case the original transition may be followed by one or more additional gamma emissions in rapid succession. The nucleus is finally left in the stable ground state. Selection rules may be formulated relating to the probability of a given transition, as is done for optical spectra. The packet of gamma radiation sent out as a consequence of a single transition is termed a "photon."

7.4. The Photon.

In attempting to explain the observed form of the distribution curve of the radiant energy from a black-body, Planck, in 1901, introduced the notion of the atomicity of energy in absorption and emission processes.[6] In 1905, Einstein proposed the now famous "photoelectric equation." [7] This states that the energy W of a light photon will on impact with an atom dislodge an electron and give it kinetic energy. The equation is

$$W = h\nu = \tfrac{1}{2}mv^2 + P \qquad (7.2)$$

where h is the Planck universal constant, ν is the frequency of the light, m and v are the mass and velocity of the ejected electron, and P is the energy of binding of the electron or the work required to free it from the atom. It was seven years before this relationship was experimentally verified.[8]

In 1906, Einstein formulated further the corpuscular notion of light by stating: "Every quantity of energy of any form whatever represents a mass which is equal to this same energy divided by c^2, where c is the velocity of light, and every quantity of energy in motion represents momentum." Thus the term photon applies to a wave-train or packet of electromagnetic radiation in motion, whose energy W is

$$W = h\frac{c}{\lambda} = h\nu = mc^2 \qquad \text{(ergs)} \qquad (7.3)$$

and whose momentum is

$$\frac{W}{c} = \frac{h}{\lambda} = \frac{h\nu}{c} = mc \qquad \text{(gm cm per sec)} \qquad (7.4)$$

The corpuscular notion of electromagnetic radiation was more firmly established by the experiments of A. H. Compton in what is now termed the "Compton effect," which will be described later.

[6] M. Planck, *Ann. Physik*, **4**, 552 (1901).
[7] A. Einstein, *Ann. Physik*, **17**, 132 (1905).
[8] K. T. Compton, *Phil. Mag.*, **23**, 579 (1912); A. L. Hughes, *Phil. Trans. Roy. Soc.*, **212**, 205 (1912); R. A. Millikan and J. Wright, *Phys. Rev.*, **34**, 68 (1912).

7.5. The Absorption of Gamma Radiation. While alpha radiation is usually completely absorbed in a fraction of a millimeter of aluminum and beta rays are absorbed by a few millimeters of the same metal, gamma rays may traverse a thickness of several centimeters. The absorption of gamma radiation by materials of different density is found to vary almost directly with the density. If radiation of intensity I is incident upon an absorbing layer of thickness dx, the amount of radiation absorbed, dI, is proportional both to dx and to I, so that

$$\frac{dI}{I} = -\mu\,dx \qquad\qquad dI = -\mu I\,dx \qquad\qquad (7.5)$$

The proportionality factor μ is a characteristic property of the medium. It is called the coefficient of absorption. It may be defined as the relative loss in intensity per centimeter of path. The negative sign indicates that I decreases as x increases. It follows from equation 7.5, by integration, that

$$\log_e I = -\mu x \qquad\qquad (7.6)$$

By evaluating at the limits, $I = I_0$ when $x = 0$, and $I = I$ at $x = x$, the emergent intensity I is

$$I = I_0 e^{-\mu x} \qquad\qquad (7.7)$$

The coefficient of absorption μ may be expressed as the reciprocal of the thickness that will reduce the intensity of an incident beam to $1/e$ or $1/2.73$ of its original value. To reduce the intensity to half its original value a thickness $x_{\frac{1}{2}}$ called the half-value thickness is required. From equation 7.7 it then follows that

$$\log_e \frac{I_0}{I} = \log_e 2 = 0.693 = \mu x_{\frac{1}{2}} \qquad\qquad (7.8)$$

and

$$\log_e \frac{I_{\frac{1}{2}}}{I} = \ln 2 = \mu = \frac{0.693}{x_{\frac{1}{2}}} \qquad\qquad (7.9)$$

Experimentally, the half-value thickness is easy to determine, and from this the absorption coefficient μ is expressed by equa-

tion 7.9.   The specimen under study is placed above an ionization chamber and the intensity I of the radiation is noted as
the thickness of an interposed absorber is increased.   The data
are represented on a log I versus thickness coordinate plot.
A straight line of negative slope will result if the gamma radiation is of single value as to energy.   In case two discrete

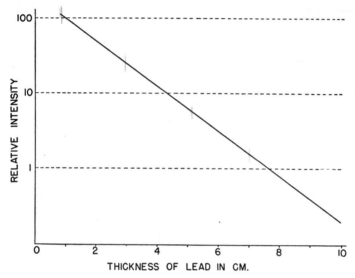

FIG. 7.4.   The decrease in intensity of the gamma radiation from zinc 65 in lead.

gamma rays are present the resulting curve may be analyzed
to yield the absorption coefficient of each, provided the radiation is sufficiently intense to be followed through a very thick
layer of absorbing substance and the two gamma rays have appreciably different absorption coefficients.

In Figure 7.4 is shown the absorption of the gamma rays
from a radioactive isotope of zinc of mass 65.   From the linear
curve the half-value thickness is 1.022 centimeters so that μ is
0.693/1.022 or 0.678 per centimeter.   It is sometimes desirable
to divide the linear coefficient μ by the density of the substance
ρ, giving what is termed the "mass absorption" coefficient μ/ρ.

This is thus the reciprocal of that number of grams per square centimeter that will reduce the intensity to $1/e$ of its original value. The same value would be found for the mass absorption coefficient for a substance regardless of its state of aggregation, that is, as gas, liquid, or solid.

On dividing the mass absorption coefficient by (n), the number of atoms per gram, an atomic absorption coefficient μ_a, defined as the relative absorption per atom per square centimeter, is obtained. On dividing further by the atomic number $\underline{Z}$, an "electronic absorption" coefficient μ_e or the relative loss in intensity per electron per square centimeter is given. Since the absorption of gamma radiation is an electronic phenomenon it might be expected for a given energy that the latter quantity μ_e would be the same regardless of the element from which it was derived. In practice this is not the case, but the electronic absorption depends upon the binding of the electron. For gamma radiation of energy 1.3 Mev, the linear, mass, and electronic absorption coefficients in different absorbers are shown in Table 7.1. The wide variation in the electronic coefficient

TABLE 7.1

Absorber	$\mu(cm^{-1})$	$\dfrac{\mu}{\rho}\left(\dfrac{cm^2}{gm}\right)$	$\mu_e = \dfrac{\mu}{\rho n Z}$
Carbon...........	0.115	0.059	1.96×10^{-25}
Aluminum.........	0.156	0.058	2.00×10^{-25}
Iron..............	0.455	0.058	2.06×10^{-25}
Copper...........	0.509	0.057	2.08×10^{-25}
Tin..............	0.345	0.060	2.36×10^{-25}
Lead.............	0.800	0.071	2.98×10^{-25}

will be seen to be due in great part to the variation in electron pair production with the atomic number Z of the element.

It is apparent that the more tightly bound the electron, the greater is its ability to reduce the intensity of the gamma radiation. Since μ_e is also the relative loss in the number of photons per electron, it really represents a cross section (σ) for this reaction.

The loss in intensity suffered by gamma radiation in its passage through matter is due to the combined effects of five processes. These are

    a. The photoelectric effect
    b. Compton scattering
    c. Pair production
    d. Nuclear photodisintegration
    e. Elastic scattering

7.6. The Photoelectric Effect. It was early known that the passage of gamma radiation through a gas rendered the gas electrically conducting. This meant that ions were produced by the gamma rays. Such ions can be readily visualized as negative orbital electrons dislodged from the atoms of the gas. The heavy atomic residues will persist only a short time as positive ions because they will soon capture other electrons. In case the gamma ray gives all its energy to the dislodged electron, the electron is termed a photoelectron. The energy balance applicable to this case was first proposed by Einstein.[9] The energy of the incident photon, W_γ, is

$$W_\gamma = h\nu = P + \tfrac{1}{2}mv^2 \qquad (7.10)$$

where h is the Planck constant, ν is the frequency of the radiation, P is the binding energy of the electron in the atom, m is its mass, and v its velocity. Since gamma rays are usually very energetic, their energy is large compared to the binding energy P. Hence the kinetic energy of the ejected electron is not much less than that of the photon, and it may be necessary

[9] A. Einstein, *Ann. Physik*, **17**, 132 (1905).

to use the relativistic expression ($mc^2 - m_0c^2$) for its evaluation. Absorption due to the photoelectric process is greater, the more tightly bound the electron. Thus in a given element, a K electron may be many times as effective as an L electron in stopping gamma radiation. Likewise for a gamma ray of given

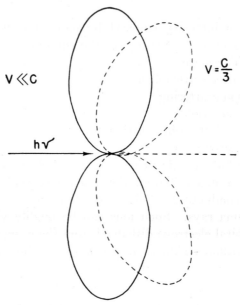

FIG. 7.5. The distribution of photoelectrons of low energy and higher energy.

energy, the absorption per K electron increases rapidly with the atomic number of the absorbing element. For heavy elements and radiation of low energy the photoelectric effect accounts for most of the absorption. The heavy residue of the atom shares in the impact by carrying off much of the momentum and little of the energy. The angular distribution of the emitted photoelectrons can be calculated. For low-energy photons, no photoelectrons will be emitted in the forward direction of the gamma quanta. A photoelectron has the greatest probability of being emitted in the direction of polarization of the incident quantum, that is, at right angles to its forward direction. As the energy increases, the tendency is for the photo-

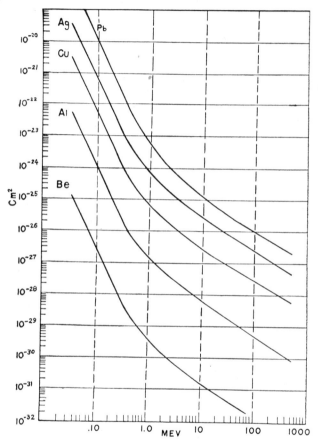

FIG. 7.6.   Photoelectric cross section for the two K electrons in Be, Al, Cu, Ag, and Pb.

electrons to have a forward component of velocity. In Figure 7.5 the distribution of electrons is shown at various angles when their energies are low and also when their velocities are of the order of one third that of light.

For energies up to 0.5 Mev, in light elements [10] the cross section σ_K for the two K electrons may be expressed as

$$\sigma_K = C \frac{Z^5}{W_\gamma^{7/2}} \text{ cm}^2 \tag{7.11}$$

Many more detailed developments capable of treating the heavy elements at high energies have been made.[11] Calculations made from these more complicated expressions give for the cross section for the two K electrons, σ_K, in the representative elements Be, Al, Cu, Ag, and Pb, the values shown graphically in Figure 7.6. For the over-all photoelectric effect not only the K but also the L and M electrons must be considered. In the heavy elements the contribution due to all outer electrons has been estimated [12] as equal to about one fourth of that due to the K electrons. Hence, the photoelectric cross section per atom σ_P is approximately equal to five fourths of σ_K.

7.7. The Compton Effect. In 1922, a very important experimental observation was made by A. H. Compton.[13] Quite independent of the photoelectric effect, it was shown beyond any doubt that photons must be considered as corpuscles, in that they exhibit mass and momentum as do ordinary material particles. It may be readily shown that a photon cannot give its entire energy to a "free" electron and satisfy both the conservation of momentum and energy. In the Compton effect the photon of frequency ν incident upon a free or loosely bound electron, converts to a new photon of lesser frequency ν' at an angle θ with the incident photon. The free electron recoils at an angle ϕ as shown in Figure 7.7.

Denoting the rest mass of the electron as m_0, then by relativity its mass, m, momentum, and energy are, respectively,

$$m_0(1 - \beta^2)^{-1/2}, \quad m_0 v(1 - \beta^2)^{-1/2}, \quad \text{and} \quad (mc^2 - m_0 c^2)$$

[10] W. Heitler, *The Quantum Theory of Radiation*, Clarendon Press, p. 126 (1935).
[11] H. Hall, *Rev. Mod. Phys.*, **8**, 358 (1936); H. Hulme, J. McDougall, R. Buckingham, and R. Fowler, *Proc. Roy. Soc. (London)*, **149**, 131 (1935).
[12] G. D. Latyshev, *Rev. Mod. Phys.*, **19**, 132 (1947).
[13] A. H. Compton, *Phys. Rev.*, **21**, 482 (1923).

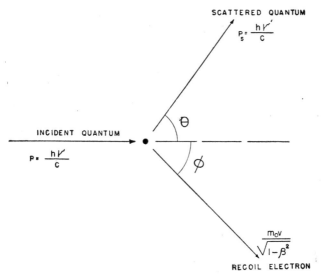

FIG 7.7. "Compton" scattering.

where β is the ratio of its velocity v to that of light c. The similar quantities for the photon are, respectively,

$$\frac{hv}{c^2}, \quad \frac{hv}{c}, \quad \text{and} \quad hv$$

From the conservation of energy, and the conservation of momentum in directions both parallel and perpendicular to the incident photon, three independent equations may be written as

$$hv = hv' + mc^2 - m_0c^2 \tag{7.12}$$

(parallel)

$$\frac{hv}{c} = \frac{m_0v}{\sqrt{1 - \beta^2}} \cos \phi + \frac{hv'}{c} \cos \theta \tag{7.13}$$

(perpendicular)

$$\frac{m_0v}{\sqrt{1 - \beta^2}} \sin \phi = \frac{hv'}{c} \sin \theta \tag{7.14}$$

The solution of these equations, which was of particular interest in X-ray spectroscopy, gave the change in wavelength in angstrom units on scattering, as

basic Eg.

$$\lambda' - \lambda = 0.0241(1 - \cos \theta)(\text{A.U.}) \quad \frac{h}{mc} \tag{7.15}$$

It is apparent that the change in wavelength at a given angle is independent of the incident energy. In the forward direction, $\theta = 0$, so that there is no loss in energy by the photon.

For each scattered photon at an angle θ, there is a particular recoil particle at an angle ϕ. The relationship between these particles, as θ takes all values from zero up to π, is shown by Figure 7.8. The angles θ and ϕ are related by the expression

$$\tan \phi = \frac{0.51 \cot \theta/2}{W\gamma + 0.51} \tag{7.16}$$

For a photon scattered directly backward, the recoil electron must go directly forward. Since

$$\lambda = \frac{hc}{W} \quad \text{and} \quad \lambda' = \frac{hc}{W'} \tag{7.17}$$

where W and W' are the photon energies before and after scattering, it follows that

$$\lambda' - \lambda = hc\left(\frac{1}{W'} - \frac{1}{W}\right) = 0.0482 \tag{7.18}$$

so that

$$W' = \frac{W}{1 + 3.9W} \tag{7.19}$$

where W is expressed in Mev. This back-scattered energy is in the neighborhood of 200 kev for a wide spread in the incident energies, and it can be bothersome in coincidence experiments with scintillation crystals.

This process of Compton scattering is effective in reducing the intensity of a beam of gamma radiation traversing matter. It is particularly important in the lighter elements for energies

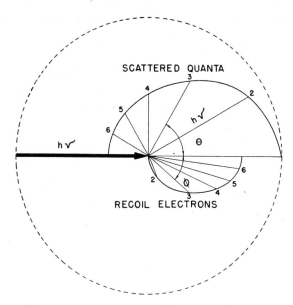

FIG. 7.8.   The scattered quanta and recoil electrons in "Compton" scattering.

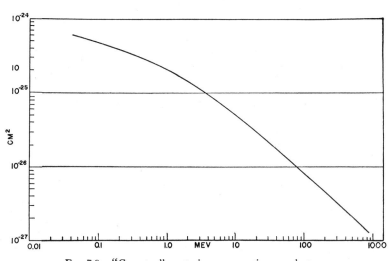

FIG. 7.9.   "Compton" scattering cross section per electron.

that are not too high. For example, it is the main contributing factor to the total absorption coefficient in such elements as copper, for energies up to 3 Mev.

The cross section, σ_c, for this scattering process per electron was first formulated [14] by Klein and Nishina. Computations based upon this rather complicated expression are shown graphically in Figure 7.9. For an atom this result must be multiplied by the number of such scattering particles, which in the light elements could be all of the electrons.

7.8. Pair Production. By 1932 many measurements of absorption coefficients had been made for high-energy gamma rays in such elements as aluminum, copper, and lead. The observed absorption coefficients [15] were found to be larger than would be expected from the combined Compton scattering and photoelectric effect. This discrepancy was at first usually explained as due to some unknown contribution to absorption by the nuclei.

In 1934 Dirac outlined a relativistic theory of the electron.[16] In the development along with the ordinary states of positive energy, he was led to the notion of the existence of negative energy states. These possible negative energy states were assumed to be normally filled with electrons and not observable. A gamma ray might remove one of these electrons of negative energy so that it became a negative electron. The "hole" remaining would appear as a positively charged particle.

Following the discovery of the positron, pair production as shown in Figure 6.6, by irradiating a lead foil with high-energy photons became commonplace. This annihilation process can occur only in the field of another particle since it may readily be shown that it is otherwise impossible to conserve both energy and momentum. The incident energy must be greater

[14] O. Klein and Y. Nishina, *Z. Physik*, **52**, 852 (1929).
[15] C. Y. Chao, *Proc. Nat. Acad.*, **16**, 431 (1930); L. Meitner and H. Hupfeld, *Z. Physik*, **67**, 147 (1931); L. H. Gray, *Proc. Cambridge Phil. Soc.*, **27**, 103 (1931); W. Gentner, *Jour. phys. radium*, **6**, 340 (1935).
[16] P. Dirac, *Proc. Cambridge Phil. Soc.*, **30**, 150 (1934); see also W. Furry and J. R. Oppenheimer, *Phys. Rev.*, **45**, 245 (1934), and H. Bethe and W. Heitler, *Proc. Roy. Soc. (London)*, **146**, 83 (1934).

than $2m_0c^2$ (1.02 Mev) and the energy excess appears as the kinetic energies of the particles.

The total cross section for pair production, σ_{PP}, may be calculated [17,18] for certain limited conditions, but in general it is

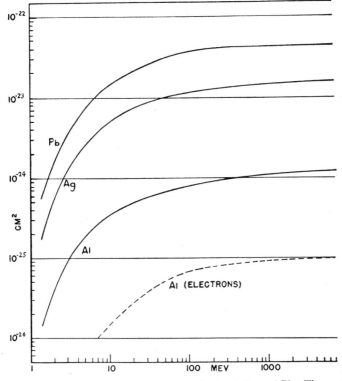

FIG. 7.10. Cross section for electron pair production in Al, Ag, and Pb. The contribution due to all electrons in Al.

difficult. The results obtained for Al, Ag, and Pb as a function of the photon energy are shown graphically in Figure 7.10. These values are based upon numerical integration calculations.

There is a slight possibility that the photon may be annihilated in the field of an electron. If this phenomenon appears

[17] H. Bethe and W. Heitler, *Proc. Roy. Soc. (London)*, **146**, 83 (1934).
[18] P. Hough, *Phys. Rev.*, **80**, 1069 (1948); L. Maximon and H. Bethe, *Phys. Rev.*, **87**, 156 (1952).

in a cloud chamber, a three-pronged pattern results, in which the third track is due to the recoil electron. The process has been treated theoretically [19] and studied experimentally.[20] In heavy elements the contribution of the electrons is only about 1% of the nuclear effect.

7.9. Nuclear Photodisintegration. For photon energies greater than the binding energy of the neutron, interactions may occur in which the neutron is ejected from the nucleus. If the product nucleus does not normally exist in nature it will be radioactive and will usually be a positron emitter. The effect was first observed in deuterium for which the threshold energy is only 2.224 Mev. For heavier elements, energies of the order of 10 Mev may be required.

The cross section, $\sigma_{\gamma n}$, for the effect is relatively small and is found to increase up to a maximum value at an energy about twice that of the binding energy of the neutron. At higher energies competing interactions, such as $\gamma,2n$ or γ,np, detract increasingly from the γ,n yield. Many theoretical treatments [21] of the effect have been developed. The cross section as observed [22] for Al, Ag, and Pb are presented in Figure 7.11. Agreement with current theory is not satisfactory.

At energies above 145 Mev it is possible [23] that a pi meson will be ejected from the nucleus instead of a neutron. Theoretical treatments of this process indicate [24] a cross-section curve similar in shape to that for neutron ejection. A maximum yield of positive mesons from hydrogen occurs at about 300 Mev with a cross section of 2×10^{-28} cm².

7.10. Elastic Scattering. A photon beam incident on matter may be reduced in intensity by "elastic" scattering. In this

[19] A. Borsellino, *Nuovo Cimento*, **4**, 112 (1947).

[20] E. Gaertner and M. Yeater, *Phys. Rev.*, **78**, 621 (1950).

[21] V. Weisskopf, *Phys. Rev.*, **59**, 318 (1941); M. Goldhaber aad E. Teller, *Phys. Rev.* **74**, 1049 (1948); J. Levinger and H. Bethe, *Phys. Rev.*, **78**, 115 (1950).

[22] R. Montalbetti, L. Katz, and J. Goldemberg, *Phys. Rev.*, **91**, 659 (1953).

[23] A. Silverman and M. Stearns, *Phys. Rev.*, **83**, 206 (1951); J. Steinberger and A. Bishop, *Phys. Rev.*, **86**, 171 (1952).

[24] K. Brueckner and K. Watson, *Phys. Rev.*, **86**, 923 (1952).

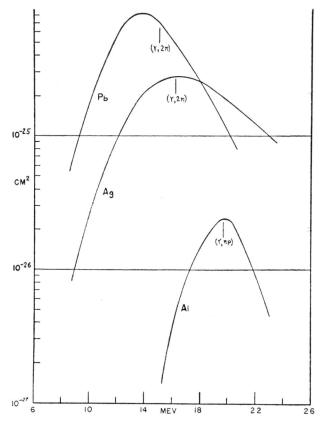

FIG. 7.11. Cross sections for photodisintegration in Al, Ag, and Pb, for varying energies.

process the direction of the photon is altered with no change in energy, except for the small amount carried away by the recoiling particle. This may be accomplished by any of the following:

    a. Thomson scattering by the nucleus
    b. Rayleigh scattering by bound electrons
    c. Nuclear resonance scattering
    d. Potential scattering by virtual pair production
The magnitude of each of these effects is small.

In the Thomson effect the charged nucleus is assumed to vibrate under the action of the incident photon and it may then re-emit the same frequency in any direction. The cross section, σ_T, has been expressed [25] as

$$\sigma_T = 1.195 \ Z^4/A^2 \ (1 + \cos^2 \theta) \times 10^{-32} \ \text{cm}^2 \qquad \textbf{(7.20)}$$

In Rayleigh scattering the electrons act coherently to change the direction of the photon much as the atoms of a crystal behave in X-ray reflection. This type of scattering [26] dominates at small scattering angles. For energetic gamma rays in lead its contribution is about 1% of that due to Compton scattering. The Thomson and Rayleigh effects are in phase with each other and are hence additive.

Nuclear resonance scattering occurs when the absorption of the photon results in exciting a virtual level which immediately re-radiates the energy in a different direction. The effect is very small except at those energies corresponding to the resonance energies, at which the absorption is large. Since the resonance widths are narrow ($\cong 10^{-4}$ ev) and relatively widely spaced (several ev), the over-all probability of scattering by this mechanism is small.

The observed over-all cross section, σ_e, for elastic scattering is found [27] to be less than would be expected for the Thomson and Rayleigh effects acting together. To account for the deficiency an additional effect has been postulated which is out of phase with the former so as to decrease the total result. Such an effect might be the formation of a "virtual" pair of electrons which are immediately mutually annihilated. The re-emission of the incident energy may occur at any angle so that in effect the incident photon is scattered. Figure 7.12 represents, for a 1.33 Mev gamma energy on lead, the cross sections as observed and as calculated at various angles. To reduce the combined

[25] P. B. Moon, *Proc. Roy. Soc.* (*London*), **A63**, 1189 (1950).

[26] F. Rohrlich and R. Gluckstern, *Phys. Rev.*, **86**, 1 (1952); P. Greifenger, J. Levinger, and F. Rohrlich, *Phys. Rev.*, **87**, 663 (1952).

[27] R. R. Wilson, *Phys. Rev.*, **90**, 720 (1953).

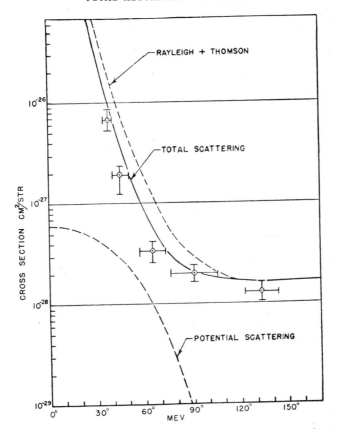

FIG. 7.12. The differential cross section due to the elastic scattering of 1.33 Mev photons in Pb.

Rayleigh and Thomson effects to good agreement with the observed points it is necessary to postulate a potential scattering as shown.

7.11. Total Absorption of Gamma Rays. The total cross section per atom for the loss of a photon from the incident beam is the sum of the previously mentioned five cross sections. The total absorption coefficient, μ, is then given by

$$\mu = \frac{\sigma_{\text{Total}}}{v} = \sigma_{\text{Total}}\rho n \ \text{Cm}^{-1} \tag{7.21}$$

where v is the volume occupied per atom, ρ is the density, and n is the number of atoms per gram. The absorption due to both the Compton and photoelectric effects decreases as the energy increases, while the contribution due to pair production increases. Photodisintegration and resonance scattering super-

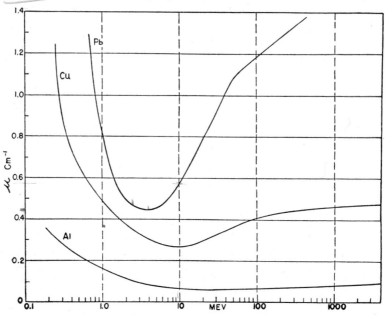

FIG. 7.13.   Absorption coefficient in Al, Cu, and Pb at various gamma energies.

pose intermediate peaks. The calculated values for the absorption coefficients, μ_{Total}, in Al, Cu, and Pb are presented graphically in Figure 7.13. It is apparent that minimum absorption occurs in the three elements at approximately 25, 10, and 3 Mev, respectively.

The minimum absorption coefficient for lead is calculated to be 0.46 per centimeter. Some experimental results seem to confirm the calculated values, while others [28] tend to show some systematic deviations.

[28] J. L. Lawson, *Phys. Rev.*, **75**, 433 (1949); DeWire, Ashkin, and Beach, *Phys. Rev.*, **79**, 210 (1950).

7.12. Gamma Spectra and Internal Conversion. Instead of a nucleus emitting a gamma ray it may happen that an equivalent amount of energy is carried off by an ejected orbital electron. This process is called internal conversion. A measure of the

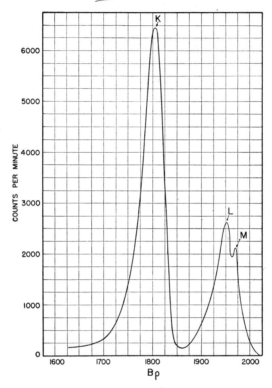

FIG. 7.14.   Internally converted gamma rays from lanthanum.

energy of the electron plus its binding energy in the atom (K, L, M, or etc.) yields the energy of the gamma transition. From a monoenergetic source containing many decaying nuclei, several groups of electrons may be observed corresponding to K, L, M, N, etc., conversion. These may be resolved in a magnetic spectrometer leading to distinct peaks or lines depending upon the type of detection used. Figure 7.14 shows

the resolution of the K, L, and M peaks for a single gamma ray
(0.276 Mev) in La^{133} following beta emission in Ba^{133} (38.8 hr
half-life), as revealed by a good constant radius magnetic spectrometer. The very superior resolution obtainable by the photographic magnetic spectrometer is shown in Figure 7.15. Since

K   L   M N

Fig. 7.15. Electron conversion lines in a magnetic photographic spectrometer for a
single gamma ray.

the energies are determinable with an accuracy of 0.2 kev and
the K-L differences of neighboring heavy elements differ by one
or more kev, it is possible to identify positively the Z for the
emitting nucleus.

The relative areas of the K, L, M, etc., peaks or the relative
intensities of the photographic lines are of value in determining
the type of transition involved. In the photographic spectrum
it is frequently possible to observe the relative intensities of the
L_1, L_2, and L_3 fine structure lines. This is also significant in
making conclusions regarding the radiation. In some emitters
the yield of converted gamma rays is large, so that the conversion coefficient, which is defined as the number of conversion
electrons divided by the number of unconverted gamma photons, may be greater than unity.

The loss of a K electron must be followed immediately by a
refilling of the K shell. This will result in the emission of a K
X-ray photon which may also eject an L, M, N, or etc., electron. The loss of one or two L electrons will be followed by L
X-ray emission. These may in turn eject M, N, or O electrons,
etc. These low-energy ejected particles are known as "Auger"
electrons. The emitting atom may be left in a multiply ionized state by the almost simultaneous loss of several electrons.[29]

[29] A. H. Snell, *Bull. Amer. Phys. Soc. Series II*, **1**, 220 (1956).

7.13. Nuclear Isomerism. In organic chemistry, molecules whose component atoms may be differently arranged and thus display different properties are called "isomers." In nuclear physics the same term is applied to those atoms whose atomic numbers Z and nucleonic numbers A are the same, yet the atoms differ in energy and in half-life. The first evidence for the existence of nuclear isomers was offered by Hahn [30] in 1921. In the uranium-radium family, on the beta emission of thorium 234 whose half-life is 24.5 days, two protactinium nuclei seemed to result, one of which (UZ) had a half-life of 5.7 hours while the other (UX$_2$) decayed with a half-life of 1.14 minutes. Both nuclei were beta-active, ending in uranium 234.

With the discovery of induced radioactivity, many examples of isomerism have been observed. One of the first of these was in bromine, which exists in nature as two stable isotopes whose masses are 79 and 81. On bombardment with slow neutrons, Fermi [31] and co-workers found three radioactivities whose half-lives are 18 minutes, 4.4 hours, and 34 hours. Subsequent production of the same radioactivities by other modes of excitation confirm that the 4.4-hour and the 18-minute activities are due to isomeric nuclei of bromine of mass 80.

On the emission of a gamma ray it must follow that any initial emitter and its product nucleus are isomeric. Usually this process occurs in a time of negligible duration, but if the half-life of the metastable state is greater than 10^{-9} second it is now possible to determine it experimentally by calibrated delay circuits. Many long-lived gamma-emitting isotopes have been identified. The emission of a gamma ray must necessarily mean a loss in momentum by the emitting nucleus and hence a probable change in its spin characteristics.

The emitted radiation is associated with a spin change, ΔI, and a possible change in parity. The multipole order describing the radiation is given by 2 raised to the ΔI power, so that

[30] O. Hahn, *Chem. Bericht*, **54**, 1131 (1926); *Z. Physik. Chem.*, **103**, 461 (1923).

[31] E. Amaldi, O. D'Agostino, E. Fermi, B. Pontecorvo, and E. Segré, *Proc. Roy. Soc.* (*London*), **149**, 522 (1935).

dipole, quadrupole, and octupole refer to ΔI values of 1, 2, and 3, respectively. The radiation may be either electric multipole or magnetic multipole. These are designated by the symbols E and M followed by numbers denoting the maximum ΔI. Thus, E1, M2, M3 represent electric dipole, magnetic quadrupole, and magnetic octupole radiations, respectively. Selection rules applying to the multipole transitions are presented in Table 7.2. Electric monopole E0 transitions proceed solely by

TABLE 7.2. SELECTION RULES FOR MULTIPOLE RADIATION

Name	Max. Spin Change, ΔI	Parity Change
E0	0	No
E1	1	Yes
M1	1	No
E2	2	No
M2	2	Yes
E3	3	Yes
M3	3	No
E4	4	No
M4	4	Yes
Etc.		

internal conversion, with no angular momentum carried off by the electron.

The type of radiation emitted may be determined by observing certain factors, such as the coefficient of internal conversion; the ratio of the "K" to the "L" conversion coefficients; the ratio of $L_1:L_2:L_3$; the half-life of the metastable state; and the angular correlation between sequential radiations. For allowed transitions, where the spin change is small and a low-order multipole radiation occurs, K conversion is about ten times more probable than L conversion. For highly forbidden transitions, particularly for large atomic numbers Z and low energy W, the L conversion may be greater than the K. Almost complete calculations have been made [32] for K shell conversion and for L_1, L_2, and L_3 transitions over a wide range in Z for electric and magnetic multipole radiations of several orders.

7.14. Directional Correlation of Successive Gamma Quanta.

It was first suggested [33] by Dunworth, and theoretically substantiated by Hamilton, that when two gamma rays are emitted

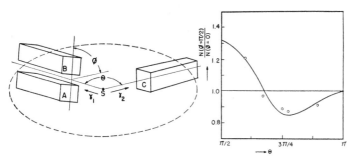

Fig. 7.16.   Arrangement of scintillation counters to correlate gamma emissions.

in succession by a nucleus their directions and planes of polarization are not entirely independent. Many attempts to detect a relationship between these gamma quanta, using coincidence counting rates, were unsuccessful. With the development of scintillation counters the effectiveness of the apparatus is increased and in several radioactive emitters a striking correlation is found [34] to exist. The apparatus as used by Dr. Deutsch and associates is shown in Figure 7.16. The naphthalene crystals A, B, and C are arranged for coincidence counting. A and B independently form a polarimeter in that a gamma ray ending in A might send a photoelectron into B with a probability

[32] M. E. Rose, G. H. Goertzel, and C. L. Perry, *Oak Ridge Nat. Lab. Report 1023* (1951); later results issued as letters.

[33] J. Dunworth, *Rev. Sci. Instruments*, **11**, 167 (1940); D. R. Hamilton, *Phys. Rev.* **58**, 122 (1940).

[34] M. Deutsch, E. Brady, and F. Metzger, *Phys. Rev.*, **74**, 154 (1948); D. Hamilton, *Phys. Rev.*, **74**, 782 (1948).

dependent upon the angular position ϕ with the horizontal plane, and the angle θ made with the counter C. The results obtained with the radioisotope rhodium 104 are presented graphically, showing a relatively large change in coincidence counting rate as the angles are varied.

7.15. The Scintillation Spectrometer and Gamma-gamma Coincidence. By placing a radioactive source between two

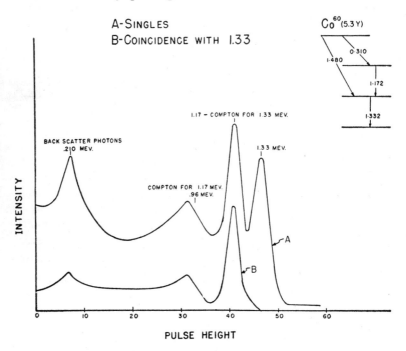

FIG. 7.17. Coincidence and singles peaks with the scintillation spectrometer.

scintillation crystals, each of which has its own phototube and pulse height analyzing circuit, nuclear level schemes may be checked. Using only one of the circuits a singles curve is first established. One of the circuits is now adjusted so as to respond only to a pulse height corresponding to a particular gamma ray. Coincidences between this and the output of the other phototube receiving all energies are observed. A peak in the coincidence curve thus shows two gamma transitions to be in rapid sequence. This is illustrated in Figure 7.17 which shows a singles and a coincidence curve for cobalt 60. The two gamma energies are resolved in the upper curve. By admitting only the 1.33 Mev peak in one circuit the coincidence peak at 1.17 Mev shows the two to be in sequence, as shown in the level scheme. Other disturbing associated peaks are due to the Compton back scattering at 210 kev and a subsidiary peak at 0.96 Mev due to subtracting the Compton back scattered gamma energy (210 kev) from 1.17 Mev.

7.16. The Wave-nature of Particles.

With the elaboration of the photoelectric and the "Compton" effects, the dual nature of electromagnetic radiation was well established, namely that it is both wavelike and corpuscular. It was soon equally well established that such entities as electrons, protons, and neutrons must be regarded not only as corpuscular but also as wavelike in nature.

The first evidence of this was presented by the famous electron reflection experiments of Davisson and Germer in 1925.[35] By using as the scatterer a crystal of nickel, they found certain well-defined beams of electrons issuing from the target for a certain definite incident angle. The theory sufficient to explain their results as a Bragg crystal reflection had already been formulated. In 1924, L. de Broglie had proposed that the particles of matter are intrinsically wavelike as well as corpuscular in nature.[36] The theory of de Broglie has been extended by Scrödinger, Heisenberg, and others to become the extensive subject of "Wave-Mechanics."

The energy W of a particle was considered associated with a frequency ν just as for a photon, namely $W = h\nu$ or $\dfrac{hc}{\lambda}$, where h is the Planck constant, c the velocity of light, and λ is the

[35] C. J. Davisson and L. H. Germer, *Phys. Rev.*, **30**, 705 (1927).
[36] L. de Broglie, Theses, Paris, Mason et cie. (1924); *Ann. Physik*, **3**, 22 (1925).

wavelength. The momentum P is the energy W divided by the velocity of light c, hence

$$P = mv = \frac{h\nu}{c} = \frac{h}{\lambda} \qquad (7.22)$$

Thus there results a wavelength λ given by

$$\lambda = \frac{h}{mv} \qquad (7.23)$$

If the particle derives its energy W from the acceleration of a charge e in falling through a potential E, then,

$$W = Ee = \tfrac{1}{2}mv^2 \qquad (7.24)$$

so that

$$v = \sqrt{\frac{2Ee}{m}} \qquad (7.25)$$

and

$$\lambda = \frac{h}{m\sqrt{\dfrac{2Ee}{m}}} = \frac{h}{\sqrt{2eEm}} \qquad (7.26)$$

For electrons accelerated by a potential of E volts

$$\lambda = \frac{6.624 \times 10^{-27}}{\sqrt{2 \times 4.8025 \times 10^{-10} \times 9.1066 \times 10^{-28} \times \frac{1}{300}} \times \sqrt{E}}$$

$$= \frac{12.2}{E^{1/2}} \times 10^{-8} \text{ cm} \qquad (7.27)$$

For protons

$$\lambda = \frac{12.2 \times 10^{-8}}{\sqrt{1838E}} = \frac{28.6}{E^{1/2}} \times 10^{-10} \text{ cm} \qquad (7.28)$$

so that at 9 Mev the wavelength of protons becomes 9.5×10^{-13} centimeter, which is approaching in magnitude the dimensions of the nuclear diameter. For very slow protons or thermal neutrons the de Broglie wavelength becomes of such an order that Bragg crystal reflection is entirely possible.

7.17. Use of Gamma Radiation in Radiology. Any sufficiently intense ionizing agent will kill living tissue. Those cells that are in the process of growth, such as most cancerous tissue, are usually more susceptible. It is the hope of the radiologist that by proper dosage the abnormal fast-growing tissue may be destroyed without seriously damaging normal cells. Therapeutic doses used in practice vary from 200 up to 3000 roentgen units. By using a filter of 0.5-millimeter platinum the alpha and beta radiations are removed. The filtered gamma radiation, at a point 10 centimeters from a source of 1 gram of radium in equilibrium with its daughter products, in 1 hour is about 85 roentgen units. The absorption coefficient of tissue for the gamma radiation from radium is about 0.067 per centimeter. The radiation thus has a very considerable penetration, losing about 7% of its intensity on passage through each centimeter of tissue, or dropping to half-value on traversing a layer of 8 centimeters.

Strong gamma sources produced in reactors are readily available. For example, a 1000 curie source of cobalt 60, with a half-life of 5.26 years, consisting of irradiated rods arranged to form a cylindrical cage 10 inches in diameter and 15 inches long will give a fairly uniform field of about 1000 r (roentgens) per minute in the central volume. To destroy some bacteria a dosage of 700,000 r may be necessary, thus requiring an exposure of several hours. Some biological processes may be controlled as desired with relatively small dosages. Certain foods sterilized in this manner will survive for long periods without the usual spoilage. The steady tolerance dosage for gamma radiation on the entire human body has been regarded to be about 0.4 r per week.

QUESTIONS AND PROBLEMS

1. The intensity of a beam of gamma rays on passage through lead of thicknesses 1, 3, 5, and 7 cm is found to be 90, 20.6, 4.78, and 1.10 divisions per minute. Express the half-value thickness and the co-efficient of absorption in cm^{-1}. What possibilities exist for the value of the energy? Calculate the atomic and the electronic coefficients of absorption.

Answer: $d_{1/2}$ = 0.95 cm, μ = 0.729 cm^{-1}, W = 1.28 Mev or 15.3 Mev, μ_a = 2.2 × 10^{-23}, and μ_e = 2.69 × 10^{-25}.

2. Prove that a gamma ray cannot give its entire energy to an electron. Demonstrate that "pair-production" cannot be accomplished by a gamma ray in free space.

3. A photoelectron from a thin lead foil in a Wilson cloud chamber describes a track whose radius of curvature is 10 cm in a magnetic field of 200 maxwells per cm^2. Assuming the electron to be from the K shell, what was the energy of the gamma ray?

Answer: W = 0.364 Mev.

4. A Compton recoil electron in the same direction as the incident photon has a radius of curvature of 15 cm in a magnetic field of 400 maxwells per cm^2. What is the energy of the gamma ray?

Answer: W_e = 1.36 Mev, W_τ = 1.59 Mev.

5. The radioactive isotope, tellurium 129, decays by internal conversion. What will be the $B\rho$ values for the K, L, and M electron groups? Decay const. = 0.102 k, L, M.

Answer: $B\rho$ (K) 924, (L) 1099, and (M) 1124 gauss cm.

6. Gamma rays whose energies are 1.5, 3.0, and 10.0 Mev, all of equal intensity, are passed through 12 cm of lead. Compare the intensities in the emergent beam.

Answer: Intensity ratio $I_{1.5}:I_3:I_{10}$ = 0.186:1.0:0.115.

7. What minimum energy would enable a gamma ray to make carbon 11 from carbon 12 by photodisintegration?

Answer: Δm = 0.0201 mass units or 18.7 Mev.

8. What is the de Broglie wavelength of a 10 Mev deuteron? Of a thermal neutron at 27° C.?

Answer: λ = 6.39 × 10^{-13} cm and 1.46 × 10^{-8} cm.

CHAPTER 8

NEUTRONS

8.1. Discovery. In 1930, Bothe and Becker noticed that light elements, particularly boron and beryllium, when bombarded by the alpha rays from polonium seemed to emit very penetrating gamma rays.[1] They concluded that the gamma radiation was characteristic of the target element. I. Curie-Joliot[2] and F. Joliot,[3] measured the absorption coefficients of the supposed gamma radiations in lead. For the radiations from beryllium and boron, respectively, linear absorption coefficients of 0.147 and 0.227 per centimeter were observed. They interpreted this as meaning that the gamma radiation from the beryllium had an energy between 15 and 20 Mev and that from boron about 11 Mev. At that time only the Klein-Nishina formula was considered. It was not yet known that such low-valued absorption coefficients were impossible for any substance because of the absorption due to electron pair formation.

It was observed that when carbon, in the form of paraffin sheets, was placed in the path of the supposed gamma radiation as shown in Figure 8.1, a new radiation seemed to come from the carbon. This latter radiation behaved like proton radiation but it had a very long range, up to 26 centimeters in air. Assuming these particles were generated in the carbon by a process similar to the Compton effect, it was necessary to postulate that the energy of the incident gamma quanta was of the order of 55 Mev.

[1] W. Bothe and H. Becker, *Z. Physik*, **66**, 5–6, 289 (1930).
[2] I. Curie-Joliot, *Compt. rend.*, **193**, 1412 (1931).
[3] F. Joliot, *Compt. rend.*, **193**, 1415 (1931).

J. Chadwick [4] conducted experiments confirming the conclusion that the particles emanating from the carbon were protons. The only way he could justify their presence and satisfy conservation laws was to assume that the radiation from the beryllium or boron was not gamma radiation but rather consisted of energetic neutral particles. These neutral particles were assumed to have arisen from nuclear disintegration induced by the alpha particles and, because of their lack of electric charge, they could penetrate matter with little absorption. He called the particles "neutrons."

$B_e(\alpha, n)C$ $C(n, p)B$

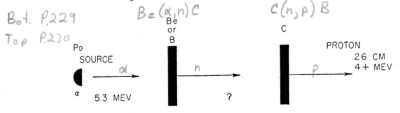

Bot. P.229
Top P.230

FIG. 8.1.   Arrangement used in the discovery of the neutron.

Subsequent experiments have shown that neutrons may be given off when almost any element is bombarded with high energy particles, such as protons, deuterons, photons, or neutrons. Being neutral in charge, they are the disintegration particles that can most easily escape through the nuclear barrier, provided enough energy exists for their formation.

8.2. The Mass of the Neutron.   Since the neutron carries no net electric charge it cannot be deflected in either a magnetic or electric field. Hence the conventional methods cannot be applied to determine its mass. Only indirect methods may be employed to this end. The masses of the deuterium and the hydrogen atoms as determined in a mass spectrometer are 2.014740 and 1.008145 mass units. The threshold energy for photoelectric disintegration has been variously reported, but the best current value is perhaps 2.226 Mev. This is equivalent to

[4] J. Chadwick, *Nature*, **129**, 312 (1932).

0.002391 mass units. Hence the energy equation in terms of mass becomes:

$$_1H^2 + h\nu \rightarrow {}_1H^1 + {}_0n^1 \tag{8.1}$$

$$\underset{2.014740}{} \quad \underset{0.002391}{} \quad \underset{1.008145}{} \quad \underset{1.008986}{}$$

The masses involved in this reaction have recently been revised, so that the mass of the neutron is greater than the older value [5] by more than had been thought to be its uncertainty. Other indirect methods [6] have been pursued in which the mass difference between the neutron and the hydrogen atom appear. For example, deuterium bombarded by deuterons may yield either $H^3 + H^1$ or $He^3 + n^1$ particles. The relative masses of H^3 and He^3 are precisely known from the beta decay of tritium H^3, for which the maximum energy is 18.3 kev. By determining the energy of the H^3 and He^3 particles in a spectrometer, Lauritsen and his co-workers expressed the mass difference as 789 kev or 0.00085 mass unit. This should agree with the hydrogen-neutron mass difference.

8.3. The Life of the Neutron. In the vicinity of cyclotrons or reactors a cloud of neutrons might be expected to exist. When slowed to thermal energy, these particles in many ways behave as hydrogen gas. In the presence of many materials, however, they will suffer inelastic impacts and terminate their existence. It is reasonable to inquire what might be their fate if no such reacting matter is encountered. It has been postulated that the neutron could convert to a proton plus a negative electron. Since the spin of each of the particles is one half, it becomes necessary to admit the simultaneous emission of the neutrino ν. Thus

$$_0n^1 \rightarrow {}_{+1}P^1 + {}_{-1}e^0 + {}_0\nu^0 + Q \tag{8.2}$$

$$\underset{1.008986}{} \quad \underset{1.007597}{} \quad \underset{0.000549}{} \quad \underset{(783\ kev)}{}$$

showing that the energy release is represented by the mass dif-

[5] D. J. Hughes, *Phys. Rev.*, **70**, 219 (1946); J. Mattauch, *Phys. Rev.*, **57**, 1155 (1940); W. E. Stephens, *Rev. Mod. Phys.*, **19**, 19 (1947).

[6] R. E. Bell and L. G. Elliott, *Phys. Rev.*, **74**, 1552 (1948); A. Tollestrup, F. Jenkins, W. A. Fowler and C. C. Lauritsen, *Phys. Rev.*, **75**, 1947 (1949); W. E. Shoupp, B. Jennings, and K. Sun, *Phys. Rev.*, **75**, 1 (1949).

ference between the neutron and the hydrogen atom, assuming the rest mass of the neutrino is negligible.

Serious attempts [7] to observe the half-life of the neutron have been made at Oak Ridge and elsewhere. The change in the proton yield along a collimated neutron beam from the pile is observed. So far it is impossible to express this quantity with certainty. It is concluded that the half-life is greater than 9 minutes and less than 30 minutes, with a most probable value of about 12 minutes. A current report gives [8] a half-life of $12 \pm$ 1.5 minutes.

8.4. Neutrons from Natural Alpha Emitters. The yield of neutrons from beryllium bombarded with alpha particles is greater than that from any other substance, although appreciable yields are obtained with boron, lithium, and many other elements. Although there is considerable disagreement on the efficiency of neutron production, Table 8.1 represents averaged observed yields for a thick beryllium target.

TABLE 8.1.   Neutron yield—thick beryllium target

Alpha Source	Neutrons for 10^6 Alphas	Neutrons per Sec per Curie
Radium....	55	17×10^6
Radon.....	90	15×10^6
Ra A.......	120	....
Ra C'......	200	....
Polonium...	80	3×10^6

The mass of the beryllium required to react effectively with all alpha particles present depends upon the mass of the alpha source. Thus, for a source of radium bromide plus beryllium,

[7] A. H. Snell and L. C. Miller, *Phys. Rev.*, **74**, 1217 (1948); **78**, 310 (1950); J. M. Robson, *Phys. Rev.*, **78**, 311 (1950).

[8] P. E. Spivac, *Report of the Geneva Conference*, **8**, 650 (1955).

the yield has been expressed as [9]

Neutrons/sec/gm Ra

$$= 1.7 \times 10^7 \frac{(\text{Mass})_{Be}}{(\text{Mass})_{Be} + (\text{Mass})_{RaBr_2}} \quad \text{(8.3)}$$

so that for 1 gram of radium at least 10 grams of beryllium should be used. It is apparent that by using radon with its small mass of 6.6 micrograms per curie, exceedingly compact neutron sources can be made. Such sources have the disadvantage of rapid decay so that they change in intensity appreciably during a single observation.

The energy of the emitted neutrons may be derived by noting the masses of the atoms in the reaction. Thus, if the alpha particles from polonium, whose energy is 5.3 Mev, are incident on beryllium, then

$$_2\text{He}^4 + 5.3 \text{ Mev} + _4\text{Be}^9 \rightarrow _6\text{C}^{12} + _0n^1 + Q + 5.3 \text{ Mev} \quad \text{(8.4)}$$

4.003873 $\qquad$ 9.015046 $\quad$ 12.003804 $\quad$ 1.008986 $\quad$ 0.006130

Q represents a mass of 0.00613 unit that disappears in the reaction, so that there is an energy release of 5.71 Mev. The total energy to be carried off in each disintegration is, then, the sum of this plus the incident energy 5.3 Mev or 11.0 Mev. To satisfy the conservation of momentum at the break-up of the product nucleus, the greater share of the energy must be carried by the neutron. In practice the energy of the neutrons will be less because the alpha particles will very likely be slowed down before reacting with the beryllium atoms, so that the 5.3 Mev is a maximum figure.

The yield of neutrons from various thick targets exposed to identical alpha bombardments as expressed by different observers shows a wide divergence in values. In Table 8.2 a rough average of some observations is presented. The energy of the emitted neutrons from the various emitters will be dependent

[9] H. L. Anderson, Prel. Report No. 3, *Natl. Research Council, Nuclear Sci. Ser.* (1948).

TABLE 8.2. NEUTRON YIELD FROM THICK TARGETS

Element	Neutrons for 10^6 Alphas	Element	Neutrons for 10^6 Alphas
Lithium......	3.5	Nitrogen......	0.01
Beryllium.....	76.0	Fluorine......	12.0
Boron........	22.0	Magnesium...	1.4
Carbon.......	0.1	Aluminum....	0.7

upon the mass discrepancy in the reaction equation and is greatest for lithium.

8.5. Neutrons from Accelerated Particle Reactions. Following the discovery of the neutron in 1932, a search was made to observe such particles near the targets of the then existent proton accelerators. It was found [10] that when certain light elements were bombarded by either protons or deuterons, copious neutron emission occurred. Numerous investigations followed in which the reactions with their associated energies have been well established. In deuteron bombardment the energy of the released neutron is progressively larger for the target elements: deuterium, beryllium, boron, and lithium. Those neutrons which are emitted in the direction of the incident beam of deuterons will have a maximum energy, equal approximately to the sum of the incident and the reaction energies. The total energy available, assuming 10 Mev for the incident deuterons, for a target of deuterium is calculable from the reaction equation:

$$_1H^2 + 10 \text{ Mev} + {}_1H^2 \rightarrow {}_2He^3 + n + Q + 10 \text{ Mev} \qquad (8.5)$$

$$\underset{2.014740}{} \qquad \underset{2.014740}{} \quad \underset{3.016986}{} \quad \underset{1.008986}{} \underset{0.00351}{}$$

The deficiency of 0.00351 mass units corresponds to an energy of 3.268 Mev so that a total energy of 13.268 Mev is

[10] H. R. Crane, C. E. Lauritsen and A. Solton, *Phys. Rev.*, **44**, 692, 783 (1933); E. O. Lawrence, M. Henderson and M. S. Livingston, *Phys. Rev.*, **44**, 781 (1933); M. L. Oliphant, P. Harteck and Lord Rutherford, *Proc. Roy. Soc.*, **A144**, 692 (1934).

available. To satisfy the conservation laws in the most favorable case, i.e., neutrons directly in the forward direction, the energies of the He³ and neutron particles are 0.252 and 13.016 Mev, respectively. Similar calculations for the same deuterons

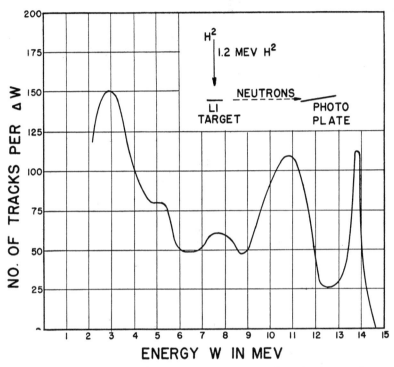

FIG. 8.2. Distribution of neutrons with respect to energy from the *d, n* reaction on lithium. [H. Richards, *Phys. Rev.*, 59, 796 (1941).]

incident upon targets of Be, B, and Li, show that the neutrons will have maximum energies of the order of 14, 23, and 25 Mev, respectively. High energy protons will similarly produce fast neutrons when incident upon the same targets.

The energies of the neutrons which are emitted in a particular direction will not all be alike. A typical distribution for the neutrons from a lithium target bombarded by 1.2-Mev deuterons, observed [11] at an angle of 90 degrees, is shown in Figure 8.2. In addition to the group with maximum energy around 14.5 Mev, other clearly defined maxima appear as 10.8, 7.5, and 5 Mev. These are interpreted as associated with the existence of excited levels in the product Be^8 nucleus, such that the energy of the excited level plus the neutron energy adds to the maximum value.

The relative yield of neutrons from various targets bombarded with 10-Mev deuterons as determined [12] by Smith and Kruger is presented in Table 8.3. The absolute value given for

TABLE 8.3. THE NEUTRON YIELD BY 10-MEV DEUTERONS ON THICK TARGETS

Target	Number of Neutrons per Microcoulomb	Target	Number of Neutrons per Microcoulomb
Deuterium........	310.0×10^8	Nickel............	36.0×10^8
Beryllium.........	370.0	Copper...........	62.0
B_4C..............	200.0	Molybdenum......	48.0
Carbon...........	130.0	Platinum.........	6.9
Oxygen...........	70.0	Gold.............	5.4
Aluminum........	99.0		

the reaction $D(d,n)$ He^3 namely, one neutron for every 200 deuterons, is greater than that observed by other investigators. It may be that all of the values are consistently large.

On comparing Tables 8.3 and 8.2, it can be seen that the neutron generation within a cyclotron operating at a 200-microampere current on beryllium is equivalent to that developed by about 3 million grams of radium plus a sufficient amount of accompanying beryllium.

The energy distribution of the neutrons from the 184-inch Berkeley cyclotron is shown in Figure 8.3. The beam of 190-Mev deuterons impinges on a beryllium target. By virtue of

[11] H. T. Richards, *Phys. Rev.*, **59**, 796 (1941).
[12] L. W. Smith and P. G. Kruger, *Phys. Rev.*, **74**, 1258 (1948); A. O. Hanson and R. F. Taschek, Report No. 4, *Natl. Research Council, Nuclear Science Series* (1948).

its small binding energy a splitting or "stripping" of the deuteron occurs.   In this process the energy is not divided equally
between proton and neutron as might be expected.[13]   The
incident nucleon within the deuteron possesses motion relative
to the center of mass of the deuteron.   At stripping this relative

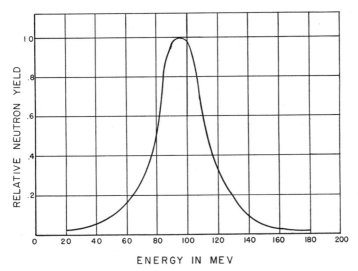

Fig. 8.3.   The energy distribution of neutrons from 190-Mev deuterons in the 184-
inch cyclotron.

motion is superimposed upon the forward motion of the deuteron resulting in an energy spread centered about half of the
average value of the deuteron energy, as shown in Figure 8.3.
The total energy is proportional to the square of the sum of
terms involving the square roots of the kinetic energy and of the
binding energy.   The full width of the energy spread at half-
maximum is expressed as

$$\Delta W = 1.5(W_B W_D)^{\frac{1}{2}} \text{ Mev}$$

where W_B and W_D are binding energy and kinetic energy of the
deuteron, respectively.   This gives a value of about 33 Mev.

[13] R. Serber, *Phys. Rev.*, **72**, 1008 (1947).

8.6. Neutrons from Gamma Ray Reactions.

When gamma rays of sufficient energy are incident upon light elements a probability exists that neutrons will be emitted by the energized nuclei. In some elements by virtue of the variation in binding energies of neighboring isotopes, the added energy need not be very large. For example, in beryllium 9 the binding energy per nucleon is 6.92 Mev, whereas in beryllium 8 the binding energy is 7.57 Mev per nucleon. In order that the Be^9 nucleus emit a neutron, it is only necessary to add about 2.3 Mev. In general, when masses of the initial and final isotopes differ by one atomic mass unit as can be seen to be very nearly true except for the very light atoms from the Table of Isotopes, then about 8.5 Mev of energy are required to free the neutron. It can similarly be noted that to eject a neutron from the tightly packed helium 4, beryllium 8, or carbon 12 nuclei, energies of the order of 20 Mev are required.

By mixing together a monoenergetic gamma-emitting radioactive isotope with deuterium or beryllium it is possible to construct [14] a source of monoenergetic neutrons. In general, however, most sources emit gamma rays of more than one energy. For example, antimony 124 emits gamma rays of energy 1.71 Mev and 0.732 Mev and many others of low energy together with a weak gamma ray at 2.04 Mev. By mixing this antimony isotope together with beryllium only the two higher energies will yield neutrons, and their relative abundance is such that the source may be regarded as monoenergetic.

8.7. Neutrons from the Reactor.

It will be shown later that the fission of each heavy nucleus by slow neutron capture is accompanied by the release on the average of about 2.5 neutrons. Their production and partial absorption in other fissionable nuclei lead to the continuous operation of the reactor. The energy distribution of the excess primary neutrons for uranium

[14] A. Wattenberg, *Phys. Rev.*, **71**, 497 (1947); D. J. Hughes and C. Eggler, *Phys. Rev.*, **72**, 902 (1947); A. O. Hanson, *Phys. Rev.*, **75**, 1794 (1949); A. Wattenberg, Prel. Report No. 6, *National Research Council, Nuclear Science Series* (1949).

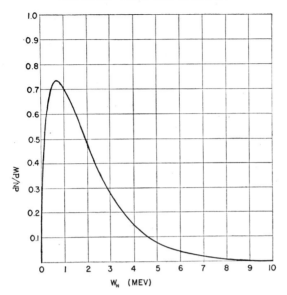

FIG. 8.4*A*. Distribution of neutrons with energy, as derived from slow neutron fission in uranium 235, unmoderated.

235 is shown [15] in Figure 8.4*A*. Following a broad maximum at about 0.75 Mev the curve descends rapidly but with some neutrons at energies as great as 17 Mev. An equation for the number of neutrons N, in a small energy interval at the energy W, of the form

$$dN/dW = cPe^{-W/1.3}$$

seems to represent satisfactorily the main portion of the curve, where c is a constant and P is the reactor power. The average energy is about 1.5 Mev.

After scattering in moderating materials, the form of the distribution changes to emphasize the increase in the number of neutrons at low energies. By a channel through the shielding, strong collimated beams of such neutrons as shown in Figure 8.4*B* may be withdrawn for study.

[15] W. T. Bonner, R. A. Ferrell, and M. C. Rinehart, *Phys. Rev.*, **87**, 1032 (1952); D. L. Hill, *Phys. Rev.*, **87**, 1034 (1952); B. E. Watt, *Phys. Rev.*, **87**, 1037 (1952).

It has become common practice to describe the neutron population erroneously by the use of the term "neutron flux" instead of neutron flux density. This is defined as the integral of the

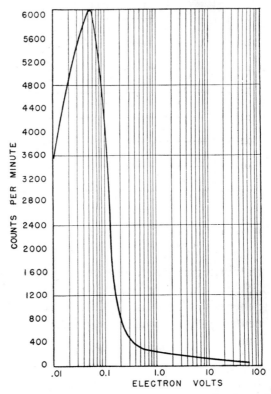

Fig. 8.4B.   Energy distribution of the neutrons in an exit column of a reactor.

number of neutrons per unit volume, each multiplied by its velocity regardless of direction. It is thus expressed as a number per square centimeter per second. In the most active region of a modern reactor the steady flux density is about 2×10^7 for each watt of power. Thus at a power level of 1000 kilowatts a maximum neutron flux density of 2×10^{13} might be expected.

8.8. The Absorption of Neutrons and Their Range in Matter.

Charged particles exert electric or magnetic forces capable of ionizing the atoms through which they pass and capable of interacting with the positively charged atomic nuclei. The neutron, however, can experience a force only when it comes within extremely close range of a nucleus. The interaction with the nucleus may be regarded as a collision, which may be either elastic or inelastic.

a. Elastic Collision. In an elastic collision the ordinary conservation laws apply. A portion of the energy of the striking neutron is transferred to the struck nucleus. If the target nucleus is extremely heavy, such as lead, then the energy loss by the striking neutron is very small. Light atoms, on the other hand, will at each collision reduce materially the energy of a high-speed neutron. Thus a centimeter of a light material, such as water or paraffin, will reduce more effectively the intensity of a beam of energetic neutrons than the same thickness of lead. A beam of fast neutrons is reduced in intensity to half-value by a thickness of about 5 centimeters of water. For lead a similar reduction in intensity is accomplished by an absorber having 50 grams per square centimeter.

Any single neutron will behave as a gas particle and its energy may be represented by the classical expression $\frac{3}{2}kT$, = W where k is the Boltzmann gas constant per particle, 1.37×10^{-16} ergs per degree C., and T is the temperature on the absolute scale. As the energy of the neutron decreases it will ultimately be in equilibrium with its surrounding molecules. It is then termed a "thermal" neutron or a "C" neutron. At a temperature of 300° K. this energy amounts to about 0.038 electron volt.

For elastic collision in the case of the neutrons from (Ra + Be), Dunning observed the variation in the cross section for atoms of various atomic weights.[16] The results are summarized in Figure 8.5.

[16] J. Dunning, G. Pergram, G. Fink, and D. Mitchell, *Phys. Rev.*, **48**, 265 (1935).

The cross sections are found to increase with atomic weight roughly in the same manner as the geometrical cross section of a sphere whose volume increases proportionally with the number of particles.

A similar relationship between the total collision cross section and the nuclear mass A has been found [17] for neutrons of 90

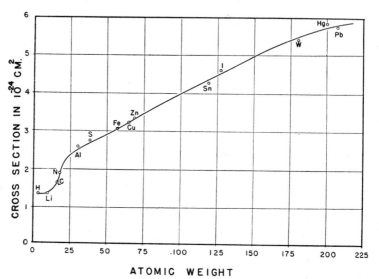

FIG. 8.5. The variation in cross section for the elastic collision of 10-Mev neutrons with various nuclei.

Mev energy. By plotting the observed cross sections in barns versus the atomic weight to the $\frac{2}{3}$ power, a straight line is obtained as shown in Figure 8.6. A theoretical treatment of the results has been presented, [18] showing that the nuclei are partially transparent to high energy neutrons and the nuclear radius R may be satisfactorily expressed as:

$$R = 1.37 A^{\frac{1}{3}} \times 10^{-13} \text{ cm} \qquad (8.6)$$

[17] L. J. Cook, E. M. McMillan, J. M. Peterson and D. C. Sewell, *Phys. Rev.*, **75**, 7 (1949).

[18] S. Fernbach, R. Serber and T. B. Taylor, *Phys. Rev.*, **75**, 1352 (1949).

By placing a source such as (Ra + Be) at the center of a sphere of paraffin and increasing the thickness progressively, an optimum radius will be found for which a maximum yield of slow neutrons exists outside the sphere. Using a lithium-lined detecting chamber, Dunning found an intensity variation

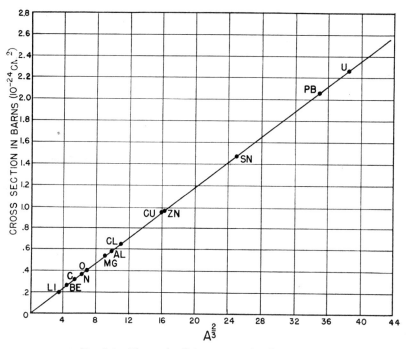

FIG. 8.6. The total collision cross section for neutrons.

as shown in Figure 8.7. A maximum neutron intensity exists for a thickness of paraffin of about 10 centimeters. This phenomenon can readily be explained by assuming that fast neutrons are being converted into slow neutrons by the paraffin and if this conversion gives rise to more slow neutrons than are lost by absorption then the emergent intensity will be augmented. For a thickness greater than 10 centimeters the absorption predominates and the intensity decreases. A detector for fast neutrons, however, will show a decreasing activity continuously as the thickness increases.

b. Inelastic Collision—Neutron Capture. The impinging neutron will occasionally enter the struck nucleus and unite with

Fast converted to slow neutrons.

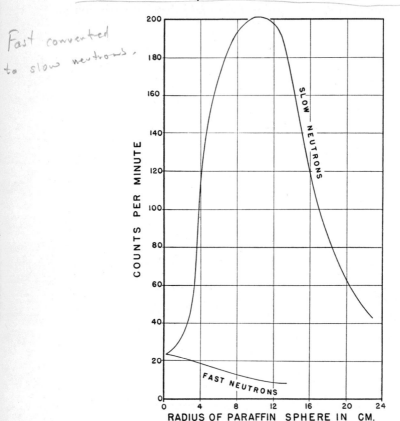

Fig. 8.7. The neutron yield at a fixed distance from a neutron source as influenced by the thickness of intervening paraffin.

the other particles thereby forming a new isotope of the bombarded element. As a result the nucleus is left in an excited state. The excess energy may be carried off by the re-emission of another particle or by gamma radiation. In the latter case the new isotope will have a mass one unit greater than that of the target nucleus. This process is termed neutron "capture." The newly formed isotope may have an atomic weight not existing for that element in nature. If this is the case, then this newly created nucleus is radioactive, that is, it will, by the emission of radiation, convert to a stable nucleus.

A survey of this neutron capture reaction for the available elements of the periodic table was made by Fermi and his associates at Rome.[19] He used the neutrons from a strong (Ra + Be) source, whose energy has a value up to 10.9 Mev. The radioactivity persisting in the element after bombardment was taken as an indication of the capture reaction. Some elements developed a strong radioactivity while others were inert after bombardment. The half-lives of the activities induced varied from a few seconds up to several days.

Certain elements which show no delayed radioactivity do emit gamma rays during the bombardment and show a large coefficient of absorption for neutrons. The product nuclei in this case are stable isotopes. The cross section for capture is found to vary greatly from element to element. In some elements, such as cadmium and the rare earths, the cross section is found to be as large as $100,000 \times 10^{-24}$ square centimeter, whereas for other elements it may be less than 0.1×10^{-24} square centimeter. The element boron has a large cross section for neutron absorption, and it is believed that the absorption coefficient varies strictly inversely with the velocity of the neutrons.

The extraordinary absorption in cadmium has been shown [20] to be due largely to the isotope of mass 113 whose normal abundance is 12.3%. By bombarding cadmium persistently with a large neutron flux the isotope of mass 113 is converted to 114 so that in the mass spectrometer such a bombarded specimen shows almost a complete absence of mass 113. A

[19] E. Fermi, F. Amaldi, O. d'Agostino, F. Rasetti, and E. Segré, *Proc. Roy. Soc.* (*London*), **146**, 483 (1934).
[20] A. J. Dempster, *Phys. Rev.*, **71**, 829 (1947).

beautiful spectrogram, prepared by A. J. Dempster and showing this effect, is presented in Figure 8.8.

It was noted that the radioactivities induced in silver, rhodium, indium, and many other elements were greatly enhanced by surrounding them with paraffin or other hydrogenous material. Since the layers of hydrogen slowed the incident fast

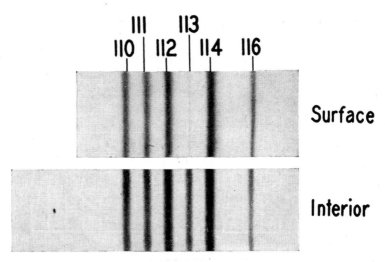

FIG. 8.8. Showing the depletion of Cd 113 from the surface layers by neutron capture.

neutrons, this phenomenon was interpreted as showing that the capture cross section varied inversely with the velocity. However, in many substances there was evidence that a resonance capture occurred. That is, at some definite energy between the high range and that of thermal neutrons, a particular isotope might exhibit an enormously large absorption.

8.9. Neutron Resonance Absorption. Since there is no delayed emission of neutrons in an accelerator, the instant that the bombardment ceases, the neutrons at a station a few meters away begin to die out. By arranging a delayed detecting circuit it is thus possible to exclude neutrons with a speed greater than that for which the circuit is set. The primary beam may be pulsed by any one of several methods. At 10 kev the effective neutron velocity is about 1.4×10^6 meters per second and in the earlier methods it was not possible to make measurements on neutrons of greater energy.

More recent methods are represented by the apparatus shown in Figure 8.9. This device is known as a "chopper" and is used [21]

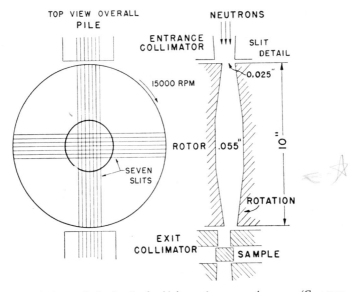

FIG. 8.9. Overall view and slit detail of a high-speed neutron chopper. (Courtesy Argonne National Laboratory.)

in connection with the beam of neutrons from a reactor. A massive cylindrical rotor penetrated by two sets each of seven slits, whose single detail is shown in the right of the figure, can be spun at a maximum speed of 15,000 revolutions per minute. At this speed a pulse of neutrons is transmitted every one thousandth of a second. The shaping of the slit allows the exclusion of very slow neutrons. The receiver is placed more than 60 meters away. By proper regulation of circuits it is possible to observe the behavior of neutrons at energies greater than 100 kev.

The cross section for neutron capture in a particular element is likely to show peak values at certain definite energies. The

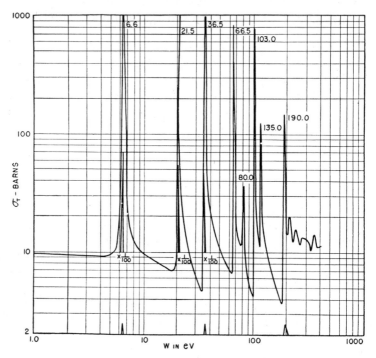

FIG. 8.10. Capture cross sections for neutrons of varying energy in uranium 238. (Argonne National Laboratory).

data observed for an isotope of special interest, namely, uranium 238, are presented in Figure 8.10. These neighboring peaks must correspond to close lying excited levels in the product nuclei uranium 239, as shown in Figure 8.11. Decay may occur promptly either by gamma emission, known as capture gamma rays, or by the emission of particles or by nuclear fission.

8.10. Transmutations Produced by Neutrons. There is no effective nuclear potential barrier to the approach of the uncharged neutron. This capture process may lead to new, unstable, or radioactive isotopes of either the bombarded element

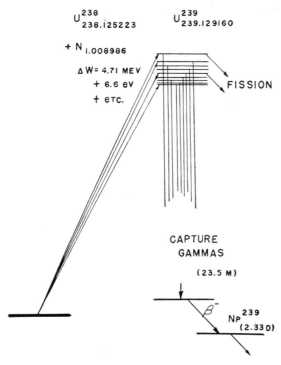

FIG. 8.11. Nuclear levels in uranium 239 following neutron capture in uranium 238.

or an element standing near it in the periodic table. The type of reaction induced by the bombardment depends largely upon the kinetic energy of the incident neutron. The disintegration occurring at impact may consist in the ejection from the compound nucleus of any one of the following: (*a*) gamma ray, (*b*) proton, (*c*) alpha particle, (*d*) two neutrons, (*e*) three or more particles, or (*f*) fission of the nucleus.

a. Neutron-Gamma Ray. This is a very likely reaction when the energy of the incident neutron is low. The abbreviated representation of the reaction is $_zA^N(n, \gamma)_zA^{N+1}$. Any release of energy because of the mass difference between initial and final products, plus the energy of the incident neutron, will be conveyed away by "capture" gamma rays.

The systematic survey of the elements of the periodic table for this reaction as carried out by Fermi and his associates at Rome has been mentioned. Extensive studies have been made to evaluate the energies of the capture gamma rays for most of the known elements. For each element many high energy [22] and several low energy transitions [23] have been reported.

b. Neutron-Proton. This process may be regarded as a competing mode of decay and becomes relatively more important for incident neutrons of large energy and for elements of low atomic number. The reaction may be represented as $_zA^N(n, p)$ $_{z-1}A^N$ or in equation form as

$$_zA^N + _0n^1 \rightarrow _{z-1}A^N + _1H^1 + Q \tag{8.7}$$

The energy Q together with any incident kinetic energy is shared by the resultant particles. The product nuclei are usually emitters of negative electrons and by this emission revert to the original isotope.

c. Neutron-Alpha Particle. Certain light elements on being bombarded with energetic neutrons give evidence of disintegrating by emitting alpha particles. This phenomenon has been observed directly in Wilson cloud chambers. A trace of boron trifluoride added to the gas in the chamber will on exposure to a neutron beam occasionally give rise to a disruption showing two heavy tracks. This reaction for the case of boron may be represented as $_5B^{10}(n, \alpha)_3Li^7$ or by an equation as

$$_5B^{10} + _0n^1 \rightarrow _3Li^7 + _2He^4 + Q \tag{8.8}$$

---

[22] B. Kinsey and G. Bartholomew, *Phys. Rev.*, **89**, 375 (1953).
[23] B. Hamermesh and R. Culp, *Phys. Rev.*, **92**, 211 (1953); D. Rose and B. Hamermesh, *Bull. Amer. Phys. Soc. Series II*, **1**, 189 (1956).

in which a mass loss of 0.0030 mass unit occurs, corresponding to a value for Q of 2.79 Mev.

On bombarding lithium 7 in a similar way, each disintegration leads to the formation of two alpha particles together with an electron. A reproduction of these oppositely directed tracks in a photographic emulsion is shown in Figure 5.2C. Together the two alpha tracks make almost a continuous straight line.

d. Neutron-2 Neutrons. If an incident neutron possessing 10 or more Mev enters a nucleus, it may result that two neutrons simultaneously are ejected. In this event the new isotope formed is less in atomic weight by one than the parent nucleus. If the product nucleus does not normally exist in nature, it is almost certain to be a radioactive emitter of positive electrons. This reaction may be represented in general as $_zA^N(n,2n)_zA^{N-1}$.

A rather comprehensive survey in which most of the elements of the periodic table were bombarded by 24 Mev neutrons was carried out at the University of Michigan.[24] The neutrons were obtained by the bombardment of lithium with 10 Mev deuterons. From the elements bombarded a total of 115 radioactivities was observed. Of this number about one third were emitters of negative electrons and were identified to be the same activities produced by Fermi in neutron capture. The remainder of the observed activities were positron emitters of the type here described.

e. Neutron-3 or More Particles. The detachment of each neutron from a nucleus requires 8 to 10 Mev. Thus an incident neutron of energy greater than 20 Mev has in some elements the possibllity of inciting a struck nucleus to give off three or more neutrons or equivalent particles in disintegration. This was first done in the case of sulfur exposed to 24 Mev neutrons.[25] The product isotope was identified as phosphorus of mass 30 by its positron emission with a 2.55-minute half-life. The reaction

[24] M. L. Pool, J. M. Cork, and R. Thornton, *Phys. Rev.*, **52**, 239 (1937).
[25] J. M. Cork and W. Middleton, *Phys. Rev.*, **58**, 474 (1940).

may be represented by the symbol $_{16}S^{32}(n, 2np)_{15}P^{30}$ and the equation is

$$_{16}S^{32} + _0n^1 + W \rightarrow _{15}P^{30} + _0n^1 + _0n^1 + _1H^1 + Q + w \quad \text{(8.9)}$$

which requires that $(W - w)$ be greater than 21.2 Mev.

For the higher energy neutrons which are now obtainable, the emission of multiple particles from the highly excited nucleus is commonplace. In the competition between possible disintegration processes those activities are more probable in which the energy is carried off by several low-energy particles rather than a single particle of high energy.

f. Fission by Neutrons. Very heavy nuclei made unstable by the addition of a neutron will sometimes, instead of sending out a small particle, break up into two parts of comparable size. The process is called "fission." This has been found to be possible for all elements whose atomic number is 73 or above. The energy required for fission in the case of two of these isotopes, namely, uranium 235 and plutonium 239, need be only that of a low-speed neutron. Other isotopes undergo fission when the incident neutron carries an amount of energy greater than their threshold values, which in some cases is as high as 1.5 Mev. The threshold energies reported for uranium 238 and thorium 232 are [26] 1.0 ± 0.1 and 1.10 ± 0.05 Mev, respectively.

8.11. The Scattering of Neutrons. Direct neutron-neutron scattering cannot be accomplished because neutrons cannot be produced and held as a target. The nearest approach is to project a beam of neutrons into hydrogen gas. Observations can be made on either the scattered neutrons or on the recoil protons.

It is common experience that a moving billiard ball, on striking head-on another similar ball at rest, will communicate all of its energy and momentum to the struck ball and itself remain at rest at the point of impact. In the same manner, an incident neutron or proton of not too high energy on striking a

[26] W. E. Shoupp and J. E. Hill, *Phys. Rev.*, **75**, 785 (1949).

hydrogen nucleus directly will transfer its entire energy. When a glancing collision occurs, the conservation of momentum and the conservation of energy relate the motions of the two scattered particles as shown in Figure 8.12A. Since the masses,

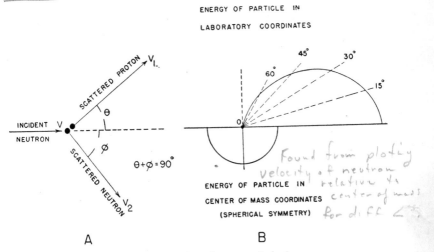

FIG. 8.12. The scattering of neutrons in hydrogen.

whether neutrons or protons, are essentially the same, they need not appear in the equations, so

$$V_1 \cos \theta + V_2 \cos \phi = V \qquad (8.10)$$

$$V_1 \sin \theta - V_2 \sin \phi = 0 \qquad (8.11)$$

$$V_1{}^2 + V_2{}^2 = V^2 \qquad (8.12)$$

where V, V_1, and V_2 are the velocities of the incident neutron, the scattered proton, and scattered neutron, respectively.

On squaring equations 8.10 and 8.11 and adding, and substituting for V^2 its value from equation 8.12, it follows that

$$\tan \theta = \cotan \phi \qquad (8.13)$$

Hence $(\theta + \phi)$ must always add to 90 degrees, and the paths of the two particles are at right angles. The energy W_θ of the particle scattered at an angle θ is the energy W of the incident particle times $\cos^2 \theta$, or

$$W_\theta = W \cos^2 \theta \tag{8.14}$$

In this case, there can be no back-scattering and θ cannot exceed 90 degrees. This variation in the energy of the scattered particle at different angles is shown in the upper portion of Figure 8.12B. The angles mentioned are measured in the fixed laboratory coordinate system.

It is frequently of interest to consider the scattering as it would appear in a coordinate system whose origin is the center of mass of the two interacting particles. Scattering angles in this system would be double those in the laboratory system. For the direct collision the velocity in the forward direction would be only half that in the fixed system and hence the energy would be only one quarter as large. This same energy would characterize particles scattered at every other angle. This spherical distribution is shown in the lower part of Figure 8.12B.

In the symmetrical, center-of-mass system, the number of particles per unit solid angle (σ) is the same in every direction. Hence the number of particles (dn) scattered between an angle θ and $\theta + d\theta$ is

$$dn = \sigma \frac{2\pi r^2 \sin \theta \, d\theta}{r^2} \tag{8.15}$$

At neutron energies up to 14 Mev the total cross sections for scattering in hydrogen are shown [27] in Figure 8.13. Theoretical explanations of the variation with energy include a consideration of the spins of the colliding particles. These may be anti-parallel (singlet) or parallel (triplet) with statistical weights of one and three, respectively. A complete satisfactory theoretical development is still to be presented. As the energy of the

[27] C. Bailey, W. Bennett, T. Bergstrahl, R. Nuckolls, H. Richards, and J. Williams, *Phys. Rev.*, **70**, 583 (1946); H. H. Barschall and R. F. Taschek, *Phys. Rev.*, **75**, 1819 (1949).

incident neutron is increased the scattering process becomes more complicated. It now becomes necessary to introduce short range "exchange" forces in which a charged particle such as an electron or a meson is exchanged by virtual absorption

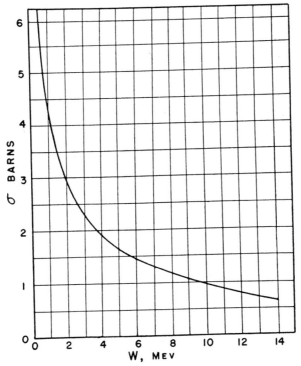

FIG. 8.13. Total neutron scattering cross section for energies up to 14 Mev in hydrogen.

and re-emission between the two nucleons. This sharing of the charged particle leads to an attractive force between the nucleons which increases rapidly as the distance between them decreases. It results in a variation in intensity with the angle of scattering.

It is common practice to show the angular distribution of the scattered neutrons by expressing a "differential cross section,"

$d\sigma/d\omega$, which is measured in barns per steradian. This is usually given in the center-of-mass system. The averaged results obtained by various observers for energies of 40, 91, and 260 Mev are shown graphically in Figure 8.14. One of many

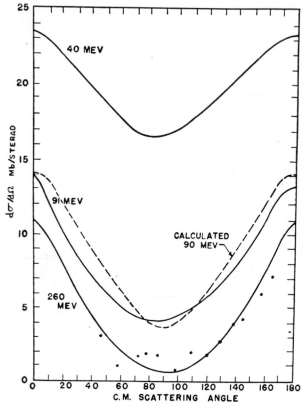

FIG. 8.14. The differential cross section for high-energy neutron scattering in hydrogen.

suggested theoretical curves as developed [28] for 90 Mev neutrons is shown by the dotted trace. By varying the assumed nuclear potentials this can be greatly altered to obtain satisfactory agreement with experiment.

[28] R. S. Christian and E. W. Hart, *Phys. Rev.*, **77**, 441 (1950).

8.12. The Magnetic Moment of the Neutron and Anomalous Scattering.

Like all fundamental particles as previously noted, the neutron has a spin and a consequent magnetic moment. It was calculated that because of this magnetic moment the scattering of neutrons from the two kinds of molecular hydrogen known to exist would be quite different.[29] In orthohydrogen the spins of the two nuclei are in the same sense, while in parahydrogen the spins of the two hydrogen nuclei are opposite. Alvarez and Pitzer found that for 20° K. neutrons, orthohydrogen gave about nineteen times the scattering observed for parahydrogen.[30] The hydrogen was in each case at 20.4° K.

The scattering of thermal neutrons in iron should be influenced by the state of magnetic saturation existing in the iron, because of the interaction between the magnetic moment of the neutron with that of the atoms in the substance. Calculations have been made of the magnitude of the effect to be expected.[31] It has been found experimentally that a change in transmission of about 8% takes place as the state of magnetization of the iron changes from zero to 97% saturation.[32]

It has also been predicted that the scattering of neutrons in matter depends upon the temperature of the scatterer.[33] Calculations indicate that an increase in temperature from 0° C. to 750° C. should cause a decrease in the scattered radiation by about 7%.

A small angle scattering of neutrons, less than 1 degree, in unmagnetized iron has been observed [34] and attributed to refraction at the boundaries of the microscopic crystalline domains.

8.13. The Reflection of Neutrons.

Two types of reflection have been observed in experiments with the strong neutron beams obtained with reactors. Neutrons may be reflected by

[29] J. Schwinger and E. Teller, *Phys. Rev.*, **51**, 775 (1937); **52**, 286 (1937).
[30] L. Alvarez and K. Pitzer, *Phys. Rev.*, **55**, 596 (1939); **58**, 1003 (1940).
[31] O. Halpern and T. Holstein, *Phys. Rev.*, **59**, 960 (1941).
[32] F. Block, M. Hamermesh, and H. Staub, *Phys. Rev.*, **64**, 47 (1943).
[33] R. Weinstock, *Phys. Rev.*, **65**, 1 (1944).
[34] D. Hughes, M. Burgy, R. Heller, and J. Wallace, *Phys. Rev.*, **75**, 565 (1949).

crystalline materials according to the Bragg law for the de Broglie wavelength characteristic of their energy. They may also be totally reflected by highly polished surfaces of selected materials at incident angles greater than their critical angle.

It was observed that thermal neutrons on being filtered through a block of graphite 23 centimeters thick, behaved quite differently than they did initially.[35] Their absorption in boron indicated that their energy corresponded to that of neutrons at a temperature of only about 18° K. The de Broglie wavelength for this energy is about 7.15 angstroms. The longest wavelength regularly reflectible by a graphite crystal is limited by the grating constant to 6.69 angstroms. It might therefore be expected that of the initial spread of wavelengths starting out through the graphite, those higher energy neutrons whose wavelengths are within the Bragg reflecting limit will be scattered out of the forward-proceeding beam, leaving in the end only those low-energy neutrons of longer wavelengths.

With the well-collimated beams of neutrons, spectrometers quite like those used in X-ray spectroscopy have been successfully employed.[36] Crystals of calcite and lithium fluoride are satisfactory. The intense reflected beam is thus an ideal monoenergetic group of particles and may be used for studying resonances or allied problems.

The fact that neutrons are scattered by atoms leads to speculation regarding the index of refraction (μ) of various materials for a neutron beam. Experiments on the form factors obtained by the regular reflection of neutrons from various crystal planes indicated that ($\mu - 1$) was of the order of 10^{-6}, and that it might be positive in sign for some elements and for other elements negative in sign.

Those elements for which ($\mu - 1$) is negative should exhibit a regular reflection within the critical angle. This is similar to the well-known corresponding phenomenon with X-rays. With

[35] H. Anderson, E. Fermi, and L. Marshall, *Phys. Rev.*, **70**, 102 (1946).
[36] E. Fermi and W. Zinn, *Phys. Rev.*, **70**, 103 (1946); W. C. Koehler and E. O. Wollan, *Phys. Rev.*, **92**, 1380 (1953).

mirrors of graphite, aluminum, beryllium, copper, zinc, nickel, and iron, intense regularly reflected beams are observed at glancing angles up to 10 minutes of arc. Manganese appears to behave differently, in that its index of refraction for neutrons is greater than unity.

8.14. The Antineutron. To complete the symmetry of the fundamental particles, after the discovery of the antiproton, one still unobserved particle was necessary, namely, the anti-neutron. As the magnetic moment of the ordinary neutron indicates a spin in the regular fashion of negative electricity, then another similar particle could be envisioned in which an ordinary spin of positive electricity takes place. Evidence for the existence of such a particle has now been obtained.[37]

By passing the 6.2 Bev beam of protons from the Berkeley bevatron into a beryllium target, many disintegration products are formed and leave the target. By the use of strong mag-netic fields the charged particles can be deflected out of the emergent beam and the decay of the uncharged particles in the beam observed. It was noted that in addition to the numerous flashes of energy due to ordinary neutron and meson decay events, occasional cascades of energy as great as 2 Bev occurred. This has been interpreted as evidence for the decay of an anti-neutron. Its origin could be explained by the surrender of a negative charge by an antiproton as it passed close to an ordi-nary proton in the target. It is then converted into energy by annihilation with an ordinary neutron.

8.15. The Physiological Effect of Neutrons and Dosage. It is well known that a sufficient dosage of any ionizing radiation will kill living tissue. Since neutral radiations like gamma rays and neutrons give rise to energetic charged particles they may be equally effective in destroying living cells. The use of this radiation in medicine is discussed later.

The intensity of neutron radiation may be measured by the same technique and instrument, such as the Victoreen meter,

[37] B. Cork, G. Lamberton, O. Piccioni, and W. Wentzel, *Phys. Rev.*, **104**, 1193 (1956).

used in evaluating the intensity of gamma radiation or X-rays. The indication of the instrument on a scale calibrated in roentgen units, is expressed as the same number of "n" units when neutron radiation is being measured. In biological processes one n unit is equivalent in effect to from 2 to 40 r units of X-rays, depending largely upon the hydrogen content of the specimen. Because of the lethal effect of neutron radiation on tissue, care must be observed by workers exposed to it. Since the long-range effect is still not known, a conservative figure of 0.15 n per month is recommended as a maximum exposure.

QUESTIONS AND PROBLEMS

1. A neutron has an energy of 5 electron volts. What is its effective velocity? With what temperature would you associate it?

Answer: 3.08×10^6 cm/sec, 38,600° K.

2. Lithium is bombarded by 10 Mev deuterons and neutrons are observed leaving the lithium at right angles to the direction of bombardment. By writing expressions for the conservation of momentum and energy determine the energy of one of the neutrons observed. Calculate the energy and the angle of recoil of the associated beryllium 8 nucleus.

Answer: $W_b = {\sim}5$ Mev, $\theta = {\sim}45°$.

3. If the intensity of a beam of neutrons is reduced to half-value by a thickness of 5 cm of water, express the absorption coefficient. Calculate the effective cross section in cm^2 for the process, dealing only with the hydrogen.

Answer: $\mu = 0.1386$ cm^{-1}, $\sigma = 2.08 \times 10^{-24}$ cm^2.

4. If the intensity of a neutron beam 50 cm from its source is 10 "n" units per minute, what thickness of water would safely shield an operator so as to keep the dosage to 0.005 n for an 8-hour day? The operator is 10 m from the source. What would be the effect of scattering around the wall?

Answer: Thickness = ${\sim}56.3$ cm.

5. What is the product formed in the water tanks shielding a cyclotron as a result of neutron absorption? Describe the gamma rays produced by a 5 Mev neutron on absorption in a single step.

Answer: $_1D^2$, $W\gamma$ (forward) = 4.93 Mev.

6. Assuming that 5 out of every 10^5 alpha particles from radon will produce a disintegration in the surrounding beryllium, how many neutrons are emitted per second from a mixture of 100 millicuries of radon and beryllium?

Answer: 18.5×10^4 neutrons/sec.

7. A 10-gm piece of Mn^{55} (S.G. = 7.2) is placed in a reactor where the neutron flux density is 5×10^{13}. The cross section for neutron capture is 12.5 barns. Mn^{56} decays by beta emission (half-life 2.6 hr) to stable Fe^{56}. (*a*) How long an exposure would convert 1% of the Mn to Fe? (*b*) What is the number of curies of Mn^{56} existing at the end of one day? (*c*) One week?

Answer: (*a*) 185 days. (*b*) ~1840 curies. (*c*) 1840 curies.

Fundamental Laws of Mechanics

(cm²) /cm²/sec

CHAPTER 9

PROTONS, DEUTERONS, AND TRITIUM

9.1. The Proton. The first measurements made on protons were carried out by W. Wien [1] and later by J. J. Thomson [2] in his investigation of the specific charge of the particles comprising the "canal" rays in a discharge tube. The particles were found to be positively charged and, if the charge was assumed to be that of the electron, then the mass was shown to be that of the hydrogen atom or the hydrogen molecule.

The proton is the positive nucleus of a hydrogen atom. It can be produced by ionizing atomic or molecular hydrogen by electron impact. In the Bohr theory of the atom it was assumed that the nuclei of all heavy atoms were made up of combinations of protons and electons. With the discovery of the neutron as a particle emitted by the nucleus, it became more rational to regard all nuclei as built of protons and neutrons. The number of neutrons that will combine with a definite number of protons is seldom unique. For each such combination a particular isotope of the element results.

Protons were first observed as particles emitted in disintegration, by Rutherford in 1919.[3] Nitrogen gas, on exposure to alpha particles from radium, was found to emit protons in all directions. These particles were identified by the scintillations they produced on a zinc sulfide screen in an apparatus shown in Figure 4.1.

9.2 Transmutation by Protons. After the discovery by Rutherford that energetic alpha particles would induce atomic

[1] W. Wien, *Wied. Annal.*, **65**, 440 (1898).
[2] J. J. Thomson, *Phil. Mag.*, **13**, 561 (1907).
[3] E. Rutherford, *Phil. Mag.*, **37**, 537 (1919).

transmutation, numerous attempts were made to accomplish the same end by the controlled acceleration of other particles. As previously mentioned, it might have been expected that such reactions would proceed even in the light elements, only if the incident particles had an energy of several million electron volts. From simple electrostatics the potential due to a charge (Q), at a distance (r), is Q/r and the work required to transport any charge (e) through a potential difference, $(V_2 - V_1)$ is $(V_2 - V_1)e$. Hence to bring a charge (e) from infinity up to a distance (r) from the nuclear charge (Ze) beyond which point it will be carried forward by attractive forces, is Ze^2/r ergs. By knowing the potential for one or more elements from experiments on alpha particle scattering, it becomes possible to deduce the distance (r) as a function of the atomic weight (A). This was expressed as

$$r = 1.4 \times 10^{-13} \times \sqrt[3]{A} \text{ cm} \tag{9.1}$$

Hence for a proton able to penetrate the barrier of lithium 7, the energy W would be expected to be

$$W = \frac{Ze^2}{r} = \frac{3 \times (4.8)^2 \times 10^{-20}}{1.4 \times 10^{-13} \times \sqrt[3]{7}} \text{ ergs} = 2.6 \text{ Mev} \tag{9.2}$$

For any other element the threshold energy is

$$W = 1.25 Z^{2/3} \text{ Mev} \tag{9.3}$$

However, it had been shown form the standpoint of quantum mechanics that a certain probability existed for the penetration of the nuclear barrier by particles with much less energy.[4]

The first successful transmutation induced by energetic protons was accomplished by Cockcroft and Walton in 1931.[5] Protons were accelerated by a potential of only 280 kv and were allowed to impinge on lithium as a target. It was found

[4] R. W. Gurney and E. Condon, *Nature*, **122**, 439 (1928); G. Gamow, *Z. Physik*, **51**, 204 (1928).

[5] J. D. Cockcroft and E. Walton, *Proc. Roy. Soc.*, **129**, 477 (1931); **136**, 619 (1932).

that alpha particles with a range in air of 8.4 centimeters were emitted from the lithium during the bombardment. This represents an energy of about 8.5 Mev. An improvement in the accelerating equipment soon allowed the production of protons with an energy of 800 kev. The yield of disintegrations at this energy was many times that at the lower potential. This reaction can be represented by the equation

$$_1H^1 + {_3}Li^7 \to {_2}He^4 + {_2}He^4 + Q \ (17.4 \ \text{Mev}) \qquad (9.4)$$

The difference in mass on the two sides of the equation is 0.01863 mass units. This mass deficiency means that an energy of 17.4 Mev was set free by the insignificant amount of energy of the incident proton. Even though the energy set free at each disintegration is 1000 times that of the particle initiating the reaction, the probability of the transmutation is so small that no total gain in the release of energy can be anticipated.

As the energy of the incident proton increases, the number of disintegrations per incident particle increases. For a thin target the yield approaches a limiting value as the incident energy approaches in value the height of the nuclear potential barrier characteristic of the bombarded element.

Many subsequent studies have been made in which transmutations have been induced in elements by protons. Figure 9.1 shows [6] a typical excitation curve as the energy of the incident particles is varied. A "threshold" energy of about 2.5 Mev is apparent, below which the reaction will not proceed. At about 9 Mev a saturation yield is attained.

With the good control of voltage offered by Van de Graaff generators these threshold potentials can be determined with accuracy. Typical of such measurements are [7] the following results: 1.88 Mev for the reaction $_3Li^7(p, n){_4}Be^7$, and 3.20 Mev

[6] L. DuBridge, S. Barnes, J. Buck, and C. Strain, *Phys. Rev.*, **53**, 447 (1938); L. DuBridge and J. Marshall, *Phys. Rev.*, **58**, 7 (1940).

[7] R. O. Haxby, W. Shoupp, W. Stephens, and W. Wells, *Phys. Rev.*, **57**, 348 (1940).

for the reaction $_6C^{13}(p, n)_7N^{13}$. The capture of a proton without the accompanying emission of a particle, other than a gamma ray, has rarely, if ever, been observed. It can be noticed by referring to the Table of Isotopes that both the (p, n) and the (p, α) reactions usually result in the formation of positron-emitting radioactive isotopes.

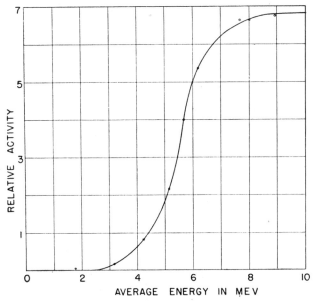

FIG. 9.1. Variation in radioactive yield with the energy of the incident particles.

In the 184-inch cyclotron energetic protons were first obtained by the stripping of the deuteron. The arrangement of the stripping target and the proton target is shown in Figure 9.2. The proton target is raised slightly out of the median plane so as not to interfere with the deuteron beam. The distribution of the protons due to stripping is very similar to that for neutrons presented in Figure 8.3. Incidentally the magnetic field serves as a proton spectrometer so that protons at a given radius have uniform energy. By modifying the

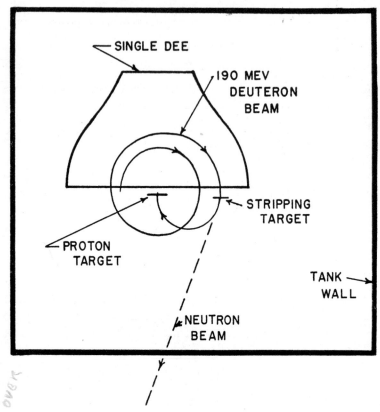

FIG. 9.2. The arrangement for stripping 190-Mev deuterons in the 184-inch cyclotron at Berkeley.

magnetic field it is now possible to accelerate protons directly in the 184-inch cyclotron up to about 700 Mev in energy.

In both the cosmotron and the bevatron the projectiles are protons. On reacting with the nucleons of the target, disruptions occur in which pi mesons (pions) are copiously emitted. At 6.2 Bev there is evidence [8] that new particles, namely, the antiproton and the antineutron may be created. The yield at

[8] O. Chamberlain, E. Segré, C. Wiegand, and T. Ypsilantis, *Phys. Rev.*, **100**, 947 (1955).

this energy is about two such particles for 10^5 pions. The anti-proton may be created as a member of a pair as in positron production, shown as follows:

$$H + n \rightarrow H + n + {}_+P + {}_-P \qquad (9.5)$$

where n is the target nucleon. To satisfy conservation laws the incident energy should be greater than $6M_P C^2$ or about 5.6 Bev. If the momentum of the nucleon ($\sqrt{25}$) be such as to combine with the momentum of the incident particle ($\sqrt{W}$), then W need be only about 4600 Mev to yield sufficient energy.

9.3. The Deuteron. The atomic weight of hydrogen as found by Aston with the mass spectrograph differed slightly from that deduced on the basis of its chemical activity.[9] Birge and Menzel [10] proposed that the difference could be accounted for by assuming the presence of a trace of hydrogen of mass 2, present to the extent of about 1 part in 4500.

The first success in concentrating and identifying the heavy isotope of hydrogen was attained by Urey, Brickwedde, and Murphy in 1932.[11] They evaporated large quantities of liquid hydrogen at its triple-point temperature and collected the last fraction. On a spectroscopic examination, they found certain lines not agreeing with those of any molecule reported in the literature. These lines did, however, occur in positions predicted for the spectrum of hydrogen 2. This has been taken as evidence of discovery and the heavy hydrogen isotope was termed deuterium.

The deuterium isotope was positively identified by W. Bleakney by the use of the mass spectrograph.[12] The percentage difference in the atomic weights of the two hydrogen isotopes is so appreciable that their separation by physical methods is a relatively easy matter. It is rendered difficult by the fact that deuterium is normally present only to about 0.018% in ordinary

[9] F. W. Aston, *Isotopes*, Arnold, London (1924).
[10] R. T. Birge and D. Menzel, *Phys. Rev.*, **37**, 1669 (1931).
[11] H. Urey, F. Brickwedde, and G. Murphy, *Phys. Rev.*, **39**, 164 (1932).
[12] W. Bleakney, *Phys. Rev.*, **39**, 536 (1932).

hydrogen. In diffusion, distillation, or electrolysis the lighter component is more active. Consequently, these processes result in a progressive enrichment of the heavier isotope in the residuum. In general in these processes the action proceeds at a rate proportional to the velocity of the particles and hence inversely as the square roots of their masses, since on the average their kinetic energies are the same.

9.4. Transmutation by Deuterons. The deuteron proved at once to be an effective projectile for producing nuclear disintegration. It might have been expected that, because of the high energy of the nuclear barriers in all but the very light elements, transmutations could not be induced by deuterons with energies less than several million electron volts. This was found not to be the case. Two factors contribute to the explanation of this result. As mentioned previously, by wave-mechanics a certain probability exists that the approaching charged particle will filter through the nuclear barrier even though the energy of the barrier is much greater than that of the particle.

A second possibility to explain an induced nuclear reaction by a low-energy deuteron was proposed by Oppenheimer and Phillips.[13] It was considered that the deuteron in approaching close to a nucleus in the target might break up into a neutron and a proton provided its kinetic energy was greater than its own binding energy. The neutron, because of its lack of charge, could proceed into the nucleus, but the proton, by virtue of its positive charge, would be repelled or scattered away. The entering neutron could then incite any of the characteristic neutron reactions. Many different types of transmutation can be attributed to the deuteron bombardment, based upon the nature of the particle that escapes from the excited nucleus.

a. The Deuteron-Neutron Reaction. One of the reactions first studied was the bombardment of ice, made from heavy water, by deuteron projectiles.[14] For incident deuterons of very low

[13] J. R. Oppenheimer and M. Phillips, *Phys. Rev.*, **48**, 500 (1935).
[14] M. L. Oliphant, P. Harteck, and E. Rutherford, *Proc. Roy. Soc. (London)*, **144**, 692 (1934).

energy a reaction occurred in which neutrons were copiously emitted. At 100 kev it was estimated that one in every 10^6 incident deuterons produced a disintegration. At higher energies the disintegration yield increases rapidly. The (d, n) reaction when applied to boron, beryllium, or lithium serves as a source of high-energy or fast neutrons.

  b. *The Deuteron-Proton Reaction.* Other competing processes exist in excited nuclei resulting from the entrance of the deuteron. If the energy is sufficient a proton may be ejected. It might be expected that this would have a low probability compared to that for the escape of a neutron, since the nuclear barrier which made it difficult for the charged particle to enter the nucleus would to the same degree offer resistance to its departure. This is often found not to be the case. For certain elements the relative probability for the two competing processes can be determined.

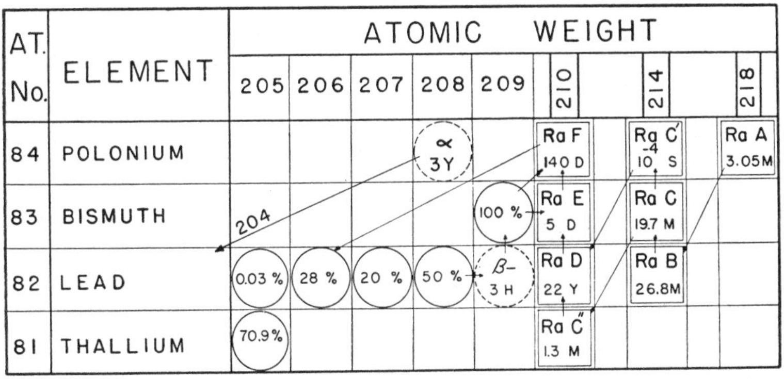

AT. No.	ELEMENT	ATOMIC WEIGHT							
		205	206	207	208	209	210	214	218
84	POLONIUM				α 3Y		Ra F 140 D	Ra C' 10^{-4} S	Ra A 3.05M
83	BISMUTH	204				100 %	Ra E 5 D	Ra C 19.7 M	
82	LEAD	0.03 %	28 %	20 %	50 %	β− 3 H	Ra D 22 Y	Ra B 26.8M	
81	THALLIUM	70.9%					Ra C'' 1.3 M		

FIG. 9.3. Isotopes, stable and radioactive, for the elements near bismuth.

Figure 9.3 shows the possibility for such a study with bismuth. This element has a single natural isotope of mass 209 and atomic number 83. The deuteron-neutron reaction results in the production of polonium 210, called radium F, while the deuteron-proton process yields bismuth 210, called radium E. Radium E has a half-life of 5.0 days, emitting a beta particle

$$_{83}Bi^{209} + {}_1H^2 \rightarrow {}_{83}Bi^{210} + {}_1p^1$$

$$_{83}Bi^{209} + {}_1H^2 \rightarrow {}_{84}Po^{210} + {}_0n^1$$

and becoming radium F.   Radium F, however, emits only alpha particles and has a half-life of 140 days.   By recording the intensity of alpha emission immediately after bombardment, the yield of radium F is established.[15]   Then by noting the increase in alpha activity on successive days, as shown in Figure 9.4, the initial yield of radium E can be calculated.

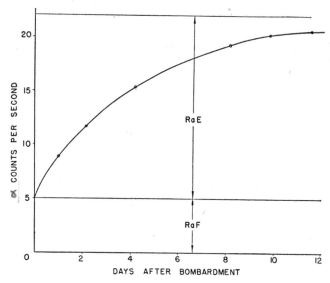

FIG. 9.4.   The yield of radium E and radium F from (Bi + H²).

These relative yields for identical targets bombarded with the same number of deuterons but with varying energy were first observed up to 14 Mev.   It appeared that at low energies the (d, p) reaction is much more probable than the (d, n) process, and at 9 Mev it is still five times as likely to occur. This apparent anomaly is not unexpected when the Oppenheimer-Phillips process is considered.

On extending the energy of the incident deuterons to 19 Mev

[15] J. M. Cork, J. Halpern, and H. Tatel, *Phys. Rev.*, **57**, 371 (1940); D. Hurst, R. Lantham, and W. B. Lewis, *Proc. Roy. Soc. (London)*, **174**, 126 (1940); J. M. Cork, *Phys. Rev.*, **70**, 563 (1946).

Segré has [16] shown that the (d, p) yield of radium E goes through a maximum as shown in Figure 9.5. The decreased yield at the higher energies is due to the increased probability of the competitive process $(d, 3n)$, ending in polonium 208

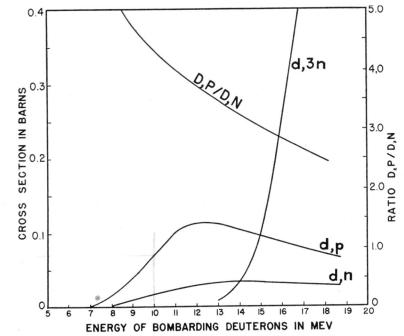

FIG. 9.5. Relative yields by the (d, p), the (d, n) and the $(d, 3n)$ reactions with bismuth.

which is an alpha emitter of 3.0-year half-life. The yield of this isotope was observed to increase rapidly as the deuteron energy exceeded 15 Mev.

   c. The Deuteron-Alpha Reaction. There is conclusive evidence that nuclei bombarded by deuterons may, at impact, sometimes emit alpha particles. This fact can be established both by observing in a cloud chamber the particles ejected during the exposure and by studying and identifying the radio-

[16] E. L. Kelly and E. Segré, *Phys. Rev.*, **75**, 999 (1949); D. C. Peaslee, *Phys. Rev.*, **74**, 1001 (1948).

active isotopes resulting from the bombardment. In certain elements it is possible quantitatively to follow this process and compare its probability with that of the reaction in which a neutron escapes from the excited nucleus.

By bombarding pure iron with deuterons, a radioactive isotope of cobalt whose half-life is 18.2 hours and a radioactive isotope of manganese whose half-life is 21 minutes are formed. Both radioactive elements emit positrons and they are believed to be derived from the same isotope of iron, of mass 54. The former would be produced by a deuteron-neutron reaction and the latter by a deuteron-alpha process as shown in Figure 9.6. This, then, offers an opportunity to observe the relative probability for the two reactions.

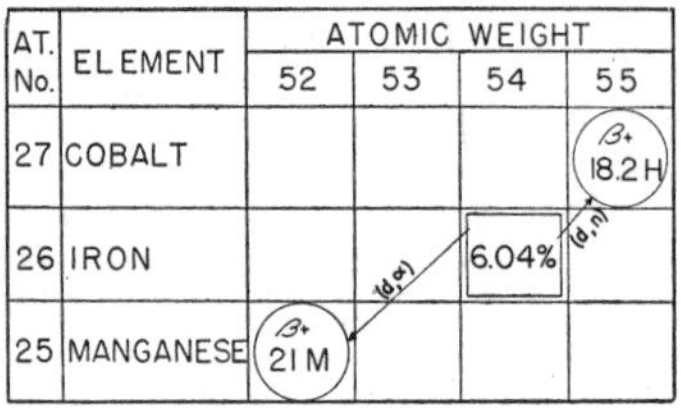

AT. No.	ELEMENT	ATOMIC WEIGHT			
		52	53	54	55
27	COBALT				$\beta+$ 18.2H
26	IRON			6.04%	
25	MANGANESE	$\beta+$ 21 M			

FIG. 9.6. Indicating the possible transitions for (Fe^{54} + H^2).

To study the variation in the probability at different excitation energies a stack of thin foils of pure iron is exposed to a beam of deuterons.[17] The cover foil is traversed by deuterons with a maximum energy. Each succeeding underlying foil will transmit practically the same number of deuterons but with a continually decreased energy until the deuterons are completely stopped.

Each foil is then studied individually so as to yield the initial intensities of the 21-minute and 18-hour radioactivities. These quantities for each foil are plotted together with the average energy of the deuterons in that layer, yielding curves as shown in Figure 9.7. The yield from the deuteron-neutron reaction seems to approach a maximum for deuterons of energy about 7.5 Mev and then to show a very slight decrease at higher energies. The yield of the deuteron-alpha reaction increases progressively with increasing deuteron energy. In both cases the deuteron as a whole has entered the nucleus through the poten-

[17] J. M. Cork and J. Halpern, *Phys. Rev.*, **57**, 667 (1940).

$$_{26}Fe^{54} + _1H^2 \rightarrow _{27}Co^{55} + _0n^1$$

$$_{26}Fe^{54} + _1H^2 \rightarrow _{25}Mn^{52} + _2He^4$$

tial barrier. The Oppenheimer-Phillips splitting of the deuteron in the external field plays no role, since the reactions considered could not be initiated by a single neutron entering the nucleus.

It has now been demonstrated [18] that alpha-emitting isotopes may be produced by the bombardment of elements as light as the rare earths, with 190 Mev deuterons.

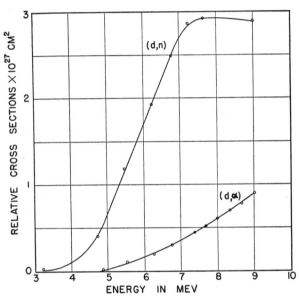

Fig. 9.7. Excitation curves for cobalt and manganese from the reaction iron plus deuterons.

9.5. The Production of X-Rays by Deuteron Bombardment.

The possibility of producing X-rays by the bombardment of targets with heavy particles was demonstrated [19] as early as 1913 by Chadwick and by Rutherford and Richardson.

If it be assumed that the deuteron collides elastically with the electron, then the energy communicated to the electron ac-

[18] S. Thompson, A. Ghiorso, J. Rasmussen, and G. Seaborg, *Phys. Rev.*, **76**, 406 (1949).
[19] J. Chadwick, *Phil. Mag.*, **25**, 193 (1913); E. Rutherford and H. Richardson, *Phil. Mag.*, **25**, 722 (1913).

cording to classical mechanics is only $4m/M$ times the energy of the deuteron, where m and M are the masses of electron and deuteron, respectively. Hence, deuterons of energy 10 Mev could give to an electron an energy of only 10.9 kev. This potential would be sufficient to excite the "K" series in elements only up to about atomic number 30. In practice,[20] for 10 Mev deuterons, "K" radiation has been observed for elements up through atomic number 38. This ability of the heavy particle to communicate more energy to the electron than simple theory would predict has been theoretically explained by Henneberg.[21]

9.6. The Scattering of Protons in Hydrogen. The nature of the forces acting between fundamental particles can be revealed by observing the scattering of these particles by the same or other nuclei. It is important to note the intensity of the scattering at various angles as the energy of the incident particles is given increasingly large values.

Many relationships dealing with the scattering of incident charged particles by the Coulomb fields of other particles were developed.[22] The problem was treated both nonrelativistically and relativistically with wave mechanics. For energetic protons scattered by hydrogen, experimental results were not in agreement with theoretical predictions. At an angle of 45°, 900 kev protons were scattered [23] about four times more abundantly than expected from the coulomb force alone. This anomalous effect was reconciled by assuming the presence of an attractive nuclear force between the protons at close range. It was predicted [24] that because of the interference between the repulsive coulomb scattering and the attractive effect, at an angle of 45 degrees a minimum scattering should be expected

[20] J. M. Cork, *Phys. Rev.*, **59**, 957 (1941).

[21] W. Henneberg, *Z. Physik*, **86**, 592 (1933).

[22] W. Gordon, *Z. Physik*, **48**, 180 (1928); G. Temple, *Proc. Roy. Soc.*, **A121**, 673 (1928); C. G. Darwin, *Proc. Roy. Soc.*, **A118**, 654 (1928); N. F. Mott and H. S. Massey, *Theory of Atomic Collisions*, Oxford Press (1933).

[23] M. Tuve, N. Heydenburg, and L. Hafstad, *Phys. Rev.*, **49**, 402 (1936); **50**, 806 (1936).

[24] G. Breit, E. Condon, and R. Present, *Phys. Rev.*, **50**, 825 (1936).

for particles whose energy was about 400 kev. The existence of this minimum is shown in Figure 9.8.

The scattering of protons, with energies up to 430 Mev, at various angles up to 90 degrees, in the center-of-mass system, has been intensively studied.[25] Typical results at the low or intermediate energies (<10 Mev) are shown graphically in

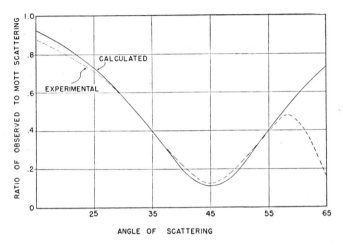

FIG. 9.8. Proton scattering at 45 degrees compared with the calculated distribution.

Figure 9.9. The differential cross section is plotted as a function of the scattering angle in the center-of-mass system. At very high energies, averaged results as reported from various laboratories are similarly presented in Figure 9.10. The striking features of the very high energy scattering are (a) the slight variations in cross section with angle, (b) relatively small change in cross section with incident energy, and (c) a larger absolute value of σ than generally expected from theory. It is possible to conjecture nuclear potentials such that agreement is obtained between calculated and any particular observed angu-

[25] R. Birge, U. Kruse, and N. Ramsey, *Phys. Rev.*, **83**, 274 (1951); O. Chamberlain, E. Segré, and C. Wiegand, *Phys. Rev.*, **83**, 923 (1951); C. L. Oxley and R. D. Shamberger, *Phys. Rev.*, **85**, 416 (1952); J. Marshall, L. Marshall, and V. Nedsel, *Phys. Rev.*, **92**, 834 (1953); B. Cork, L. Johnson, and C. Richman, *Phys. Rev.*, **79**, 71 (1950).

lar distribution. At the present time, however, considerable lack of agreement exists [26] between various theoretical treatments of the subject. The total elastic cross section at 429 Mev is about 20.7 millibarns. An additional component due to

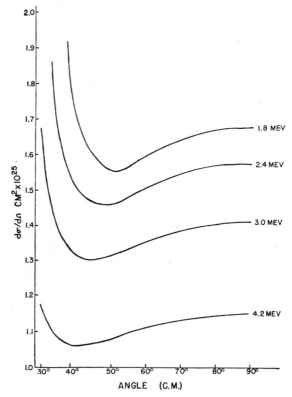

FIG. 9.9. The scattering of low-energy protons in hydrogen.

pion production amounts to about 3.8 millibarns making an over-all cross section at this energy of 24.5 millibarns.

9.7. Inelastic Scattering of Protons. When protons approach very close to other nuclei, in the scattering process, they

[26] R. S. Christian and H. P. Noyes, *Phys. Rev.*, **79**, 85 (1950); K. M. Case and A. Pais, *Phys. Rev.*, **80**, 203 (1950); R. Jastrow, *Phys. Rev.*, **79**, 389 (1950).

may transfer some of their energy to the struck nuclei. The proton with its reduced energy is scattered, but the bombarded nucleus is left in an excited energy state. This process was first reported by Wilkins in bombarding lithium and magnesium in

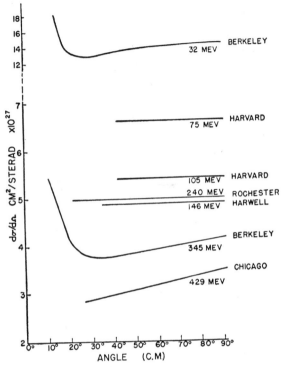

Fig. 9.10. The angular distribution of scattered protons by hydrogen.

photographic emulsions.[27] The scattering has been observed directly with a proportional counter, by Dicke and Marshall, using Cr, Al, and Mg as scattering agents.[28] A typical scattering curve showing the number of particles scattered in various

[27] T. R. Wilkins, G. Kuerti, and G. Wrenshall, *Phys. Rev.*, **57**, 1082 (1940); **60**, 365 (1941); **63**, 56 (1943).
[28] R. Dicke and J. Marshall, *Phys. Rev.*, **63**, 86 (1943); H. Fulbright and R. Bush, *Phys. Rev.*, **74**, 1223 (1948).

energy groups at the fixed angle of 135 degrees, for incident protons of 6.9 Mev on aluminum is presented in Figure 9.11.

The elastically scattered protons have an energy of 6.08 Mev as shown in Figure 9.11A, but the inelastic collisions lead to certain groups of particles of lower energy at the same angle, as shown by the definite peaks in Figure 9.11B. The energy

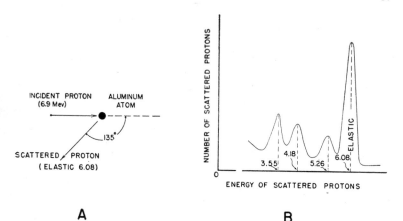

A   **B**

FIG. 9.11.   Elastic and inelastic scattering of 6.9-Mev protons from aluminum at an angle of 135° (Dicke and Marshall).

represented by these peaks, namely 5.26, 4.18, 3.55, and 2.82 Mev, is what remains after the nuclei have taken out their respective characteristic energies, to become excited. These excitation energies, characteristic of aluminum, are accordingly 0.87, 2.03, 2.70, and 3.5 Mev. Similar characteristic excitation energies have been observed for many other substances.

In case the incident particle is a deuteron, it has been shown by Guth that it may be polarized by the nuclear field.[29] In this way the neutron may come close enough to the struck nucleus to transfer energy from the deuteron, producing an excited state, yet the deuteron as a whole will be scattered. This process, originally called "polarization scattering" was first

[29] E. Guth, *Phys. Rev.*, **68**, 280 (1945).

observed [30] in the excitation of indium 115 by 1.7 Mev deuterons. It has been shown [31] that protons, deuterons, or alpha particles whose energies are so low that they have little chance of penetrating a nuclear barrier, may still transfer some of their energy to the struck nucleus. This process is called "Coulomb excitation" and results in the formation of isomeric states of the target nucleus.

9.8. The Range of Protons and Deuterons.

Except for the straggling introduced by statistical fluctuations, the range of a collection of monoenergetic protons in passing through normal air is unique. This variation in range as the energy of the protons is varied up to 450 Mev is shown [32] graphically in Figure 9.12. A beam of deuterons will behave similarly except that their range for the same energy is much less than that of the proton. The range-energy relationship for deuterons up to 3 Bev is included in Figure 9.12.

The range-energy relationship for charged particles is not simple. For low ranges it may be empirically expressed. According to the Geiger rule the range R of a charged particle of a particular kind varies as the cube of the velocity v. Since the energy W involves the square of the velocity, then it follows that

$$R \propto v^3 \propto W^{3/2} \tag{9.6}$$

The energy loss per centimeter of path dW/dR can be found since

$$\frac{dR}{dW} \propto \sqrt{W} \propto v \quad \text{or} \quad \frac{dW}{dR} \propto \frac{1}{v} \tag{9.7}$$

The specific ionization along the path of the singly charged proton or deuteron thus depends upon the reciprocal of the velocity. This indicates that the longer the particle takes to pass an atom the greater is its probability of producing ioniza-

[30] M. L. Wiedenbeck, *Phys. Rev.*, **69**, 47 (1946).
[31] C. L. McClelland and C. Goodman, *Phys. Rev.*, **91**, 760 (1953); J. Bjerregaard and T. Huus, *Phys. Rev.*, **94**, 204 (1954).
[32] J. H. Smith, *Phys. Rev.*, **71**, 32 (1947).

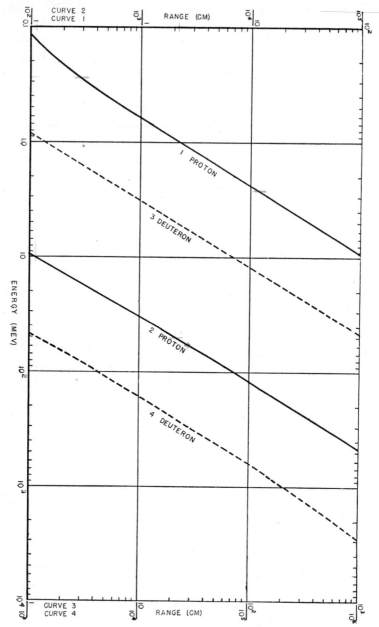

Fig. 9.12. Proton and deuteron ranges in air.

280

tion. At the same energy the velocity of a proton is $\sqrt{2}$ times that of the deuteron, and hence it produces only 0.70 times as many ions per centimeter.

It can be noted from the data shown in Figure 9.12 that over quite a range the following relationship holds, namely, "the

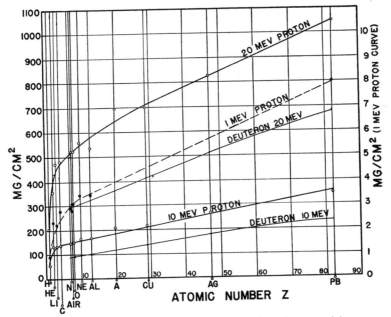

FIG. 9.13. The range of protons and deuterons in various materials.

range of a proton, whose energy is half that of a deuteron, is half the range of the deuteron."

The stopping power of various materials is often expressed in the number of milligrams per square centimeter needed to stop completely the incident energetic particles. Since the stopping is largely an electronic process and the number of electrons per gram of any element does not differ greatly from 3×10^{23}, it might have been expected that the stopping power of the various elements is a constant. Actually this is very far from true as evidenced by Figure 9.13 which shows the stopping power as observed in several elements for protons and deuterons of energy 1, 10, and 20 Mev. For example, it takes 350 milligrams per square centimeter of lead to stop completely 10-Mev protons, whereas only half that amount of aluminum will produce the same effect. The tightly bound electrons in the inner orbital shells of the heavy element are not so easily dislodged and hence they are less effective in the stopping process.

9.9. Particles of Mass Three. An isotope of helium of mass 3 occurs in nature. For helium derived from the atmosphere, He^3 is present to $1.2 \times 10^{-4}\%$ and gas-well helium contains about $1.5 \times 10^{-5}\%$ He^3.

Hydrogen of mass 3, sometimes called "tritium," does not exist in nature. It can be produced in such nuclear reactions as

$$Be^9(H^2, n)H^3, Be^7 \quad \text{or} \quad {}_5B^{10}(n, H^3)2_2He^4$$

or

$$_7N^{15}(n, H^3)_6C^{13}$$

It has been estimated that for high-energy neutrons on boron or nitrogen the cross section for the production of H^3 is about 10^{-26} square centimeter. The bombardment of deuterium by deuterons yields both tritium and He^3.

$$H^2 + H^2 \rightarrow H + H^3 \quad \text{or} \quad n + He^3$$

At 10 Mev the numbers of H^3 and He^3 particles produced and their angular distributions are almost identical.[33] Similar yields are also found at bombarding energies up to 190 Mev. This is interpreted as evidence of "charge symmetry" or the equality, except for the Coulomb effect, of n,n and p,p nuclear forces of the same spin state. The half-life of tritium is 12.4 years, decaying by beta emission with an energy maximum [34] of 17.95 kev to He^3.

---

[33] J. Allred, D. Phillips, and L. Rosen, *Phys. Rev.*, **82**, 782 (1951); C. S. Godfrey, *Phys. Rev.*, **96**, 1621 (1954).
[34] L. M. Langer and R. Moffat, *Phys. Rev.*, **88**, 689 (1952).

QUESTIONS AND PROBLEMS

1. A 10-microampere beam of protons at 10 Mev is incident upon a 1-mil (0.001 in.) foil of aluminum for 2 sec. Assume that neutrons are emitted isotropically in the disintegration. A neutron counter 20 cm from the target offers an effective area of 5 sq cm and indicates that 2000 neutrons are received per sec. What is the cross section for the reaction? What is the energy of one of the forward neutrons?
Answer: $\sigma = 2.09 \times 10^{-28}$ cm^2, $W_F = 3.17$ Mev.

2. The half-life of the silicon isotope formed in problem 1 is 4.9 sec, and it emits positrons of maximum energy 3.64 Mev. How many curies of activity exist in the target at the end of the bombardment? How many curies would exist at the end of a bombardment for 1 hr?
Answer: 13.4 and 54.3 microcuries.

3. By bombarding a thick target of phosphorus 31 (30.9836) with 10-Mev deuterons, it is found that 35 microampere hours will produce 1 millicurie of radioactive phosphorus. Assuming a threshold of 3 Mev for the reaction, what is the effective cross section for the process? If the cyclotron beam is 120 microamperes and its operation is valued at $12.00 per hr, what is a fair value for 10 millicuries of radioactive phosphorus?
Answer: $\sigma = 5.9 \times 10^{-26}$ cm^2, cost, $35.00.

4. In problem 3, what is the energy and range in air of the protons emitted at right angles to the deuteron beam?
Answer: 14.9 Mev. Range = 235 cm.

5. A proton whose energy is 0.200 Mev is elastically scattered in hydrogen through an angle of 20 degrees. Describe the behavior of the scattering particle.
Answer: $\theta = 70$ degrees, $W = 0.0236$ Mev.

6. If the average energy per ion pair is 35 electron volts, how many ions are produced by a 10-Mev proton? What is the average distance traveled in normal air between ionizing impacts? Why should a deuteron of the same energy produce more ions per cm of path?
Answer: $N = 2.8 \times 10^5$, $l = 0.0004$ cm.

$$\frac{dN}{dt} = (\alpha - \lambda N$$

Check for answers on graphs or charts.

CHAPTER 10

MESONS

10.1. The Meson and Its Discovery. In 1935, H. Yukawa presented a theoretical discussion of the short-range forces acting between a neutron and a proton in the nucleus.[1] In accounting for beta disintegration he was led to a prediction of the existence of quanta or particles whose mass should be about one tenth that of the proton.

An estimate of the expected mesonic mass can be gained by a consideration of its role within the nucleus. A neutron within the nucleus may convert momentarily into a proton plus a pi meson which is later reabsorbed and then again emitted, and so on. The nuclear field involved in this oscillation will extend as far as the emitted pi meson can travel. The energy of the meson is $M_m C^2$, where M_m is its mass in grams. From the Heisenberg uncertainty relationship the time of the meson flight will be of the order of $h/M_m C^2$. During this interval it cannot travel farther than the time multiplied by the velocity of light, which distance may be designated as d. If this distance is assumed to be 10^{-12} cm and M_e is the rest mass of the electron, then

$$d = \frac{h}{M_m C^2} \times C = \frac{h}{M_m C}$$

and

$$\frac{M_m}{M_e} = \frac{h}{M_e dC} = \sim 240$$

In 1936, Anderson and Neddermeyer observed, among their many cloud chamber photographs of cosmic radiation, several

[1] H. Yukawa, *Proc. Phys. Math. Soc. Japan*, **17**, 48 (1935).

tracks of particles whose penetration was much greater than it should have been, as indicated by their radii of curvature, if they were electrons.[2]   In order to determine more definitely the nature of such particles it was considered desirable to observe them at the end of their range when they have lost most of their energy.   Street and Stevenson, accordingly, arranged a system of four vertical coincidence Geiger tubes with a Wilson cloud chamber placed between the lower two.[3]   The circuit was arranged so that heavy particles that penetrated all tubes gave no response, but any particle actuating the first three tubes, and not the fourth, set the cloud chamber in action. In this way they obtained a photograph of a negatively charged particle whose mass, as determined by its specific ionization and curvature in a strong magnetic field, was about 200 times the mass of the electron.   Many subsequent investigations confirmed the existence of such particles.

10.2. Classification of Mesons.   It has now been fairly well established that there are many different kinds of mesons.   By general agreement the particles are divided into three broad divisions, according to their masses.   These are given in Table 10.1.

TABLE 10.1.   MESON DIVISIONS

Names	Mass (m_e)
L—Light	<275
K—Heavy	$>275, <1830$
Y—Hyperon	$>1830, <3660$

Within each division are several clearly distinct types of particles differing from each other by either mass, charge, or mode of decay.   They are designated by Greek letters with superscripts denoting their charge.   Small letters are used in the first two divisions and capital Greek letters for established hyperons.   V-events indicate the decay in flight of hyperons or K mesons, as opposed to S-events which occur when they are at

[2] C. D. Anderson and S. Neddermeyer, *Phys. Rev.*, **50**, 263 (1936).
[3] J. Street and E. Stevenson, *Phys. Rev.*, **52**, 1003 (1937).

rest. In Table 10.2, which shows the current belief regarding the characteristics of various mesons, the following abbreviations are employed: e (electron), P (proton), n (neutron), ν (neutrino), γ (gamma), and η, η' (neutral unspecified). The spin of the π^+ particle has been experimentally determined to be zero. This is also probably the spin of π^- and π^0. The spin of the muon particles is believed to be one half.

TABLE 10.2. MESON CHARACTERISTICS

Name	Mass (m_e)	Mean-Life (sec)	Decays to
	times the mass of an electron.		
L Mesons			
$\pi^\pm$	273.0	2.55×10^{-8}	$\mu^\pm + \nu$
π^0	263.8	5×10^{-15}	$2\gamma; \gamma + e^+ + e^-$
$\mu^\pm$	206.6	2.15×10^{-6}	$e^\pm + \nu + \nu$
K Mesons			
$\tau^\pm$	965.2	1×10^{-8}	$\pi^\pm + \pi^+ + \pi^-$
θ^0	965	1.6×10^{-10}	$\pi^+ + \pi^-$
χ	965	$\sim 10^{-8}$	$\pi^\pm + \pi^0$
$K_{\mu 2}$	965	$\sim 10^{-8}$	$\mu + \nu$
$K_{\mu 3}$	965	$\sim 10^{-8}$	$\mu + \eta + \eta'$
$K_{e 3}$	965		$e + \eta + \eta'$
Y Hyperons			
Λ^0	2181	3.7×10^{-7}	$P + \pi^-$
Σ^+	2325	$\sim 10^{-10}$	$P + \pi^0; n + \pi^+$
Σ^-	2325	$\sim 10^{-10}$	$n + \pi^-$
Ξ	2580	$\sim 10^{-10}$	$\Lambda^0 + \pi^0$

[handwritten margin notes: $\tau = 3.7 \times 10^{-10}$, arrow to Λ^0 row; -10 above 3.7×10^{-7}]

10.3. The Production of Mesons. With the availability of 190-Mev deuterons and 380-Mev alpha particles in the 184-inch cyclotron, the possibility of controlled meson production was explored. It might have been expected that the maximum energy per nucleon in either of these accelerated particles would be 95 Mev and hence not adequate to produce a meson. Actually this is not the case and the energy available in the nucleon-nucleon impact within a carbon nucleus may be as great as 200

Mev. This has been explained [4] by the combination of the momentum of the incident nucleon, $\sqrt{95}$, with that of the "Fermi" energy of the struck nucleon, $\sqrt{20}$, giving 14.2, which when squared gives approximately 200 Mev.

The first observation of controlled meson production was reported by Gardner and Lattes [5] in 1948. The arrangement of the carbon target and the NTB photographic plates within the 184-inch cyclotron is shown in Figure 10.1. Success was

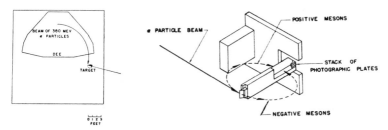

FIG. 10.1*A*. The arrangement of carbon target in the 184-inch cyclotron.

FIG. 10.1*B*. The mounting of target and photographic plates within the cyclotron.

achieved largely through the ability to use the improved photographic-emulsion technique. A typical photogram of an incoming negative meson and the disruption caused by its impact with a nucleus is shown in Figure 10.2. At impact with a silver or bromine nucleus many heavy particles such as protons or alpha particles are ejected, forming what is termed a star. In Figure 10.2 one of the emitted protons is scattered through almost 90 degrees and accidentally stays in the emulsion so as to trace out a path over 400 microns in length, thus indicating that its energy is about 10 Mev. Another particle ends in a "hammer track" due to a splitting of a struck lithium nucleus into two heavy parts leaving in opposite directions.

The ranges of various particles expressed in microns in the NTB emulsion, as a function of energy, are shown in Fig. 10.7.

[4] R. Serber, *Phys. Rev.*, **72**, 1114 (1947).
[5] E. Gardner and C. Lattes, *Science*, **107**, 270 (1948); *Phys. Rev.*, **75**, 364, 379 (1949).

It is reasonably certain that the nucleon-nucleon impact at energies less than 200 Mev yields only pi mesons and hence requires a minimum of about 140 Mev. Theoretically they are the mesons envisaged in the Yukawa theory which, coupled with nucleons, account for the nuclear forces. Hence they are called

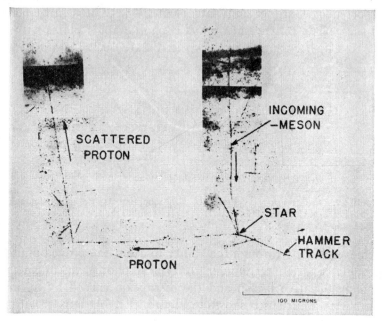

Fig. 10.2. Production of a star in the photographic emulsion by a meson (Gardner and Lattes).

N.F. mesons, by Heitler,[6] who showed that the cross section for meson production when the energy is sufficient, is of the order of the area presented by one nucleon in the nucleus. This cross section is of the order of $(h/2\pi MC)^2$ or 10^{-27} square centimeter, where h is the Planck constant, M the mass of the meson, and C the velocity of light. Theoretically the probability for the production of a positive meson is much greater than for a negative meson.

[6] W. Heitler, *Rev. Mod. Phys.*, **21**, 113 (1949).

The mu mesons are produced from the decay of pi mesons, as shown in Figure 10.3 and although they may appear abundant in the irradiated emulsions or in cosmic-ray cloud chamber pictures, they are intermediate particles in the decay process.

At the very high energies now available in the Bev accelerators, K mesons are produced [7] in considerable number. The heavier hyperons are found only in cosmic rays.

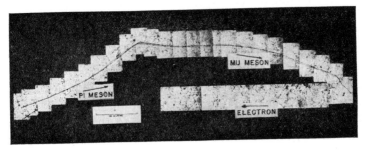

FIG. 10.3.   Emulsion photogram showing the decay of a pi meson to mu meson to electron (Gardner and Lattes).

10.4. The Half-life of the Pi Meson.   The mesons emerging from the carbon target (shown in Figure 10.1) will describe circular or helical paths in the uniform magnetic field. By collimating the beam with a semicircular spiral channel, it is possible by photographic emulsions to observe the mesons along a particular path. Their number per second may be observed after they have described 180-degree, 540-degree, or 900-degree transits. If the falling off in number is greater than would have been expected from the geometry, then it is reasonable to assume that the spontaneous decay of the mesons is responsible. The time for one complete circular trip for a singly charged meson of mass 273 M_e in a magnetic field of 15,000 gausses is from equation 3.16 equal to 6.7×10^{-8} second. It was concluded [8] that negative mesons have a half-life of only 7.7×10^{-9}

[7] D. Ritson, A. Pevsner, S. Fung, M. Widgoff, G. Zorn, S. Goldhaber, and G. Goldhaber, *Phys. Rev.*, **101**, 1085 (1956).

[8] J. R. Richardson, *Phys. Rev.*, **74**, 1720 (1948).

second. An identical time was [9] also found for the half-life of positively charged mesons. In order to observe solely negative pi mesons, only stars produced in the emulsion were counted.

10.5. The Half-life of Mu Mesons. In the absence of colliding nuclei, both positive and negative mu mesons probably decay spontaneously into electrons and neutrinos. An estimate of their half-life of 1.6×10^{-6} second, or a mean-life of 2.3×10^{-6} second was made [10] by Rossi.

This conclusion on half-life was established by the following experiment. The number of vertical counts in a coincidence circuit was observed, first at a high altitude and then at a low. The difference in the readings might be expected to be due to the absorption in the intervening mass of air. Another reading was now taken at the original high altitude with an additional dense absorber just equivalent in mass to the intervening attenuated air, placed above the counter. It might be expected that this added absorber would reduce the intensity to the same value first observed at the low altitude. Actually this was found by Rossi to be not the case. The condensed absorber produced a much smaller reduction in the reading than did the same mass of attenuated air. This was interpreted as indicating that the mesons in traveling the distance in the air were reduced in intensity by absorption but also by their death or conversion into other types of radiation.

Later measurements have shown that in the presence of interacting nuclei, the half-life of negative mu mesons is shorter than that for the positive meson.[11] By an arrangement as shown in Figure 10.4, downcoming mesons of either sign may be focused upon the absorber, which may be any element whose stopping power is to be studied. A, B, C, and D are trays of Geiger-Müller counters which are connected in the order, $A +$

[9] E. Martinelli, *Bull. Am. Phys. Soc.*, **24**, E7 (1949); R. Lattes and R. Christy, *Phys. Rev.*, **75**, 1459 (1949).

[10] B. Rossi and N. Neherson, *Phys. Rev.*, **62**, 417 (1942); P. Blackett, *Nature*, **142**, 992 (1938).

[11] M. Conversi, E. Pancini, and O. Piccioni, *Phys. Rev.*, **71**, 209 (1947); H. Ticho, *Phys. Rev.*, **71**, 463 (1947); **74**, 1337 (1948).

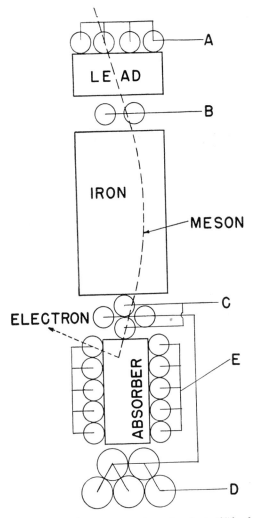

Fɪɢ. 10.4. Arrangement of apparatus to determine the half-life of mu mesons.

$B + C - D.$ This means that a penetrating particle which passes through A, B, and C but does not arrive at D must have terminated in the absorber and probably given rise to an electron. The electron in escaping might trigger the counter array E, but if some time elapses between the meson being slowed to rest and its release of the electron then a delay circuit can measure this time.

It is noted that when positive mesons are employed, a half-life time of 1.5 microseconds is observed regardless of the material of the absorber, as shown in Figure 10.5. With negative mesons, however, the decay time is dependent upon the material of the absorber. It may be noted that half-lives rather than mean-lives are shown in Figure 10.5.

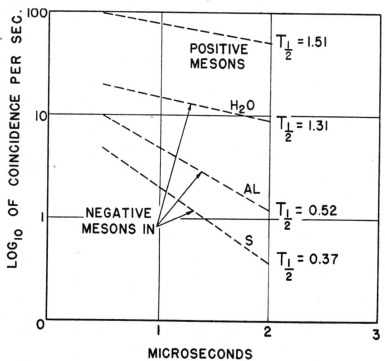

FIG. 10.5. Logarithmic decay of positive and negative mu mesons in various materials.

This phenomenon is rationally explained by considering the interaction between the negative meson and the heavy nucleus as a capture process, much like the "K"-electron capture observed with positron emission. The heavier the nucleus, the greater is the speed of the capture process.

10.6. Energy Loss of High-energy Electrons and Mesons. When an energetic charged particle passes through matter it loses energy by two processes. These are, namely:

(*a*) Collision with the orbital electrons of the atoms through which it passes. These electrons may be ejected from the atoms or they may be lifted to levels so as to leave the atoms in excited states.

(*b*) Interaction with the strong field surrounding the atomic nucleus, resulting in large accelerations, and consequent radiation losses. These photons radiated may produce high-energy secondary electrons.

The energy loss by collision for an electron, decreases [12] rapidly to a minimum at about 1 Mev and then rises slowly as its energy is steadily increased. For a meson, minimum ionization occurs at about 10^8 electron volts. For different elements the energy loss per centimeter of path by collision is proportional to the number of electrons per cubic centimeter.

The radiation loss in different elements increases with the square of the atomic number. In lead, above 10 Mev, and in water above 1 Bev, electrons lose energy mainly by radiation loss. Mesons lose energy mainly by this process at energies greater than 500 Bev.

The energy loss per centimeter of path in any material, for high-energy electrons, by each of the two processes, as computed by Heitler, follows:

(*a*) By radiation

$$\frac{dW}{dx} = \frac{NZ^2}{137} \left(\frac{e^2}{mc^2}\right)^2 W \left(4 \log \frac{183}{Z^{1/3}} + \frac{2}{9}\right)$$

[12] W. Heitler, *Quantum Theory of Radiation*, Oxford Press (1936).

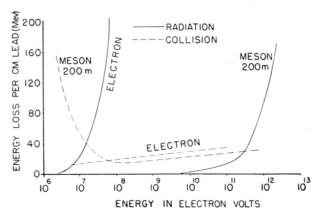

FIG. 10.6. Energy loss per centimeter of lead for mesons and electrons at high energies

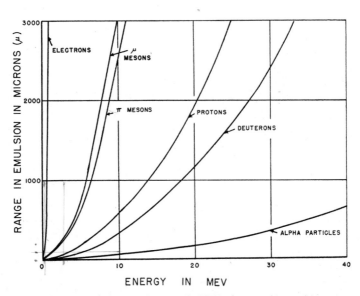

FIG. 10.7. The range of mu and pi mesons in NTB photographic emulsions compared with the ranges of other particles.

(b) By collision

$$\frac{dW}{dx} = \phi_0 \frac{NZ}{\beta^2} \left[\log \frac{(W - \mu)W^2\beta^2}{2\mu I^2 Z^2} + \frac{\mu^2}{W^2} \right]$$

where μ is the rest energy of the electron $= m_0c^2 = 0.51$ Mev.
    W is the energy of the electron in terms of m_0c^2 or μ.
    I is the average ionization energy per pair, usually about
        35 electron volts.

    ϕ_0 is defined as unit cross section $= \dfrac{8\pi}{3} \left(\dfrac{e^2}{mc^2} \right)^2 = 6.57$

        $\times 10^{-25}$ square centimeter.
    N is the number of electrons per cubic centimeter.
    Z is the atomic number.

These losses at different energies are shown in Figure 10.6.
It should be noted that the energy is plotted logarithmically
as abscissas. The ordinate indicates the loss in energy in Mev
per centimeter of lead traversed. This shows that for mesons
of energy less than 10 Bev, energy is lost solely by collision.

QUESTIONS AND PROBLEMS

1. A 10-Mev alpha particle suffers a head-on collision with an electron at rest. Prove that the velocity of the "knock-on" electron cannot be greater than twice the velocity of the alpha particle. Express
the energy of the electron, (a) if its change in mass is neglected, and
(b) giving consideration to the relativity mass.
    Answer: (a) 5.47 kev, (b) 5.53 kev.
2. Prove that a pi meson at rest gives rise to a mu meson whose
energy is 4.05 Mev, and a neutrino whose mass is 58.5 times the rest
mass of an electron.
3. A pi meson whose energy is 6 Mev converts into a mu meson and
a neutrino (assume zero rest mass). Compute the energy of the mu
meson if the neutrino has the exact forward direction of the incident particle.
    Answer: 23.2 kev.
4. A primary proton whose energy is 900 Mev produces on collision with a bromine nucleus in a photographic emulsion a star with

$\pi + 6 \, Mev \geq \mu$

36 prongs. Assuming the tracks to be protons, (*a*) express the approximate average energy, and (*b*) the average range of the charged particles emitted.

Answer: (*a*) 2.5 Mev, (*b*) ~40 microns.

5. At what energy would the specific ionization along the track of a pi meson be indistinguishable from the track (*a*) of a 10-Mev mu meson, and (*b*) of a 100-Mev mu meson?

Answer: (*a*) 13.3 Mev, (*b*) 133 Mev.

6. (*a*) Compare the specific ionization along the paths of a 10-Mev electron, a 10-Mev mu meson, and a 10-Mev alpha particle all under identical conditions, assuming Z^2 dependence. (*b*) Do the same at 100 Mev.

Answer: (*a*) 1, 2.5, 55.6.
        (*b*) 1, 1.18, 17.8.

7. Compare the radii of curvature of the above paths in a perpendicular field of 4000 gausses.

Answer: (*a*) 8.8 cm, 39.9 cm, 114 cm.
        (*b*) 84 cm, 149 cm, 363 cm.

8. Show that on the decay of a mu meson at rest the maximum energy of the created electron is about 53 Mev.

Handwritten annotations:

1,2,3, 8   Conserv mom, mass, Energy

Convasion factor

(charge)^2 H_e = charge 2 ; Z^2 = 4

$p = 183$ electronic m.u. = 931 Mev

~ 2:1

pion mass 283

muon " 215

#8

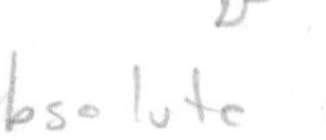

Use Absolute units

Mom   Eh

$\sqrt{2mE}$ E

$\dfrac{h\nu}{c}$ $h\nu$

CHAPTER 11

COSMIC RADIATION

11.1. Historical. In studying radioactivity by electroscopes it was noticed that with no emitting source present, any charged electroscope would always exhibit a residual rate of discharge. This phenomenon was first studied by Rutherford and Cooke,[1] who found that with all radioactive sources carefully removed, about 10 ions per cubic centimeter per second were continuously formed in a brass vessel filled with air. By completely shielding the electroscope with many layers of iron and lead the production of ions was reduced by about 40%. They therefore concluded that some very penetrating radiation was arriving continuously from outside, which excited a secondary activity in the room. It is now known that the cosmic radiation alone produces at sea level only about 1.8 ion pairs per cubic centimeter per second in air under standard conditions.

In a balloon flight from Zurich in 1909, Gockel[2] noted the rate of discharge of a Wulf electroscope at several different altitudes up to a height of 4500 meters. The rate of discharge seemed to vary erratically from about 60% of normal rate up to three times that value with no general proportionality with altitude. It was generally assumed at that time that the penetrating radiation observed by Rutherford really came from the earth. To test this assumption more carefully, Hess[3] in 1911 made a balloon flight to 1070 meters and later to greater heights

---

[1] E. Rutherford and H. L. Cooke, *Phys. Rev.*, **16**, 183 (1903).
[2] A. Gockel, *Physik. Z.*, **11**, 280 (1910).
[3] V. Hess, *Akad. Wiss. Wien*, **120**, 1575 (1911); **122**, 1053 (1913); W. Kolhorster, *Physik. Z.*, **14**, 1153 (1913).

with free balloons. He found no diminution, but rather an increase in the penetrating radiation at greater altitudes. He therefore was convinced that the radiation was coming to the earth from interstellar space.

In 1913, simultaneous observations were made over a period of several weeks on the penetrating radiation at five different laboratories widely dispersed throughout Europe. No concordance appeared in the observed variations of intensity at the several stations.[4]

11.2. Nature of Cosmic Rays. From the fact that cosmic radiation was able to penetrate the entire atmosphere it was generally taken for granted that it consisted solely of energetic gamma rays. This view was supported by an absorption experiment conducted by Millikan in 1928.[5] In noting the absorption of the radiation in water, as the thickness of the water was increased, a complex absorption was observed. On analyzing the data, absorption coefficients of 0.35, 0.08, 0.04, and possibly 0.019 per meter of water were thought to represent satisfactorily the observed results. By extrapolating the well-established relationship between X-ray wavelength and absorption coefficient, Millikan concluded that these observed coefficients represented the radiation that would be emitted in the process of the building of the four most common elements of the universe, namely, helium, oxygen, silicon, and iron, from hydrogen. This interpretation was of course meaningless with the discovery of pair formation with its resulting increased absorption for higher-energy gamma radiation.

Studies on the variation of the intensity with latitude and with altitude, as well as the east-west asymmetry made it seem certain [6,7] that the primary cosmic radiation consists largely of high-energy protons.

[4] H. Benndorf, C. Dorno, V. Hess, E. v. Schweidler, and T. Wulf, *Physik. Z.*, **14**, 1141 (1913).

[5] R. A. Millikan, *Phys. Rev.*, **32**, 533 (1928).

[6] W. Heitler and H. Peng, *Proc. Roy. Irish Acad.*, **49**, 101 (1943); *Phys. Rev.*, **64**, 78 (1943); J. Hamilton and H. Peng, *Proc. Roy. Irish Acad.*, **49**, 197 (1944).

[7] O. Wollan, M. Schein, and W. Jesse, *Phys. Rev.*, **59**, 930 (1941).

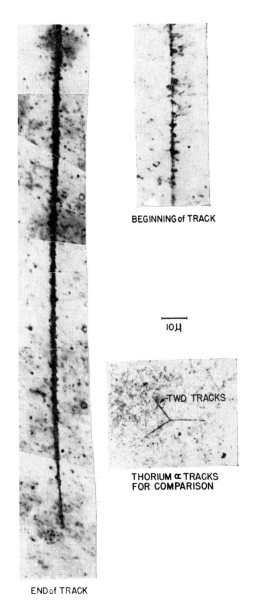

BEGINNING of TRACK

10 μ

TWO TRACKS

THORIUM α TRACKS
FOR COMPARISON

END of TRACK

FIG. 11.1 Primary cosmic particle of large atomic mass. Narrowing at end may be due to electron capture, thus reducing its electric charge (Bradt, Freier, Lofgren, Ney, Oppenheimer, and Peters).

It has been established [8] that other heavy particles with atomic numbers up to 40 are also present in primary cosmic radiation.   Figure 11.1 is an emulsion track of one of these heavy particles taken at an altitude of 90,000 feet at which altitude the atmospheric pressure is only about 10 millimeters of Hg.   The relative abundance of certain elements in the universe as spectroscopically determined is compared with the relative abundance of the same items in primary cosmic radiation, in Table 11.1.   Any satisfactory theory of the origin of cosmic rays must account for this close correlation in composition.

TABLE 11.1.   RELATIVE ABUNDANCE OF CERTAIN ELEMENTS IN THE UNIVERSE AND IN COSMIC RADIATION

Z	Element	Universe	Cosmic Radiation
1	Hydrogen	100,000	100,000
2	Helium	10,000	10,000
8	Oxygen	63	
7	Nitrogen	46	520
6	Carbon	23	
10	Neon	5	30
26	Iron	5	30
14	Silicon	2.9	40
12	Magnesium	2.5	30
30	All others	2.7	30
30	All others	0.005	1

In examining cosmic radiation near the earth's surface, two components appear to be present.   One is a very penetrating or hard component, while another portion is stopped by a few centimeters of lead.   The total atmosphere is equivalent in its absorbing power to about 100 centimeters of lead or 10 meters of water.   It must be, therefore, that the softer component is

[8] G. Freier, E. Lofgren, E. Ney, and F. Oppenheimer, *Phys. Rev.*, **75**, 340, 1451 (1949); H. Bradt and B. Peters, *Phys. Rev.*, **76**, 156 (1949); *Progress in Cosmic Ray Physics*, Interscience Publishers, New York (1952).

created continuously at successive depths in the atmosphere by conversion of the penetrating radiation. The softer component probably consists of charged heavy particles of low energy, electrons, or gamma rays. The hard component consists of the remaining primary energetic heavy particles, pi mesons, mu mesons, and neutrons. The detectors generally employed are relatively insensitive to neutrons.

11.3. The Earth as a Magnetic Spectrometer; The East-West Effect.

Although the atmosphere extends, at most, but a few hundred miles upward, the magnetic field is appreciable up to a distance of 10,000 miles. At 400 miles, the magnetic field intensity is about one eighth that at the surface. It is obvious that a charged particle approaching the earth at its magnetic equator, moving at right angles to the magnetic field, will experience a force at right angles to its velocity and hence may be bent around and away from the earth. This is illustrated by Figure 11.2, in which the observer is looking geographically north along the magnetic axis of the earth. The magnetic field outside the earth is directed into the page and hence any approaching positively charged particles will, by the motor rule, be bent as shown.

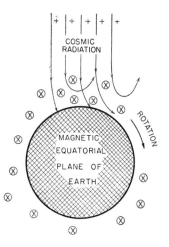

Fig. 11.2. Showing deflection of incident positively charged particles by the magnetic field of the earth, looking north along the magnetic axis.

Since the earth rotates so as to carry an observer toward the east it is apparent that positive particles will be deflected so as to approach any observer more from the west than from the east. Negatively charged particles would of course act oppositely.

An analysis of the motion of charged particles approaching the earth in the field of the magnetic dipole was made by

Stormer.[9] Figure 11.3 shows the minimum energy that particles may have and yet reach the earth at various latitudes.
Curve A is for particles arriving along the most favorable direction, curve B is for particles arriving at the zenith, and curve
C is for particles along the most difficult direction. Only those
particles can possibly reach sea level, at the magnetic equator in

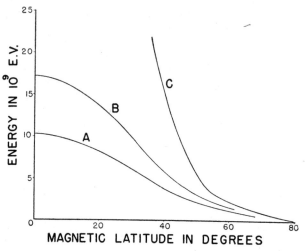

Fig. 11.3.   The minimum energy of charged particles able to reach the earth.

a vertical direction, that have energies greater than a certain
minimum energy of about 17 Bev. Lemaitre and Vallarta [10]
showed that for energies greater than this minimum, access is
possible only for particles within a cone with complicated
boundaries.

By using a system of two or more Geiger tubes arranged in a
line and connected in a coincidence circuit so as to record an
impulse only when the same ionizing particle passes all tubes,
an effective cosmic-ray telescope results. With an arrangment
of this sort the intensities of radiation from the east and from
the west at various latitudes and altitudes have been recorded.

[9] C. Stormer, *Terr. Mag. and Atm. Elec.*, **37**, 375 (1932).
[10] G. Lemaitre, M. Vallarta, and L. Bouckaert, *Phys. Rev.*, **47**, 434 (1935).

An early measurement was made by Johnson [11] at Cerro de Pasco, Peru, situated on the magnetic equator at an altitude of 4300 meters. He reported an asymmetry with a preponderance from the west, varying with the zenith angle, from 8% at 15 degrees with the vertical, up to 17% at a 60-degree zenith angle. Numerous subsequent observations [12] at various altitudes and latitudes have been made both with and without absorbing materials so as to observe the effect for the hard component alone and for the total cosmic radiation.

Perhaps the most complete results are those taken [13] on a continuous flight in a B-29 plane to Peru at an altitude of 30,000 feet. Observations were made at various zenith angles using no absorber and then 10 centimeters and 20 centimeters of lead in front of each counter. With no absorber, and zero zenith angle, at an altitude of 32,000 feet (3.1 meters of water) the normal counting rate was about 500 counts per minute. As the zenith angle was increased, the excess from the west over the east became as large as 30%. These results are presented in Figure 11.4. Values are shown for no absorber and for 10 centimeters of lead, thus observing the total radiation and the hard component after filtering. From these and other, previously reported, results it may be concluded that (*a*) the west excess in the total radiation at high altitudes is approximately the same as for the penetrating component alone, (*b*) the asymmetry increases with altitude and with the zenith angle, and (*c*) only one kind of incident primary particle, positive in sign, is necessary to account for the penetrating and the soft components of cosmic radiation at the equator.

11.4. The Latitude Effect. If cosmic radiation consists of charged particles, then a variation in intensity with latitude must be expected. Many particles that would otherwise reach

[11] T. H. Johnson, *Phys. Rev.*, **48**, 287 (1935); *Rev. Mod. Phys.*, **10**, 194 (1938).
[12] L. Janossy and P. Nicholson, *Proc. Roy. Soc. (London)*, **192**, 99 (1947); M. Schein, V. Yngre, and H. Kraybill, *Phys. Rev.*, **73**, 928 (1948); W. C. Barber, *Phys. Rev.*, **75**, 590 (1949); G. Groetzinger and G. McClure, *Phys. Rev.*, **75**, 349 (1949); A. Biehl, R. Montgomery, V. Neher, W. Pickering, and W. Roesch, *Rev. Mod. Phys.*, **20**, 353 (1948).
[13] A. T. Biehl, V. Neher, and W. Roesch, *Phys. Rev.*, **75**, 688 (1949).

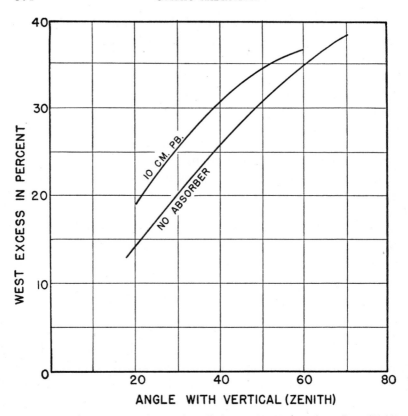

Fig. 11.4. The asymmetry in cosmic radiation at 30,000 feet above Peru (Biehl, Neher, and Roesch).

the earth will be deflected away by the magnetic field. Early measurements by Clay [14] on voyages between Holland and Batavia through the Suez Canal indicated a decrease in the sea-level ionization, due to cosmic radiation, of from 10 to 20% in equatorial latitudes. Other measurements made by Neher [15] on trips from Pasadena (34° N.) to Mollendo (17° S.) failed to observe any deviations in the sea-level ionization greater than

[14] J. Clay, *Proc. Roy. Acad.*, Amsterdam, **30**, 1115 (1927); *Naturwissenschaften,* **37**, 687 (1932).
[15] R. A. Millikan and H. V. Neher, *Phys. Rev.*, **43**, 661 (1933).

the uncertainties in the measurement of from 6 to 7%. Later, more accurate measurements revealed a definite diminution in intensity in equatorial latitudes.[16] A rather complete survey of this effect from magnetic latitudes 59° N. to 45° S., has been made by Compton and co-workers.[17] These data averaged for four trips from Vancouver to Auckland are shown in Figure 11.5. It is apparent that the intensity at the equator falls to

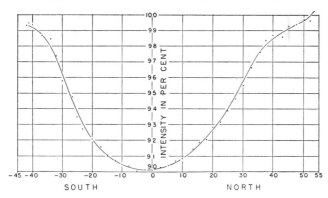

FIG. 11.5. The variation in the intensity of cosmic radiation with magnetic latitude.

about 90% of that at the terminal latitudes. For latitudes greater than 40 degrees only a slight change occurs. There is in effect a polar cap including all areas at a latitude greater than about 45 degrees, in which the intensity is essentially constant.

On several B-29 flights at 33,000 feet, along the meridian 117° W., the total vertical component of cosmic radiation was found [18] to be constant at all latitudes greater than 51° N. In going southward a rather abrupt decrease of from 5 to 6% intensity occurred between latitudes 51° N. and 46° N. For the next few degrees southward the intensity appeared to be constant and then around 41° N. another break of about 5% occurred. A similar investigation [19] by the Bartol Laboratory

[16] I. Bowen, R. A. Millikan, and V. Neher, *Phys. Rev.*, **44**, 246 (1933).
[17] A. Compton and R. Turner, *Phys. Rev.*, **52**, 799 (1937).
[18] A. Biehl, H. V. Neher, and W. Roesch, *Phys. Rev.*, **75**, 1457 (1949).
[19] W. Swann, P. Morris, and D. Seymour, *Phys. Rev.*, **75**, 1317 (1949).

scientists confirmed a break in intensity of about 10%, for a change in latitude of about 10 degrees at an altitude above 30,000 feet. On corresponding flights below 25,000 feet no such abrupt variation was observed. The phenomenon is explained in terms of the variation of meson production with altitude.

11.5. The Altitude Effect. The variation in intensity of cosmic radiation with altitude is different at different latitudes. It

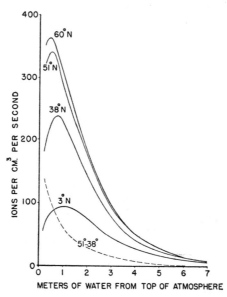

FIG. 11.6. The intensity of cosmic radiation as a function of altitude at four different latitudes.

has been quite fully investigated[20] with small unmanned balloons carrying recording ionization electrometers.

The type of curve obtained[21] by plotting the total cosmic-ray intensity as a function of the altitude expressed in terms of meters of water below the top, is shown in any one of the solid curves in Figure 11.6. Each curve is taken at a different lati-

---

[20] R. Millikan and V. Neher, *Phys. Rev.*, **50**, 15 (1936).
[21] I. Bowen, R. A. Millikan, and V. Neher, *Phys. Rev.*, **53**, 219 (1938).

tude as designated. It is apparent that a maximum occurs at a level about 0.6 meter of water below the top of the atmosphere. The position of the maximum indicates that the exceedingly energetic primary particles react with the outer layer of the attenuated atmosphere producing secondaries. This progressively increases the total number of ionizing particles traveling downward in spite of absorption until an equilibrium state is reached. From the maximum point downward the intensity decreases almost exponentially.

On forming the difference of any two of the curves in Figure 11.6 it is possible to note the absorption for those particles having an energy lying between the minimum possible energies able to reach the earth at the two respective latitudes. Thus for the curves at latitudes 51° N. and 38° N., the corresponding minimum normal energies are 3.5×10^9 and 6.7×10^9 electron volts. The difference curve therefore shows the absorption of particles in this energy band, whose effective value is about 5 Bev.

Millikan and Cameron [22] had studied the absorption of the penetrating radiation in water by lowering an electroscope to various depths below the surface at Muir Lake (alt. 11,800 feet) and at Arrowhead Lake (alt. 5100 feet). At the same depth, the ionization in Muir Lake was greater than in Arrowhead by an amount corresponding to 6 feet of water. This is just the water equivalent of the 6700 feet of air between the two elevations.

Studies have been made of the radiation at considerable depths below sea level. The intensity appears [23] to fall off in a uniform manner with the absorber thickness. At the greatest depth where such studies were made, namely in the Shimizu tunnel, at 3000 meters of water equivalent or 30,000 gm cm^{-2} the intensity is approximately 1/100,000 that at sea level. At

[22] R. Millikan and G. Cameron, *Phys. Rev.*, **28**, 851 (1926).
[23] See P. Barrett, L. Bollinger, G. Cocconi, Y. Eisenberg, and K. Greisen, *Rev. Mod. Phys.*, **24**, 133 (1952).

80,000 gm cm^{-2} in deep salt mines the intensity is [24] about 1/3000 of that at the surface.

The decrease in intensity with thickness of absorber for the ten billion electron volt band of particles, as shown by the difference in the curves at 3° N. and 38° N. in Figure 11.6, indicated a coefficient of absorption of 0.54 per meter of water.[25]

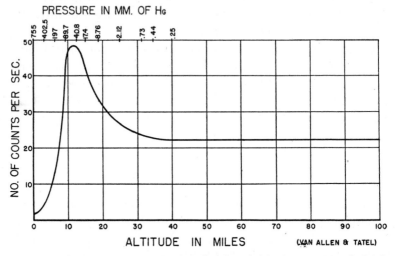

FIG. 11.7. Total cosmic-ray activity as a function of altitude up to 100-mile height in V-2 rocket.

This means that 1.28 meters of water reduce the intensity to half its initial value. A computation of this value based on the Bethe-Heitler theory has been carried out by many investigators.[26] When only pair production by photons and the energy loss of electrons by radiation is considered, the absorption coefficient predicted is much greater than that experimentally observed.

[24] C. A. Randall and W. E. Hazen, *Phys. Rev.*, **81**, 144 (1951).
[25] R. A. Millikan, *Cosmic Rays*, p. 99, Macmillan (1939).
[26] J. Carlson and J. R. Oppenheimer, *Phys. Rev.*, **51**, 220 (1937); H. Bhabha, *Proc. Roy. Soc. A*, **166**, 257 (1938); W. Heitler, *Proc. Roy. Soc. A*, **166**, 529 (1938); R. Serber, *Phys. Rev.*, **54**, 317 (1938).

Sensitive G-M tubes have been placed in the extreme nose of several V-2 rockets, and records made of the over-all cosmic-ray intensity up to the highest altitude. Data obtained [27] on one of these flights at a latitude of 43° N. are portrayed in Figure 11.7. A maximum counting rate of 49 counts per second, almost 25 times that at sea level, occurs at an altitude of about 12 miles (60 gm cm^{-2}). At altitudes greater than 35 miles (0.6 gm cm^{-2}), the intensity is constant at about 23 counts per second. The apparent incompatibility between the ratios of maximum to sea level in the two curves is probably largely due to the different types of detector employed. In the former using an ionization chamber, energy per cubic centimeter per second is measured, whereas in the latter, using a counter, numbers of particles are recorded without regard to their energy.

The variation in intensity of the hard component with altitude has been the subject of many investigations. An average of several reported [28] values at geomagnetic latitudes near 54 degrees is presented in Figure 11.8. The vertical flux of particles per square centimeter per second per steradian is shown as a function of the altitude expressed in grams per square centimeter. The counters are shielded by eight or more centimeters of lead. In general, observers agree that the hard component shows a monotonic increase from sea level up to the highest altitudes. The projected value for the intensity at zero depth is 0.171 ± 0.005 cm^{-2} sec^{-1} sterad^{-1}. At sea level the intensity is only about one fourteenth the maximum value.

This curve has been analyzed into its constituent parts, namely, that due to primary particles together with secondary nucleons and that due to pi and mu mesons. The latter shows a maximum at about 150 gm cm^{-2}, whereas the former decreases steadily from zero atmospheric depth to sea level. At a

[27] J. A. Van Allen and H. E. Tatel, *Phys. Rev.*, **73**, 245 (1948).
[28] See *Progress in Cosmic Ray Physics*, Interscience Publishers, New York, p. 119 (1953).

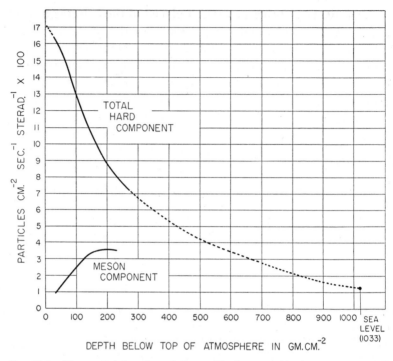

FIG. 11.8. The vertical flux through 8 cm of lead versus altitude at a geomagnetic latitude of 54 degrees.

level of 200 gm cm^{-2} the meson intensity as shown by the dotted curve in Figure 11.8 is about 40% of the total hard component.

11.6. The Longitude Effect. The many observations of the variation of cosmic-ray intensity with latitude were made on as many different oceanic voyages. These various paths crossed the equator at different longitudes and the apparent equatorial intensities showed a considerable range in values. This variation is illustrated by Table 11.2, showing the intensities observed at sea level for various locations. These data may be interpreted as an indication that the earth's magnetic

TABLE 11.2

Position	Longitude	$Ions/cm^3/sec$	Per Cent Diminution
Pasadena.................	117° W	1.75	..
Equator (Singapore)........	105° E	1.53	12
Equator (Center Pac.)......	165° W	1.57	10
Equator (Near S. A.).......	90° E	1.60	8

field even at great heights is not symmetrical but exhibits a definite geographic lopsidedness.

11.7. Cosmic-ray Showers and Bursts. In the use of ionization chambers to observe cosmic-ray intensity, it was noticed that superimposed on the steady ionization current there were occasionally large pulses much beyond any possible random fluctuation. This effect was first reported by Hoffmann and Lindholm.[29] By arranging Geiger counter tubes in a horizontal plane and connecting so as to actuate a coincidence circuit, Rossi showed that at times a coincidence would occur indicating that several high-speed particles were proceeding downward in almost parallel paths as a group. With the counter at a high altitude, increasing thicknesses of some heavy material, such as lead, were placed above the tubes. Up to about 2 centimeters of lead, the number of these coincidence-producing showers increased as shown in Figure 11.9. On further increasing the thickness of lead, the number of showers per second fell off rapidly until for about 8 centimeters an almost-saturation value was reached. For thin layers of various materials above the counters, it was found that the shower production per atom varied approximately as the square of the atomic number Z.

[29] G. Hoffmann and F. Lindholm, *Berlin Beitr.*, **20**, 12 (1928); B. Rossi, *Z. Physik.*, **68**, 64 (1931); *Physik. Z.*, **33**, 304 (1932).

In order to observe more directly the cosmic-ray particles, especially designed vertical Wilson cloud chambers have been devised.[30] By using a very powerful magnetic field up to 24,000 gausses, Anderson and Neddermeyer [31] were able to estimate the energies of electrons up to several billion electron volts. These observations showed that a typical shower was a complicated phenomenon. Some representative photographs are shown in

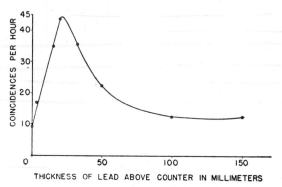

FIG. 11.9.   Increase in shower production by interposing lead above coincidence counters (Rossi).

Figure 11.10.   By putting one or more horizontal layers of metal inside the chamber it is frequently observed that a single incident particle will initiate a great number of forward secondary particles in its passage through one of the plates.[32]   These secondary particles may in turn initiate additional showers on traversing the next metal plate. This phenomenon is shown in Figure 11.10*A*. The primary shower originates in the upper wall of the chamber and numerous additional secondaries arise in the metallic layer. It is estimated that in total the energy of the numerous particles is greater than 20 Bev. Sometimes these showers seem to originate in the metallic plate and no ionizing incident particle is evident. These may accordingly be

[30] P. Blackett and G. Occhialini, *Proc. Roy. Soc.* (*London*), **139**, 699 (1933).
[31] C. Anderson and S. Neddermeyer, *Phys. Rev.*, **45**, 295 (1934); **150**, 263 (1936); see also R. Adams, C. D. Anderson, and E. Cowan, *Rev. Mod. Phys.*, **21**, 72 (1949).
[32] L. Fussell, *Phys. Rev.*, **51**, 1005 (1937).

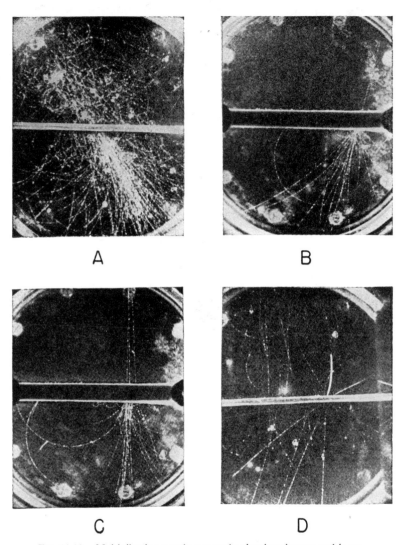

A   B

C   D

Fig. 11.10.   Multiplicative cosmic ray tracks showing showers and burst.

regarded as induced by neutrons or gamma rays arising from a previous encounter of the primary particle. It therefore appears that many showers take place as a cascade process.

In some investigations, coincidences have been observed with counters separated by horizontal distances as great as 75 meters.[33] The total energy in some of the most striking showers yet observed approaches a value of 10^{17} electron volts.

Occasionally an entirely different kind of shower [34,35] is observed in the cloud chamber. This is in the nature of an explosion, in that the particles shoot out in all directions, rather than being confined to the general direction of the incident primary. Such "bursts" are rather rare, as evidenced by the fact that in examining 900 photographs showing showers, only three bursts were noted. The particles ejected in the burst appear to ionize more heavily than electrons and they may be alpha particles, protons, or mesons with either positive or negative charges. Such a phenomenon is shown in Figure 11.10D.

With the development of the photographic-emulsion technique many previously difficult observations may be easily accomplished. For example, the phenomenon of a "burst" or a "star" in the developed emulsion is strikingly evident. Figure 11.11 shows such a many-pronged star obtained from a plate carried to an altitude of 90,000 feet by free balloons. There may be as many as 35 ejected protons or alpha particles in the disruption of a heavy silver or bromine atom of the emulsion, encouraged by the impact of a high-energy primary proton. Both the number of bursts and the number of showers per second appear to increase [36] with altitude at about the same relative rate. This increase is exponential up to a height of about 5 miles beyond which a plateau and then a decrease in the number per second appears.

[33] P. Auger, R. Maze, P. Ehrenfest, and A. Fréon, *J. phys.*, **10**, 39 (1939).
[34] L. Janossy, *Proc. Roy. Soc.*, **179**, 361 (1942).
[35] W. E. Hazen, *Phys. Rev.*, **64**, 257 (1943); **66**, 254 (1944).
[36] C. Montgomery and D. Montgomery, *Phys. Rev.*, **47**, 429 (1935); N. Hilberry, *Phys. Rev.*, **60**, 1 (1941); J. Clay, *Rev. Mod. Phys.*, **2k**, 94 (1949); H. Kraybill, *Phys. Rev.*, **73**, 632 (1948); G. Cocconi, *Rev. Mod. Phys.*, **21**, 26 (1949).

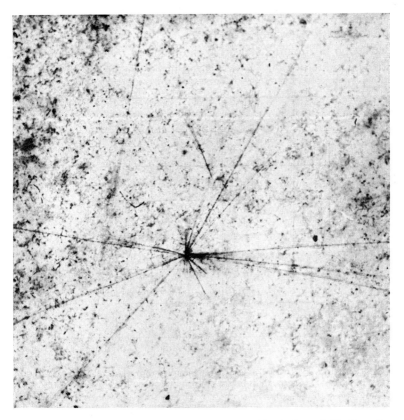

Fig. 11.11. Cosmic-ray star showing over 30 heavy particles in the probable disruption of a silver nucleus at 90,000 feet altitude. (Courtesy of W. A. Nierenberg.)

11.8. Diurnal Variation of Cosmic Radiation. By noting carefully the ionization at any station, successively, with the lapse of time, it has been well established [37,38] that a regular variation in the intensity of the cosmic radiation occurs through the hours of the day. The magnitude of the variation is about 0.3% with the maximum occurring at about 1:30 P.M. It has been

[37] R. L. Doan, *Phys. Rev.*, **49**, 107 (1936); R. Whaley and V. Long, *Phys. Rev.*, **75**, 341 (1949).
[38] J. L. Thompson, *Phys. Rev.*, **52**, 141 (1937).

suggested that this change may be due to a systematic shifting of the earth's magnetic field. A curve showing the averaged variation of the intensity with the hours of the day as observed at a latitude of 20° N. is presented in Figure 11.12.

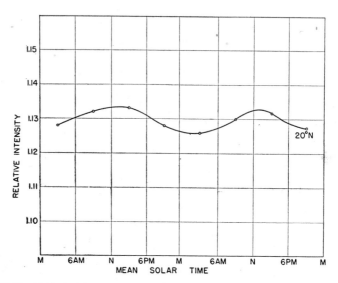

FIG. 11.12. Typical variation of cosmic ray intensity throughout the day (Thompson).

Attempts have been made [39] to correlate the variation in cosmic-ray intensity and the rate of burst formation, to the observed variations in sun-spot activity and the terrestrial magnetic field.

The possibility that beams of electrified particles might be reaching the earth from the sun was suspected a century ago. Following a brilliant eruption or "flare" on the sun's surface violent fluctuations were noted in the earth's magnetic field. This was usually followed a day or two later by strong aurora displays in the northern and southern polar regions. Modern spectroscopic studies show by the Doppler shift that hydrogen

[39] J. Broxon, *Phys. Rev.*, **72**, 1187 (1947).

atoms are moving through the upper atmosphere toward the spectrometer at great speeds during an aurora.

11.9. Neutrons in Cosmic Rays. By sending boron-trifluoride counters to various altitudes the intensity of slow neutrons in the atmosphere has been investigated.[40] The neutron intensity seems to increase with altitude in about the same way as the penetrating component of the extensive showers. The neutrons are probably the result of nuclear disruptions initiated by energetic particles on nuclei. Many experiments dealing with the capture of mu mesons in matter have been carried out to obtain a value for the neutron multiplicity. This is defined as the average number of neutrons emitted per mu meson absorbed. In lead the averaged results are about 1.8 ± 0.2 neutrons per mu meson. In lighter elements, such as magnesium and calcium, the multiplicity is only about one fifth as large as in lead. Nitrogen 14 has a large cross section for neutron capture, namely, about 10 barns. If a proton is emitted in the reaction, radioactive carbon 14 is formed.

11.10. Cosmic-ray Particles and Reactions. It seems reasonably well established that the primary particles are mainly protons, together with smaller numbers of other heavier positively charged particles, for which the atomic number might be as high as 40. The heavy particles of great energy are stripped of most of their orbital electrons and are thus multiply charged. They will accordingly produce exceptionally broad tracks because the ionization along their path is proportional to the square of the electric charge. As the particle slows up, the specific ionization will increase, giving a still broader track, as shown in Figure 11.1. Finally, however, the heavy particle will begin to recapture electrons and the track width will accordingly become narrower. Nucleons may be emitted from disruptions of the heavy particles and they may initiate cosmic showers.

---

[40] S. A. Korff, *Rev. Mod. Phys.*, **11**, 211 (1939); S. Korff and B. Hamermesh, *Phys. Rev.*, **69**, 155 (1946); V. Tongiorgi, *Phys. Rev.*, **74**, 226 (1948).

On colliding with atmospheric nuclei the primary protons may initiate a great variety of reactions, many of which at the present time are only reasonable conjectures. Many of the processes imagined to occur are shown schematically in Figure

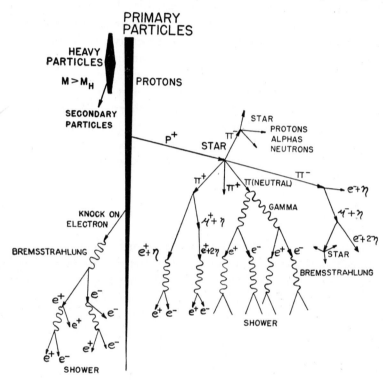

FIG. 11.13. Some probable transformations associated with cosmic radiation.

11.13. It seems reasonably certain that some protons on disruption give rise to pi mesons, forming a star. The pi mesons may be positive, negative, or neutral in electric sign. The positive and negative pi mesons each convert into mu mesons of the same sign, plus neutrinos. The neutral pi meson may convert into an electron pair, plus gamma radiation, or gamma radiation alone.

The mu meson transforms into an electron of the same sign plus two neutrinos. This process for a large number of particles is much like beta emission and may be treated theoretically in a similar manner. The distribution of energy, measured in 10 Mev intervals, for some 75 electrons derived from mesons as obtained [41] from about 15,000 cloud chamber photographs is shown in Figure 11.14. The upper limit is about 57 Mev which

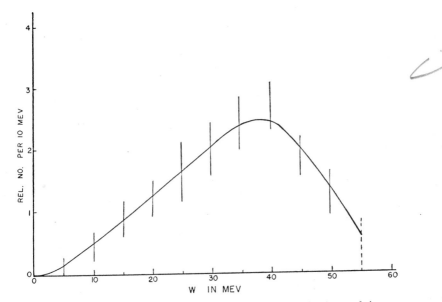

Fig. 11.14. The energy distribution of electrons derived from the decay of the mu meson.

is by conservation laws slightly larger than expected if the mesons were at rest with the mass of 206.6 M_e. The shape of the curve is regarded as evidence favoring the emission of not one, but two neutrinos in the decay.

The electrons on being slowed lose some of their energy as electromagnetic radiation known as "bremsstrahlung." This bremsstrahlung radiation may give rise to positron-electron

[41] R. B. Leighton, C. D. Anderson, and A. J. Seriff, *Phys. Rev.*, **75**, 432 (1949).

pairs which in turn reradiate electromagnetically and then produce additional electrons resulting in an electron avalanche or shower.

Some of the protons will by impact give energy to electrons, driving them forward as "knock-on" electrons. These may also induce an electron multiplication by the bremsstrahlung mechanism and hence produce showers. Some proton-induced nuclear disruptions will produce other protons of lesser energy together with neutrons and alpha particles.

Negative mesons may produce small pronged stars indicating a relatively small number of emergent nucleons. The negative mu meson may react with a proton to produce a neutron and a neutral meson. These and perhaps other reactions combine to give to cosmic radiation its apparent complicated structure and its variation with altitude and latitude.

11.11. Other Quantum Numbers. In the production, interaction, and decay of heavy particles, a quantum number, S, called "strangeness" has been proposed.[42] For L mesons it is zero, but for K mesons or hyperons it may be $+1$ or -1. For the heavy Ξ hyperon it has a value of -2. Only those transformations are probable in which the total S value is conserved. If in the decay there is a change in S, of, ±1, then the process will be relatively slow.

In the classification of the fundamental particles and their interactions another treatment [43] suggests in the selection rules an integral quantum number, a, called the attribute. This is assigned a definite value for each particle and is assumed to be additive when particles combine. Transitions in which $\Delta a = 0$ are very fast. If $\Delta a = \pm1$, the reaction is relatively slow. In addition to the usual conservation laws it is customary to assume that a heavy particle, such as a nucleon or a hyperon, can be destroyed only by annihilation against a similar antiparticle.

No examples have been found of hyperon production in which

[42] M. Gell-Mann, *Phys. Rev.*, **92**, 833 (1953); M. Gell-Mann and A. Pais, *Phys. Rev.*, **97**, 1387 (1955).
[43] R. G. Sachs, *Phys. Rev.*, **99**, 1573 (1955).

the whole mass has been created from kinetic energy. A nucleon appears to be necessary. Similarly the whole mass cannot be transformed into kinetic energy or into the rest mass of particles lighter than nucleons. This suggests that hyperons and nucleons form a class, now known as "baryons." A conservation rule then requires that in any interaction the baryon number must be conserved.

11.12. Nomograph Relating Momentum, Ionization, and Mass of Energetic Particles. It is frequently advantageous to relate graphically the various quantities pertaining to the high-

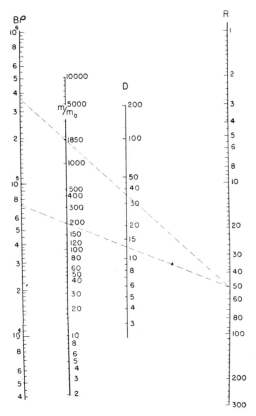

FIG. 11.15. Nomograph relating range R, ratio of ions per cm to minimum specific ionization, D, ratio of mass m to rest mass m_o, and relative momentum $B\rho$.

speed particles. Such a nomographic relationship as devised [44] by Corson and Brode and extended by D. J. Hughes is shown in Figure 11.15. The quantities represented are the range in normal air, R; the ionization expressed as a multiple of the minimum ionization per centimeter, D; the ratio of the mass m to the rest mass of the electron, m_0, and the momentum as expressed by the product of the magnetic induction, B, and the radius of the track, ρ, as observed in a Wilson cloud chamber. The dotted lines shown represent the characteristics of a proton and of a meson when the range of each is the same. It is thus possible to determine the nature of the particles and their energies uniquely when sufficient information on their ionization and their deflection is available. The nomograph as presented represents the behavior of singly charged particles. For alpha particles it is still suitable provided the $B\rho$, D, and R scales be multiplied by the simple factors $\frac{1}{2}$, 4, and $\frac{1}{4}$, respectively.

QUESTIONS AND PROBLEMS

1. A 10-billion-volt electron describes a circular track in a cloud chamber where the uniform flux density is 20,000 gausses. What is the radius of the path? What would be the radius of the track for a proton whose energy is 10,000 Mev?

Answer: 1666 cm, 1820 cm.

2. At an altitude of 29,000 ft the pressure is 3.3 meters of water. Assuming an absorption coefficient of 0.55 per meter of water and a sea-level intensity of 1.9 ions per cm^3 per sec, what is the activity at the altitude mentioned?

Answer: 89 ions/cm^3/sec.

3. The sensitivity of a certain electrometer is 0.1 volt per scale division. Its capacity is 1 electrostatic unit and the active volume of the chamber is 50 cm^3. In what time will the residual cosmic ionization cause a discharge of 10 divisions at sea level and 45° N. latitude?

Answer: 21.5 hr.

4. The solar constant at the earth is 0.135 joule per cm^2 per sec. Approximately how does this compare with the total energy received per cm^2 per sec due to cosmic radiation, at a latitude of 51° N., ob-

[44] D. R. Corson and R. Brode, *Phys. Rev.*, **53**, 773 (1938).

tained by reference to Figure 11.6, assuming 35 electron volts per ion pair?

Answer: Solar/cosmic $= 3.9 \times 10^8$.

5. The net positive charge of a star is 10^{12} coulombs. Its radius is 10^{11} cm. Neglecting gravitational effects, how much energy must be expended to bring a proton to the star?

Answer: 14.4 ergs or 9×10^6 Mev.

6. Express the intensity of cosmic radiation at sea level, 40° N. latitude, in roentgen units per day.

Answer: 7.9×10^{-5} r/day.

7. Calculate the maximum energy of an electron derived from the decay of a mu meson at rest, assuming two neutrinos to accompany the disintegration.

Answer: ~55 Mev.

#4 picture on p. 306
    area under 51°N = 2.25 Bev's/cm² sec.

1, 3, 5 electricity

CHAPTER 12

NUCLEAR FISSION

12.1. Historical: The Transuranic Elements. In his systematic survey of the elements to detect their sensitivity to neutron capture, Fermi [1] observed in uranium several new radioactivities whose half-lives were reported as 10 seconds, 40 seconds, 13 minutes, and 40 minutes. On decay these uranium activities emitted beta particles; therefore the product nuclei must have an atomic number of 93, that is, one greater than uranium, which had been regarded as the heaviest element. The question might well be asked, what becomes of these created atoms of the new element and what are its properties? From the periodic table the element of atomic number 93 should have chemical properties similar to manganese and hence might be separated from the parent element uranium. On making a rapid separation of manganese from the uranium, a beta-active precipitate was obtained. Similarly, on taking from the bombarded uranium, separations of iron, rhodium, or palladium, all were found to be radioactive.[2] The chemistry of these latter elements might have been expected from the vertical columns of the periodic table to be very similar to the elements whose atomic numbers are 94, 95, and 96. Fermi thus concluded that transuranic elements were being created from the uranium by the action of the slow neutrons.

These experiments with slow neutrons were repeated in other laboratories particularly in Berlin, by O. Hahn, L. Meitner, and F. Strassmann [3] and in Paris by I. Curie-Joliot and L. Savitch.

[1] E. Fermi, *Nature*, **133**, 898 (1934).
[2] E. Amaldi, O. D'Agostino, E. Fermi, B. Pontecorvo, F. Rassetti, and E. Segré, *Proc. Roy. Soc. A*, **149**, 522 (1935).
[3] O. Hahn, L. Meitner, and F. Strassmann, *Z. Physik*, **106**, 249 (1937).

On making more detailed examination of the chemical separations from bombarded uranium, Hahn in 1938 found an activity in a barium precipitate,[4] and I. Curie found similarly an activity in a lanthanum separation.[5] Classically the chemistry of none of the transuranic elements should have been similar to either barium or lanthanum. Hahn, at first, reasonably assumed that the radioactivity he was observing was a new form of radium, since the chemistry of radium is much like that of barium. This could be derived from the heavy new elements by the emission of alpha particles. On further tests Hahn became convinced that the activity he was observing was really in barium and not radium. It was somewhat hazardous to depend too positively on the similarity between the properties of the lighter elements and those of the transuranic elements in the same vertical column of the periodic table.

12.2. Fission. On January 6, 1939, Hahn and Strassmann in a continuing report on the radioactivities observed in barium, cerium, and lanthanum stated: ". . . with hesitation because of the strange results, we come to the conclusion our 'radium isotopes' have the properties of barium; as chemists we really ought to say these new substances are barium, lanthanum, and cerium. . . ."[6] They then proceeded to explain the implications of their proposal by showing that among the radioactivities observed was also one with a half-life the same as that of a known isotope of krypton. On combining the barium whose atomic number is 56 with krypton whose atomic number is 36, the number 92 is obtained which is the atomic number of uranium. Hence it might be that instead of the chipping-off of a small fragment from the nucleus as had always been observed in radioactivity heretofore, the nucleus now split up into two fragments of comparable size—a process that has come to be known as "fission." With scientific caution they then stated:

[4] O. Hahn and F. Strassmann, *Naturwissenschaften*, **26**, 755 (1938).
[5] I. Curie and L. Savitch, *J. phys.*, **9**, 355 (1938).
[6] O. Hahn and F. Strassmann, *Naturwissenschaften*, **27**, 11, 89 (1939).

"We cannot yet bring ourselves to make this leap in contradiction to all previous lessons of nuclear physics."

As soon as physicists in other laboratories heard of the proposal that Hahn and Strassmann had envisioned yet had been reluctant to assert, many confirming tests were begun. By the end of February, 1939, more than 40 published papers on the "fission" of uranium had appeared. The phenomenon became of particular interest because of the tremendous amount of energy released by each atom undergoing fission.

12.3. Energy of Fission Fragments. It was soon found that the particles ejected during the fission of uranium were exceedingly energetic. Meitner and Frisch [7] found that by placing

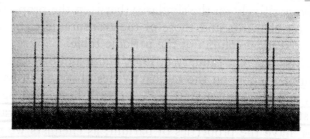

Fig. 12.1.   Deflections due to fission particles—alpha particles in dark band at bottom
(Dunning).

the uranium over water, the fission particles were driven out of the uranium and into the water, from which they then could be precipitated.

By covering a surface of bombarded uranium with a stack of thin foils and noting to what foil the radioactivity reached, McMillan was able to form an estimate of the energy per particle.[8]

More direct methods were pursued by Hafstad,[9] Dunning,[10] and Corson and Thornton.[11] An ionization chamber was

[7] L. Meitner and O. Frisch, *Nature*, **143**, 471 (1939).
[8] E. McMillan, *Phys. Rev.*, **55**, 610 (1939).
[9] R. Roberts, R. Meyer, and L. Hafstad, *Phys. Rev.*, **55**, 416 (1939).
[10] E. Booth, J. R. Dunning, and F. Slack, *Phys. Rev.*, **55**, 981, 1273 (1939).
[11] D. Corson and R. Thornton, *Phys. Rev.*, **55**, 509 (1939).

equipped with a linear amplifier and oscillograph so that the deflection observed was proportional to the energy. A copy of such a record is shown in Figure 12.1. The alpha particles from uranium whose energy is 4.1 Mev appear as the dense border at the bottom of the figure. Corson and Thornton

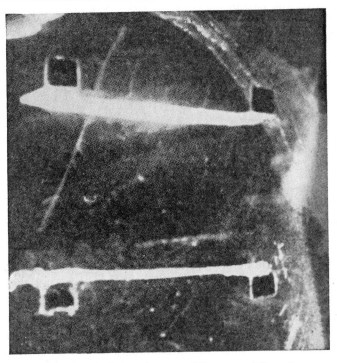

FIG. 12.2. The fission of uranium (Thornton and Corson).

placed the uranium on a thin screen inside a cloud chamber and irradiated it with neutrons during the expansion of the chamber. The heavy tracks due to the fission products, together with the alpha rays from the uranium, are shown in Figure 12.2.

By observing a large total number of fission particles and noting the number in each energy interval an interesting distribution curve results.[12]   As shown in Figure 12.3, two peaks are found to exist, one at 64 Mev and one at 97 Mev. This is about what would be expected from probability theory on, say, the splitting or fission of a raindrop. A division into two equal parts would occur only rarely. The sum of the energies represented by the two peaks is about 161 Mev.

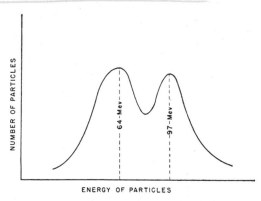

FIG. 12.3.   The distribution of energy among the fragments of fission (Kanner and Barschall).

A calorimetric determination of the total average energy per fission was carried out by Henderson.[13]   By noting the total number of disintegrations and the total energy developed in a sensitive calorimeter, it was concluded that the energy for fission was about 185 Mev. On comparing this with the energy of formation of a molecule in combustion, namely 2 to 5 electron volts, its enormous magnitude may be visualized. To represent this energy more familiarly, 1 pound of uranium 235 consists of 11.6×10^{23} particles which on complete disintegration by fission would yield 34.4×10^{19} ergs. This amount of energy is 9.55×10^6 kwh, or equivalent to the output of a 1000-kw power plant operating continuously for more than a year. The fuel consumption required for various over-all

[12] M. H. Kanner and H. Barschall, *Phys. Rev.*, **57**, 372 (1940).
[13] M. Henderson, *Phys. Rev.*, **57**, 774 (1940).

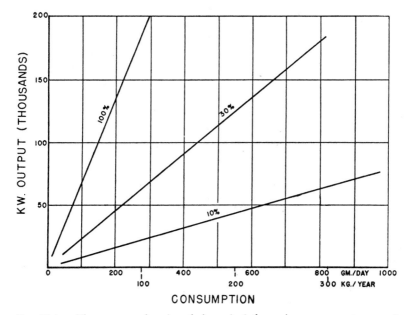

FIG. 12.4. The amount of nuclear fuel required for various power outputs and efficiencies.

efficiencies to produce a given output power is shown graphically in Figure 12.4.

12.4. Fissionable Isotopes. The natural isotopes of uranium are 234 (0.006%), 235 (0.710%), and 238 (99.28%). It was shown by Nier in cooperation with Dunning [14] that the isotope of mass 235, comprising only about $\frac{1}{140}$ of the total, undergoes fission by slow (i.e., thermal) neutron capture. For this reaction the remarkably large cross section of 400×10^{-24} square centimeter was observed. To produce fission in uranium 238 the neutron must have an energy of 1.0 ± 0.1 Mev. The natural isotope of thorium has a mass of 232, and it was shown [15] to undergo fission by 1.1-Mev neutrons. A small quantity of

[14] A. O. Nier, E. Booth, J. Dunning, and A. V. Grosse, *Phys. Rev.*, **57**, 546 (1940).
[15] Y. Nishina, Y. Yasaki, and H. Ezoe, *Nature*, **144**, 547 (1939); R. Haxby, W. Shoupp, W. Stephens, W. Wells, and M. Goldhaber, *Phys. Rev.*, **57**, 1088 (1940).

protactinium, whose mass number is 231, was found [16] to split up when the neutron energy was more than about 1.0 Mev.

With the production of energetic particles in the 184-inch cyclotron the fission of lighter nuclei was [17] attempted. Using

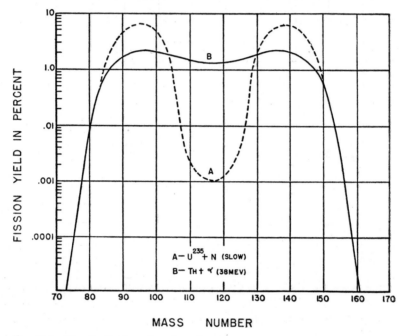

FIG. 12.5. The distribution of product elements on (*A*) the fission of uranium 235 with slow neutrons and (*B*) the fission of thorium with 38-Mev alphas (Newton).

either neutrons, deuterons, or alpha particles it was found possible to induce fission in any element with atomic number 73 or greater.

On bombarding thorium 232 with 37.5-Mev alpha particles, Newton observed [18] the masses of the fission fragments and found a distribution as shown graphically in the heavy curve of

[16] A. V. Grosse, E. Booth, and J. Dunning, *Phys. Rev.*, **56**, 382 (1939).
[17] I. Perlman, R. Goeckermann, D. Templeton, and J. Howland, *Phys. Rev.*, **72**, 352 (1947).
[18] A. Newton, *Phys. Rev.*, **75**, 17 (1949).

Figure 12.5.   The dotted line is the usual distribution of fission particles for uranium 235 plus slow neutrons.   Interestingly enough, the product nucleus just before fission for both processes should be the same, namely, uranium 236.   The added excitation energy apparently leads to a marked difference in the yield of atoms with intermediate atomic masses from 100 to 130.

12.5. Neutron Production at Fission and the Chain Reaction.
Since slow neutrons could initiate fission in uranium 235, it be-

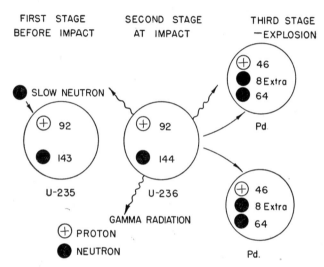

FIG. 12.6.   The imaginary fission of uranium 235 by a thermal neutron into equal palladium isotopes.

came of interest to find if any additional slow neutrons result from the process of fission.   If so, these slow neutrons could excite other uranium 235 atoms, which in turn would lead to fission in others, so that the action would proceed with increasing violence as a "chain" reaction if only uranium 235 atoms were present.

It was found [19] that neutrons were set free at fission, the number being from one to three per atom.   This number is now

[19] R. Roberts, L. Hafstad, R. Meyer, and P. Wang, *Phys. Rev.*, **55**, 664 (1939).

known to be about 2.5, varying slightly with the energy. That this should be the case is not surprising, on considering Figure 12.6. The isotope uranium 235 by capturing a neutron becomes an atom of mass 236 and atomic number 92. If it should divide into two identical parts these fragments would be palladium isotopes of atomic number 46 and mass 118. They would be highly unstable, since the heaviest natural isotope of palladium has a mass 110. By the emission of either neutrons or beta particles, or both, they would approach stability. They might

ELEMENT		ATOMIC WEIGHT														
AT. NO.	SYMBOL	106	107	108	109	110	111	112	113	114	115	116	117	118	119	120
46	P_d	27.2%		26.8%		13.5%	26 M	17 H						● ?		
47	A_g		52.5%		47.5%			7.5 D	3.2 H							
48	C_d	14%		1.0%		12.8%	13.0%	24.2%	12.3%	28.0%	2.5 D	7.3%	3.75 H			
49	I_n								4.5%	72 S	95.5%	54 M	117 M			
50	S_n							1.1%		0.8%	0.4%	15.5%	9.1%	22.5%	9.8%	28.5%

FIG. 12.7. The elements near palladium, indicating possible transitions for the two equal fission isotopes shown in Fig. 12.6.

therefore produce any one of several of the radioactivities as shown in Figure 12.7. In addition to the neutrons given off during bombardment, a delayed neutron emission with a half-life of 12.5 seconds was reported. The neutrons generated at fission were noted to be not thermal neutrons but possessing energies up to the order of 1 Mev. On further observation it was found [20] that about 1% of the neutrons emitted in fission are delayed by at least 0.01 second and about 0.07% are delayed by as much as 1 minute. This would be a satisfactory condition for a chain reaction provided the newly formed neutrons were allowed to unite with other atoms of uranium 235.

[20] A. Snell, A. Nedzel, and H. Ibser, *Smyth Report*, Princeton Press (1945).

In natural uranium this process was forbidden by the presence of a preponderant number of uranium 238 atoms. A resonance absorption for neutrons in uranium 238 was reported by Anderson and Fermi [21] at an energy of about 25 electron volts with a capture cross section of 1.2×10^{-24} square centimeter. This capture leads to the radioactivity whose half-life

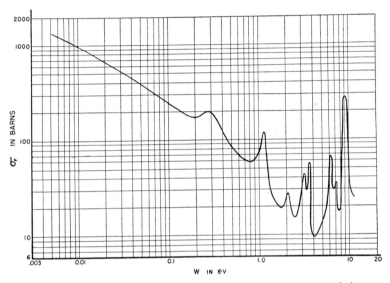

FIG. 12.8.   Neutron capture cross section in uranium 235, leading to fission.

is 23 minutes, which had been identified [22] as the only one of the many neutron-induced activities in uranium really obeying the chemistry of uranium. All the other numerous half-lives were related to elements of lesser atomic number, being fission products. The resonance cross-section curve in uranium 238 is now known to be complicated, as presented in Figure 8.10. The enormously high peaks representing cross sections of 10^5 barns, at energies of 6.5, 21, 37, 66, and 103 electron volts would very effectively absorb any high energy neutron as it

[21] H. Anderson and E. Fermi, *Phys. Rev.*, **55**, 1106 (1939).
[22] L. Meitner, O. Hahn, and F. Strassmann, *Z. Physik*, **106**, 249 (1937).

slowed down toward thermal equilibrium. If, however, it could be reduced to an energy less than 6.5 electron volts, then it could be effectively absorbed by uranium 235 as shown by the fission cross-section curve in Figure 12.8.

The problem to be solved was, how could the neutrons formed at fission be slowed to thermal neutrons without being captured by uranium 238 as their energy passed through the resonances, as shown schematically in Figure 12.9. Fermi suggested that this absorption might be averted by the judicious use of what has become known as a "moderator." This is an element of rather light atomic weight whose atoms will not accept the neutrons in capture but which will scatter them elastically. Such elements suggesting themselves were deuterium,

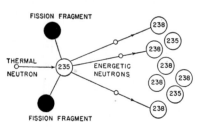

FISSION FRAGMENT

THERMAL NEUTRON

ENERGETIC NEUTRONS

FIG. 12.9. Showing the fission of a uranium 235 atom and the resonance capture in uranium 238 of the neutrons produced at fission.

helium, beryllium, and carbon. The moderating atoms will thus take a portion of the energy of the neutron at each collision, and as a result the original high-energy neutrons may be reduced to thermal neutrons. They can now diffuse back into the composite uranium and have a strong probability of inducing fission in other uranium 235 atoms. In a collision with a carbon nucleus, a neutron will lose about one sixth of its energy per collision. The scattering cross section σ_s in graphite for energetic neutrons is about 0.48×10^{-24} barn. The mean free path λ for neutrons in graphite is then

$$\lambda = \frac{1}{N\sigma_s} = \frac{1}{1.12 \times 10^{23} \times 0.48 \times 10^{-24}} = 1.86 \text{ cm}$$

where N is the number of carbon atoms per cubic centimeter. The geometry of the moderator could be arranged so that on the average about 120 elastic collisions took place, before the particle, now a thermal neutron, returned to the uranium. This behavior is suggested in Figure 12.10 and leads to a successful chain reaction.

12.6. The Separation of the Uranium Isotopes. If the spontaneous disintegration of uranium 235 is prevented by the presence of uranium 238 it might seem desirable to separate the

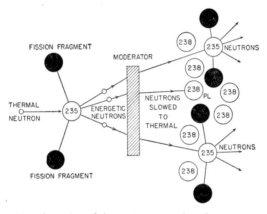

FIG. 12.10.   Showing the action of the moderator to slow the created neutrons to the thermal range.

isotopes, or at least to proceed to a product sufficiently enriched in uranium 235. The separation of heavy isotopes which differ by only a few mass units is not easy.

Four different methods suggest themselves as possible means to achieve this end. These are the magnetic mass spectrometer, molecular diffusion methods, thermal diffusion towers, and the centrifuge.

a. Electromagnetic Separator. In a strong, uniform magnetic field, singly charged particles having the same energy but unequal masses, will describe circular paths of unequal radii. The radii will be approximately in the same ratio as the square roots of the masses. The particles are given the same energy by being accelerated as ions through a fixed potential difference.

Factors important in the successful operation of such separators are (a) the size and shape of the arc source from which the ions come, (b) the accelerating voltage, (c) strength and deliberate nonuniformity of the magnetic field, (d) pressure of vapor in the ion source and in the chamber, (e) the design of the collector, and (f) the mutual interaction between particles in the beam and between neighboring beams. By successfully meeting many of these issues at Berkeley in 1942, the output of such separators was increased by an enormous factor.[23] The final practical separators of this type used successfully in large numbers were termed "calutrons." The current use of this device is to supply enriched isotopes of any of the stable elements that are sufficiently abundant.

b. Separation by Molecular Diffusion. The average kinetic energy per particle of a gas is dependent only on the absolute temperature. Hence at the same temperature, any two gas particles of masses m_1 and m_2 having velocities v_1 and v_2, respectively, will diffuse at a rate proportional to their velocities. The unequal rates of diffusion through semipermeable walls was used,[24] soon after the discovery of isotopes, to separate partially the isotopes of neon. Thus

$$\frac{v_1}{v_2} = \sqrt{\frac{m_2}{m_1}}$$

so that for the 235 and 238 isotopes of uranium the velocities are as 1.0064 to 1. Hence in any continued electrolytic, evaporation, or diffusion process the lighter particles will participate more actively. By continually collecting this first product to escape, an enrichment of the lighter isotope will be accomplished.

In attempts at separation by diffusion, the uranium is converted to the heavy, very poisonous gas, uranium hexafluoride. The two molecules UF_6 have masses 349 and 352, so that their

[23] H. D. Smyth, *Atomic Energy Report*, Princeton Press (1945).
[24] F. Lindemann and F. W. Aston, *Phil. Mag.*, **27**, 523 (1919).

relative velocities are only 1.0043 to 1. For the separation a satisfactory barrier had first to be developed. After this was successfully accomplished more than 4000 successive cycles had to be allowed to obtain the desired enrichment. An imaginary arrangement of three of the units is shown in Figure 12.11.

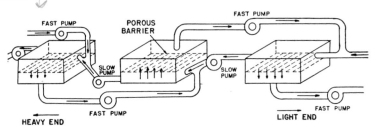

FIG. 12.11. Showing an imaginary plan for the separation of isotopes by molecular diffusion.

The scale of operation as carried out at Oak Ridge comprises what has been termed the largest continuous chemicophysical process in the world.

c. The Thermal Separating Tower. By allowing the convection of a fluid consisting of two unequal mass constituents within a vertical cylinder whose axis is maintained at a high temperature relative to the cylindrical wall, a slight separation of the components can be accomplished.

Clusius and Dickel [25] successfully operated a thermal diffusion tower for heavy isotopes. It consisted of a long vertical cylinder. A hot wire at the axis maintained a temperature difference of about 600° C. between center and outer surface. The concentration of the heavier isotope increased slightly at the cool outer surface and at the same time a convection current carried the cooler gas downward and the lighter gas upward along the wire. Thus by withdrawing the gas at the axis at the top and passing it successively through additional similar stages an enrichment in the lighter isotope is obtained. The

[25] H. Clusius and G. Dickel, *Naturwissenschaften*, **26**, 546 (1938); **27**, 148, 487 (1939).

method works particularly well if the relative mass difference is appreciable. To obtain uranium enriched in the isotope 235, mammouth thermal diffusion towers were constructed and successfully operated.

d. *The Centrifuge.* High-speed centrifuges have been used with some success in the separation of isotopes.[26] The separation factor in this case depends on the masses of the two isotopes directly rather than on the square root of their ratio as for diffusion devices. By constructing the centrifuge as a tall cylinder, advantage can also be taken of the convection currents to aid in the separation.

A separation factor S may be defined as the ratio of the concentrations of light to heavy isotopes at the axis to the same ratio at the periphery of the rotor. Assuming that the vapor obeys the ideal gas law, it has been demonstrated that

$$S = e^{(M_2 - M_1)\omega^2 r^2 / 2RT}$$

where ω is the angular velocity, r the radius, R the gas constant, T the absolute temperature, and M_2 and M_1 the masses of the isotopes. At the phenomenal speed of 800,000 revolutions per second a centrifugal acceleration of 5×10^8 g has now been attained.

12.7. The Reactor or "Pile." The first successful "reactor" or "pile," in which the unseparated isotopes of uranium maintained by themselves a continuous development of energy, was put in operation on December 2, 1942, at the University of Chicago. The structure was an oblate spheroid built up in layers of graphite bricks. In alternate layers of the graphite were lumps of uranium, situated so as to be at the corners of a cubic lattice. The pile contained 12,400 pounds of metal, together with some purified oxide, to complete the lattice. In order to control the rate of transformation, a number of rods of cadmium or boron steel were arranged so that they could be inserted or withdrawn. Because of their large absorption for

[26] J. W. Beams, *Rep. Phys. Prog. Phys. Soc.*, **8**, 31 (1942).

thermal neutrons they could if inserted shield the uranium 235, and thus retard the action.

A term called the "multiplication factor," applylng to the reactor, may be defined as the ratio of the neutron density with uranium in place to the corresponding density without the uranium. If this factor is greater than one, by any amount whatever, then the action will be self-sustaining.

The large energy carried by the fission fragments must be dissipated in the total material of the reactor as thermal energy. The action in the reactor is a continuous conversion of uranium 235 by fission into elements of lesser atomic weight, lying somewhere near the center of the periodic table. At the same time many of the surplus neutrons are being captured by uranium 238. For each neutron so captured an atom of plutonium 239 is formed by subsequent beta decay. When the action has proceeded sufficiently, this fissionable plutonium and any other by-products formed may be separated chemically from the parent uranium. Because of the exceedingly strong radio-activity of the fission products, utmost precaution must be exercised by the operators and the necessary chemical procedures are carried out by remote control. For greater power outputs provision must be made to cool adequately the large active mass of material. Simple calculation shows that to produce 1 gram of plutonium a day, the pile must operate so as to have a continuous power output of about 1000 kw.

12.8. The Enriched Atomic-fuel Reactor. By using either plutonium or uranium enriched in isotope 235, as the active agent, in a pile or reactor, remarkable outputs may be achieved with an apparatus of relatively small dimensions. With a very few pounds of active material either in the form of a solution or alloyed and sandwiched between aluminum sheets, power outputs of 1000 kw may be maintained if adequate cooling is provided. In the active region, a neutron flux density of about 2×10^7 neutrons per cm^2 per second can be expected per watt of power. Thus when operated at a level of 1000 kw a neutron flux density in excess of 10^{13} is obtained. The U. S. Atomic Energy Commission, while controlling all fissionable materials, has adopted a policy of making them available to qualified users, so that the number of reactors is multiplying rapidly.

Figure 12.12 shows a cutaway view of the heavy water enriched fuel reactor at the Argonne National Laboratory. The fuel rods of aluminum-clad uranium 235 are cooled by circulat-

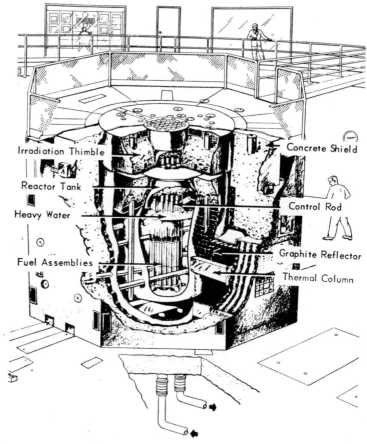

Irradiation Thimble

Reactor Tank

Heavy Water

Fuel Assemblies

Concrete Shield

Control Rod

Graphite Reflector

Thermal Column

FIG. 12.12. The heavy water enriched fuel reactor at the Argonne National Laboratory. (Courtesy of W. M. McCorkle.)

ing deuterium oxide. Maximum flux densities up to about 5×10^{13} are available in the upper irradiation thimbles.

12.9. Radioactivity Accompanying the Action of the Reactor.

For each atom of uranium 235 undergoing fission two radioactive fragments are formed. In a modest reactor operating at 1000 kw, 3.37×10^{16} particles are undergoing fission every second, forming 6.74×10^{16} radioactive atoms. The half-lives of these numerous radioactivities formed are varied, but in general for sustained operation each activity would approach equilibrium, so that in total 6.74×10^{16} radioactive disintegrations are occurring every second. Now 37×10^{9} disintegrating atoms per second were termed a curie, so that the radioactivity here displayed could be expressed as 1.81 million curies. The gamma radia-

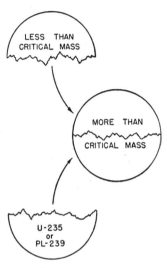

Fig. 12.13. Critical size of fissionable mass for the initiation of a chain reaction.

tion from this tremendous source presents a difficulty in shielding. Similarly in the use of nuclear fuel this same radioactivity would be developed. It is this factor that places a limitation on the use of small atomic-energy plants where weight is an important factor.

This quantity of radium would emit gamma radiation alone, capable of producing 2500 r units in 10 minutes at a distance of 10 meters from the source. This would be very close to a lethal exposure for any living organism.

In order that a rapid "chain" reaction may proceed in a quantity of a pure fissionable isotope, it is essential that the mass be sufficient in relation to the total surface area. This relationship can be calculated and is illustrated graphically in

Figure 12.13. On bringing the two nonactive masses together properly, the critical size is exceeded and the action may proceed explosively.

On analyzing the metallic uranium after the self-sustaining action in the pile has been maintained for some time, a great number of radioactive emitters would be found to be present.

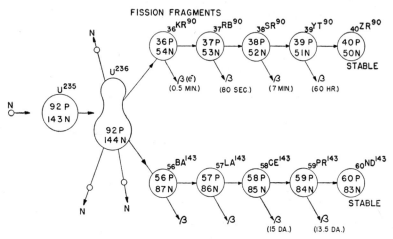

FIG. 12.14. Representing the fission of uranium 235 plus neutron, forming two short radioactive "chains".

Almost any specific element near the middle of the periodic table might be recovered in relatively large quantities. It has been possible to identify and quantitatively evaluate most of the fission products. In the decay of these radioactive products many elements are found to give rise to a series or chain of daughter products and in all about 50 such chains have been observed. The origin of two such chains may be observed in Figure 12.14 in which uranium 236 splits into barium and krypton isotopes, both of which give rise to radioactive daughter products.

The over-all decay of the fission products existing in the pile at the end of a 100-day operation is shown in the semilogarithmic plot in Figure 12.15.   For short-lived isotopes a saturation would have been attained early in the 100-day run but the longer-lived activities would still be building up.   By separating any particular isotope at some time after its removal from the

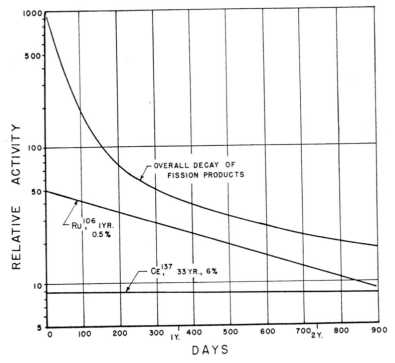

FIG. 12.15.   The radioactive decay of certain fission products.

pile, its logarithmic decay curve may be extrapolated back to zero time and the total number of such atoms, created by the fission of a fixed amount of uranium, calculated.   Thus, ruthenium 106 and cerium 137, as shown, are found to account for 0.5 and 6%, respectively, of the total number of fission particles created.   The number of fission particles would be twice or 200% of the number of uranium atoms undergoing fission.

QUESTIONS AND PROBLEMS

1. Assuming the possibility of utilizing by breeder reactor 80% of the energy of both isotopes of uranium, compare the economic advantage in heating by uranium at $20 per lb, with coal at $10 per ton. Assume 180 Mev and 4 ev for the energies respectively per reaction.

Answer: 4550:1.

2. The heat of combustion of TNT, $C_6H_2(CH_3)(NO_2)_3$ is 820,700 cal per gm molecular weight. What mass of plutonium would ideally release as much energy as a 2000-lb mass of TNT?

Answer: ~0.15 gm.

3. Assuming an average half-life of 1 hr for the radioactivities developed on the fission of plutonium, how many curies are represented in the source when 10 lb of plutonium undergo rapid binary fission?

Answer: 1.19×10^{11} curies.

4. Neglecting absorption in the air, and assuming the gamma rays to be equivalent to those from radium, at what maximum distance would a lethal dose of, say, 3000 r units be received during the first minute from the above source? Assume no dispersion of the source.

Answer: 757 meters.

5. On considering the absorption of the air, assuming standard conditions, what would be the dosage at the above-determined distance?

Answer: For $\mu/\rho = 0.058$ cm^2/gm the dosage is 10.5 r per min.

6. Assume an average specific heat of 0.8 for the fission fragments. If 10% of the heat developed is retained momentarily by the products, what maximum temperature would be attained?

Answer: 2.14×10^9 °K.

7. A piece of gold weighing 10 gm is placed in the central thimble of the Argonne pile where the neutron flux density is 6×10^{13}. The capture cross section for $Au^{197}(n, \gamma)Au^{198}$ is 95 barns. The half-life of Au^{198} is 2.7 days and its capture cross section is 38,000 barns. What are the products present at the end of a one-week irradiation? What percentage of the Au^{197} has been lost?

Answer: Au^{198}, Au^{199}, Hg^{198}, Hg^{199}; 0.35%

Chapter 13

SOME APPLICATIONS OF RADIOACTIVITY

13.1. Historical. With the discovery of natural radioactivity in 1896, it might have been expected that widespread use of the phenomenon would be found in other branches of science. The first application came in the field of medicine. In 1900, Walkhoff and Giesel announced certain physiological effects in tissue exposed to the new radiation. Madame Curie and Becquerel had both received superficial burns from close contact with the active matter. Alert to this surprising power of the rays, Pierre Curie in 1901 collaborated with two medical men, Bouchard and Balthazard, in studying the action of radium on animals. In 1902 they concluded that by "destroying diseased cells, radium cured growths, tumors, and certain forms of cancer." French practitioners then began the treatment of diseased persons with tubes of emanation loaned by Pierre and Marie Curie. To enlarge this activity the first gram of radium was successfully separated from about 8 tons of pitchblende residue, largely through the untiring efforts of Madame Curie.

Not until 1913, when Paneth and Hevesy [1] used radium D as a tracer element in chemical reactions, was the possibility of the advantageous use of radioactive elements in other branches of science recognized.

With the discovery of induced radioactivity in 1934, and its subsequent development, it became possible to render any element in the periodic table radioactive. The half-lives of these activities vary from a fraction of a second up to many years. Some emit only beta rays or positrons while others emit

[1] F. Paneth and G. Hevesy, *Akad. Wiss. Wien*, **122**, 1001 (1913).

gamma rays or a combination of both types of radiation. The availability of this wide variety of radioactive bodies stimulated their use in all related fields of science. Within a few years an avalanche of papers was appearing attesting to the efficacy of this new agent. It is apparent that by using radioactive, or tagged, detectible elements the behavior of matter in many reactions could be followed in a manner quite impossible without the radioactivity.

A few illustrations of the usefulness of radioactivity in some related branches of science will be presented. This is not intended to be a complete report on any investigation or to cover all of the applications.

13.2. Agriculture. Fundamental questions arise in the two broad divisions of (*a*) animal husbandry or (*b*) plant physiology. Problems whose solution can be materially aided by the

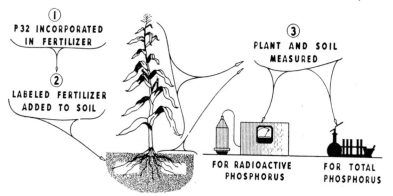

① P32 INCORPORATED IN FERTILIZER

② LABELED FERTILIZER ADDED TO SOIL

③ PLANT AND SOIL MEASURED

FOR RADIOACTIVE PHOSPHORUS

FOR TOTAL PHOSPHORUS

FIG. 13.1.   Schematic arrangement for radioactive uptake study.

use of radioactive isotopes may be typified by the following: nutrition studies by trace elements, diet additives, biochemistry of milk production, action of insecticides, mechanism of photosynthesis, metabolism rates, soil fertility, pathology of plants, uptake of fertilizers, etc. With the favorable rates existent for the purchase of radioactive materials the cost to Agricultural Experimental Stations is very modest. As an example of results obtainable in the use of fertilizer, a half-billion dollar annual industry in the United States, early experiments with radioactive phosphorus gave indications (a) that phosphate is used by corn only in the early stages of growth, (b) that potatoes use phosphate throughout the growing season, (c) that the fertility of the soil influences the uptake of phosphorus by cotton plants, (d) that growth in potatoes is retarded if phosphorus is placed too close to the plant roots, etc. The procedure is illustrated in Figure 13.1.

13.3. Archaeology—The Age of Ancient Carbon Deposits. The neutrons always present in the atmosphere by virtue of cosmic radiation may, by the capture process in nitrogen 14, produce carbon 14, which is radioactive with a half-life of 5720 years.[2] In all growing matter natural respiration effectively establishes an equilibrium between the stable carbon and the radioactive carbon present. Approximately 1 in every 10^{12} carbon atoms is radioactive. It can be computed from the known neutron production rate that the earth's total atmosphere at any time contains about 110 million curies of radioactive carbon. When an organism dies and respiration and effective diffusion ceases, then the captured content of radioactive carbon is not replenished. By virtue of its decay the amount of carbon 14 will consequently diminish and in 5720 years it would be reduced to half-normal value. By collecting a specimen from the interior of such a fossilized body, and concentrating the carbon 14 by thermal diffusion, its ratio with respect to carbon 12 may be determined. On comparing this with the normal ratio the age of the specimen is deduced. On examining a fragment of the wood from a mummy case Libby found a specific activity of 7 counts per minute per gram of carbon instead of the normal 12.5 found for other carbon. From this he deduced the age to be 4600 years, a result compatible with the archaeological prediction. Since the relative activity is so small it is

[2] E. Anderson, W. F. Libby, S. Weinhouse, A. Reid, A. Kirshenbaum, and A. V. Grosse, *Phys. Rev.*, **72**, 931 (1947); W. Libby, E. Anderson, and J. Arnold, *Science*, **109**, 227 (1949).

not possible to date accurately by this method events that occurred more than three half-lives or about fifteen thousand years ago. This period, however, includes most of the items of historical interest.

13.4. Astronomy—Solar Energy.

By using the information gained in studying nuclear reactions, it has become possible to answer one of the long-standing puzzling questions, namely, what keeps our sun at a constant temperature.

The solar constant of radiation at the surface of the earth is about 1.94 calories per square centimeter per minute. From this, one can calculate the total energy radiated by the sun in any interval of time. By assuming a reasonable value of the thermal capacity of the sun, one finds that the total radiant energy should be sufficient to reduce the temperature about 15° C. per year if the sun were simply a cooling body. Actually no drift in the solar temperature has been observed. It must therefore follow that some processes are taking place on the sun so as to release energy as fast as it is being radiated.

If the temperature and pressure are sufficiently high, various "fusion" reactions might occur. Hydrogen is the main constituent of stellar bodies and hence its capture is most important. For the less luminous stars whose temperatures are below that of the sun it has been predicted [3] that in the high energy part of the Maxwellian distribution (10 to 50 kev), two protons combine to form a deuteron and positron. The reaction chain is considered to be completed by the radiative capture of a proton by the deuteron, forming He^3, which on collision with a similar particle leads to He^4 and two protons. A net energy release of 26.2 Mev results for each He^4 nucleus formed.

For more luminous stars, whose temperatures range upward from that of our sun, the probable fusion mechanism is [4] the carbon cycle. In this process the carbon nucleus serves somewhat like a catalyst so that the four protons convert to He^4

---

[3] E. E. Salpeter, *Phys. Rev.*, **88**, 547 (1952).
[4] H. A. Bethe, *Phys. Rev.*, **55**, 434 (1939).

plus two positrons and the accompanying neutrinos. The sequential reactions are as follows:

$$_6C^{12} + {}_1H^1 \rightarrow {}_7N^{13} \rightarrow {}_6C^{13} + {}_{+1}e$$

$$_6C^{13} + {}_1H^1 \rightarrow {}_7N^{14}$$

$$_7N^{14} + {}_1H^1 \rightarrow {}_8O^{15} \rightarrow {}_7N^{15} + {}_{+1}e$$

$$_7N^{15} + {}_1H^1 \rightarrow {}_8O^{16} \rightarrow {}_6C^{12} + {}_2He^4$$

For the red giant stars found in globular structures, central temperatures greater than $10^8°K$. are predicted. Under these conditions three helium nuclei are assumed [5] to combine in two steps to form an excited carbon 12 nucleus. This emits gamma energy (7.68 Mev) in the transition to its ground state.

Some speculation might be made regarding the age of the sun by assuming that all of its present helium has been derived from hydrogen. Spectroscopically it is possible to estimate the present abundance of helium. By combining this with its known present rate of formation an estimate of several billion years results.

13.5. Botany. *a. Transport of Fluids.* Radioactive salts in solution may be taken up by the roots of plants and a subsequent analysis made of their location by noting the activity in an exploring detector. In this way by a single early experiment [6] it was shown that the long-held notion of upward transport in plants might need revision. If, as had been supposed, the upward transport takes place through the woody part of the stem alone, then on removing a section of the wood of the stem no transfer should occur. There appeared to be evidence that the radioactive material was still being carried upward, indicating an upward transport in the bark. The question is still not entirely resolved, as a somewhat contrary conclusion [7] was reached by other workers using the same technique.

[5] E. E. Salpeter, *Phys. Rev.*, **98**, 1183 (1955).
[6] F. Gustafson, *Science*, **85**, 482 (1937); *J. Applied Phys.*, **12**, 327 (1941).
[7] P. R. Stout and J. R. Hoagland, *Am. J. Biol.*, **26**, 320 (1939).

b. Photosynthesis. The reactions by which carbon dioxide in the presence of light and water proceeds to form sugars have been little understood. By using carbon dioxide consisting of radioactive carbon 11, whose half-life is only 21 minutes, Ruben and Kamen [8] were able to solve partially the difficult chemistry associated with the process. They found that the carbon dioxide united reversibly in a nonphotochemical reaction with a heavy molecule of the type *RH* where *R* is an atomic aggregate of large total weight. Thus,

$$RH + CO_2 \leftrightarrows R\,COOH$$

This carboxyl molecule unites photochemically with water to form a possible sugar, as

$$R\,COOH + H_2O + h\nu \rightarrow R\,CH_2OH + O_2$$

The formation of the sugar is thus a multiple reaction, quite different from that which had been classically assumed.

c. Selective Absorption. The selective absorption of a given radioactive element in any particular tissue of the plant may be revealed by a photographic technique. Figure 13.2 is an "autoradiogram" of a tomato plant that had been placed in a solution containing dissolved radiophosphorus.[9] After the lapse of an appropriate time the plant is removed from the solution and placed firmly against the photographic emulsion, in a darkened room. The blackening of the plate is a measure of the abundance of the radioactive element in the contiguous part of the plant. In the figure it is quite clear that the phosphorus accumulates in the stems and the conduction system of the leaves. It is also found abundantly in the seeds of the fruit.

13.6. Chemistry. *a. Adsorption.* The phenomenon of adsorption, in which solids take up on their surfaces, gases, liquids, or other dissolved solids, has been difficult to understand. Various theories have been offered. In some cases it has been

[8] M. Kamen and S. Ruben, *J. Applied Phys.*, **12**, 326 (1941).
[9] D. Arnon, P. Stout, and F. Sipos, *Am J. Bot.*, **27**, 791 (1940).

Fig. 13.2. Autoradiogram of selectively absorbed radiophosphorus.

proposed that the action is a solution, and in others a chemical combination is assumed to occur. By using radioactive sodium and bromine as tracer elements it has been demonstrated [10] that in the case of eosin and erythrosin dyes the adsorption consists entirely of an exchange between the negative ions of the solution and the negative ions of the adsorbent.

b. Synthesized Elements. There were still four unknown elements between hydrogen 1 and uranium 92 in 1937: namely, those of atomic number 43, 61, 85, and 87. The chemistry of these elements could be predicted from their position in the

[10] A. Newton and K. Fajans, *J. Applied Phys.*, **12**, 306 (1941).

periodic table and hence also their most probable source. All attempts to isolate and identify them were unsuccessful. By bombarding neighboring elements in the periodic table with various projectiles, radioactive isotopes of each of these elements have now been positively identified. In some cases the chemistry of the element has been found to be somewhat different than had been predicted. Element 87 has been found as a branching product in the actinium series.[11] A sufficient quantity of element 61 has been produced [12] to use as a target in an X-ray tube and yield its characteristic K and L series spectra.

The very heavy elements of atomic number 93, 94, 95, 96, 97, 98, 99, 100, and 101, were first known only as a result of nuclear reactions. A trace of plutonium has since been found to be present in the pitchblende from the Great Bear Lake deposit.

By bombarding gold with deuterons an isotope of mercury is formed that is quite different from ordinary mercury. Gold has a single isotope of mass 197. By a (d, p) reaction radioactive gold 198, whose half-life is 2.7 days, is formed. On the emission of a beta particle, stable mercury consisting of a single isotope of mass 198 is formed. Ordinary mercury has an atomic weight of 200.6 and consists of 7 isotopes varying from 196 to 204 in mass. Sufficient mercury 198 has been made in this way from radioactive gold to make spectroscopic studies. The radiation has been proposed as a spectroscopic standard of length, since it is free from hyperfine structure and isotope shift.

c. Radiation and Chemical Reactions. The rate of reaction in many chemical processes is known to be influenced by the application of radiation. Among the many reactions that have been studied may be mentioned (*a*) the dehydrogenation of hydrocarbon gases, (*b*) the polymerization of some liquids, such as styrene or acrylonitrile, (*c*) the synthesis of compounds from elemental matter, the cross-bonding in polyethylene, etc.

[11] Mlle. Perey, *Compt. rend.*, **208**, 97 (1939).
[12] L. E. Burkhart, W. Peed, and E. Spitzer, *Phys. Rev.*, **75**, 86 (1949).

d. Alchemy. The transmutation of base metals into gold has through the ages been the goal of a certain group of investigators, often the most erudite of their generation. From time to time success has been reported, only to be proved later to be unfounded.

The possibility of inducing transmutations by bombardment, with high-energy particles being well established, it naturally became of interest to achieve this long-sought goal and create gold from another element. This was first accomplished [13] in 1936. The luster of the achievement was somewhat dulled by the fact that the parent element in the reaction is platinum. The process as carried out is illustrated by the following equation:

$$_{78}Pt^{196} + {}_1H^2 \rightarrow {}_{78}Pt^{197} + {}_1H^1$$

$$_{78}Pt^{197} \text{ (18-hr half-life)} \rightarrow {}_{79}Au^{197} + {}_{-1}e$$

The radioactive platinum 197 formed in the bombardment decays by beta emission to ordinary gold.

13.7. Engineering. *a. Radiology.* With the development of semiportable Van de Graaff generators, and betatrons capable of delivering X-rays up to 5 Mev, defects in any engineering structure, whose thickness is not greater than about 10 inches of steel, can be expeditiously located.

Certain of the radioactive isotopes emit very penetrating gamma radiation. Cobalt 60 has a half-life of 5.3 years and emits gamma radiation having an energy 1.32 Mev. An isotope of yttrium of mass 88 is a by-product in the making of radiostrontium by the bombardment of strontium with deuterons. It has a half-life of 105 days and emits gamma rays of energy 2.8 Mev. Because of the minute size of a strong radioactive source, it can often be used advantageously to take photographs such as through a few inches of steel, in positions inaccessible to other larger equipment.

[13] J. M. Cork and E. O. Lawrence, *Phys. Rev.*, **49**, 788 (1936).

b. Thickness Measurement. Radioactivity may be employed to determine the thickness of metallic walls or plates that are not susceptible to measurement by calipers or other devices. By placing a calibrated radioactive source on one side of the wall and a receiver on the other, then the reading observed falls off with increasing thickness both because of increased absorption and decreased solid angle. By choosing a source which emits radiation of suitable energy, a sensitivity and speed of

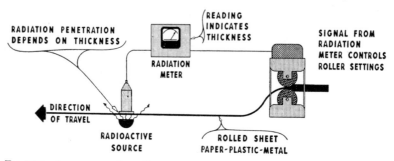

Fig. 13.3. Arrangement for radioactively controlled rolling mill for uniform thickness.

operation comparable with the use of the best conventional calipers may be attained. Figure 13.3 shows a radioactively operated automatic control for a rolling mill, capable of assuring a product of constant thickness.

An interesting modification of this apparatus permits the measurement of the thickness of walls when their back surface is not accessible. The scattering of neutrons or gamma radiation depends upon the amount and kind of matter present. The radiation from a fixed source placed near the plate will be scattered back to a neighboring receiver in amounts proportional to the thickness of the scatterer.

c. Some Other Engineering Applications. Piston rings or other motor parts may be made radioactive by placing them in the pile. Their subsequent use in friction experiments provides a method for detecting the transfer of the smallest trace of iron to an abrasive surface.

The height of molten iron within a cupola may be readily revealed by a G-M counter tube outside, by virtue of a small amount of radioactive material added to the iron.

The changes through which crude oil goes in cracking, as well as other processes in the manufacture of synthetic gasoline, are being studied by the use of radioactive carbon. There is some possibility that certain manufacturing processes may actually be accelerated by the direct use of radiation. One example is the conversion of certain fatty acids into paraffinic or straight-chain hydrocarbons, which are important in petroleum.

There has been some expectation that the combustion process in gas engines might be favorably influenced by a strong radiation field. Experiments have been carried out in which a strong radioactive palladium source is placed within the cylinder. No appreciable improvement in performance has been noted.

13.8. Medicine. *a. Radiation Therapy.* Any ionizing radiation will, if in sufficient intensity, kill all living cells exposed to it. During the process of growth the susceptibility of cells to radiation is greater than when they are in the fully developed state. In cancerous tissue the abnormal cells are undergoing rapid growth. The possibility therefore exists that by just the right dosage the abnormal tissue might be eliminated without seriously damaging the normal cells.

It is not unreasonable to suppose that neutron radiation would behave differently than X-rays on absorption. A neutron gives its energy to a recoil proton which travels only a short distance with intense ionization along its path. An X-ray photon, on the other hand, gives rise to an electron whose specific ionization is relatively small. The recoil proton might kill any single diseased cell through which it travels, whereas it might require the cumulative effect of several recoil electrons to produce the same effect.

In appraising the results in treating malignancies in man over a 10-year period,[14] with fast neutrons from the cyclotron, the

[14] R. S. Stone and J. G. Hamilton, Baruch Report, U. S. Dept. of State (1947).

conclusion appeared to be that neutrons possess no great superiority over X-rays. A possibility does exist that thermal neutrons, produced so abundantly by a pile, might be useful in destroying diseased tissue that has previously been infiltrated with some element which has an extraordinarily large capture cross section.

A promising mode of attack on the cancer problem is the use of beams of energetic particles, such as electrons or protons. At high energy the specific ionization produced by these particles is small but as they slow down the number of ions per centimeter along their path increases enormously. By proper adjustment of their energy it might then be imagined that deep-lying tissue could be given a destructive dosage without damage to the surface of the body.

b. Specific Absorption. It is well known that various tissues of the body will take up selectively specific elements from the circulating fluids. Thus after an intravenous injection of iodine, this element is found in relatively high percentages in the thyroid, liver, spleen, and heart. Phosphorus is similarly absorbed by bone marrow, and calcium and strontium are taken up in large measure by the bones. It is evident that by making the absorbed element radioactive, local destruction of the absorbing tissue may be accomplished with no general ill effects. In leukemia, a disease in which the white blood corpuscles multiply abnormally, some measure of control can be achieved by a dosage of from 2 to 8 millicuries of radiophosphorus. This element on absorption in the bone marrow and spleen can destroy the cells in their formative stage and thus control the count of the white blood corpuscles. Unfortunately it so far seems unable to produce any prolongation of life in this specific disease.

Radioactive strontium 89 has been successfully used in the treatment of bone tumors. This isotope emits solely beta particles whose maximum energy is 1.3 Mev with a half-life of 55 days. When strontium lactate is administered intravenously, as much as 35% of the dose becomes fixed in the skeleton.

Figure 13.4*A* is an ordinary photograph and Figure 13.4*B* is an "autoradiogram" of a section through the amputated knee of a patient previously given radioactive strontium. It is apparent that the radioactive material has accumulated preponderantly

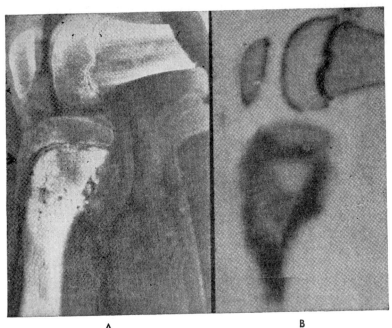

A   B

FIG. 13.4. Autoradiogram of section of amputated knee, indicating selective absorption of radio-strontium.

in the neoplastic tissue and in the epiphyseal line where growth is taking place. This is just the tissue which it is desired to have receive radiation. Radioactive gallium 67 appears to be even better in the treatment of this disease.

The most striking success so far has been achieved in the treatment of polycythemia and hyperthyroidism. Polycythemia manifests itself by an overproduction of red blood corpuscles. It has an incidence of about 1 per 100,000 population. It had previously been uncontrollable. Now, by the application of phosphorus 32, almost complete remission of the disease is obtained.

Hyperthyroidism has an incidence of about 25 per 100,000 population and seems amenable to control by the use of radioactive iodine. Thyroid cancer is often associated with cancerous growths called metastases in other parts of the body. These cells all exhibit a large characteristic uptake of administered

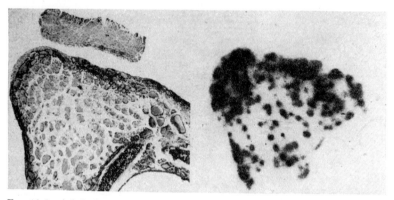

FIG. 13.5. (*A*) Stained thyroid section, (*B*) autoradiogram of same thyroid section
(S. R. Pelc).

radioiodine. However, in the presence of normal thyroid tissue a sufficient quantity of radioactive material may not reach and destroy the abnormal growths. By surgically removing the normal tissue the remaining metastases may be eliminated by the iodine radiation, wherever they may be. The remarkable uptake of radioiodine by thyroid tissue is demonstrated in Figure 13.5. A microsection, stained and enlarged, is shown in *A*, while *B* is an autoradiogram of the same section taken in a darkened room.

c. Tracer Studies. The radioactive isotope of an element behaves chemically exactly like the normal atoms of that element. The only difference is that on its disruption its presence is revealed. If administered in such small quantities that it does not alter in any way the physiological process being studied it may still disclose the behavior of the entire material of which it is a part. It is easy to visualize the importance of this technique in the study of metabolism and circulatory and chemical processes in the human body.

A most surprising observation is the extreme rapidity of certain body processes. By injecting radio sodium into the human body it has been noted that some of the radioactive material will pass through the walls of the veins, be taken up by remote sweat glands, and carried to the surface of the body, all in less than a minute. It has been learned that while the parts of the body always appear the same, they are actually always in a constant state of breaking down and renewal. Thus while an organ retains its size and shape, the individual particles of which it is composed are rapidly being replaced. It is this dynamic state of body constituents which makes possible the effective use of radioactive elements in tracer studies.

13.9. Metallurgy—Atomic Diffusion. In the alloying, case-hardening, or welding of metals it is of interest to know to what extent the atoms of one element are able to diffuse into another metal or into its own solid phase. A technique to study the behavior of the natural radioactive elements in contact with other elements was developed by von Hevesy.[15] Since any of the known elements may now be made radioactive, such investigations of self-diffusion can be carried out for every metal.

A rather complete study of the diffusion of copper atoms in copper as a function of the temperature has been carried out.[16] The results are shown on the semilogarithmic plot of Figure 13.6, in which the diffusion coefficient as ordinate is plotted against the reciprocal of the absolute temperature T. It may be recalled that almost an identical relationship exists between the vapor pressure of a liquid and its temperature. Thus the diffusion of the metallic ions may be quite similar to the process of evaporation. The diffusion coefficient η, which represents

---

[15] G. von Hevesy, *Trans. Faraday Soc.*, **34**, 841 (1938); *Z. Electech.*, **26**, 363 (1920).
[16] C. Raynor, L. Thomassen, and L. Rouse, *Proc. Am. Soc. Metals*, **30**, 313 (1942).

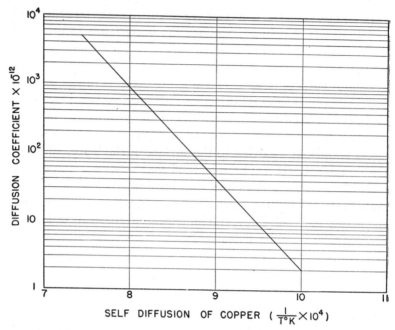

FIG. 13.6.   The self-diffusion of copper as affected by the temperature.

the number of atoms diffusing through unit area in a given time, because of the observed linear relationship, is representable as

$$\log \eta = A + \frac{B}{T}$$

where A and B are constants.   Similar measurements have been made on bismuth, gold, lead, and zinc.

A tiny quantity of radiosulfur in many tons of coal, subsequently converted to coke, enabled investigators to determine the source of sulfur impurities in the finished steel.

13.10. Mineralogy—The Color of Crystals.   It has been long known that the color of crystals can be altered by exposing them to any ionizing radiation, such as X-rays, cathode rays, or gamma rays.   Even more effective in producing alterations in color on the surface of a crystal is exposure to the deuteron beam of the cyclotron. The importance of coloration is well illustrated by considering two chemically identical crystals, aquamarine and emerald. The latter by virtue of its color has a valuation more than 100 times that of the former.

The most valued diamonds have been the very rare green crystals. On exposure to deuterons for a few seconds the most inferior amber-tinted diamond takes a permanent green tint equal to that of the best natural gems. On heating to a very high temperature the amber tint may be restored.

The coloration induced in such a crystal as rock salt, varying in shade from amber to black, may be used as an indicator of the intensity of radiation. Too strong radiation or heating to about 220° C. will restore the original clearness.

13.11. Well-logging by Radioactivity. The possibility of determining the detailed subsurface rock structure contiguous to a drill hole, by radioactive methods, has been successfully exploited since about 1940. As currently employed the analysis depends upon the interpretation of two parallel curves, each of which is obtained by recording the intensity of gamma radiation as a function of the well depth on a suitable recorder. In curve A of Figure 13.7 the natural radioactivity of the rock is recorded by a sensitive ionization chamber traveling the length of the well hole supported by a conducting cable. Only a few feet of the whole trace is shown. Curve B is independently obtained and portrays the intensity of the "capture" gamma rays arising from the absorption of slow neutrons at the same depths, in the various stratigraphic materials. The slow neutrons are derived from a Ra-Be source attached to, but well shielded from, the traveling ionization chamber.

All natural rocks are radioactive in varying degree. Petroleum is most generally associated with sedimentary rocks, particularly limestones, shales, and sandstones. Of these, the shales are the most radioactive. In the normal sequence of geologic deposition, limestone and sandstone layers are usually separated or interbedded with shales. The strongly radioactive shales are shown as peaks in curve A. It is not possible by this method alone to distinguish accurately between limestone and sandstone.

The gamma intensity associated with the neutron irradiation, shown in curve B, depends upon the relative nuclear capture cross sections and the efficiency of neutron capture gamma ray

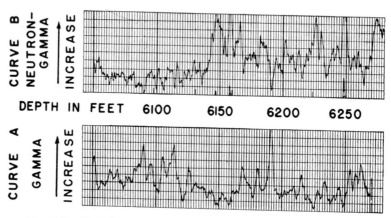

FIG. 13.7. Typical gamma and neutron-gamma traces for a deep drill hole.

emission in the surrounding materials. The neutron response for dense limestone is usually more pronounced than for sandstone and for both the intensities will be greater than that obtained for shale. The presence of a hydrogen bearing fluid in the rock, in practice acts to give a decreased neutron response and the shales are of this nature. Shales, however, are generally impervious and will usually never produce gas, oil, or water. Porous zones in the neighboring sandstone or limestone which may be productive layers, can be identified by a relatively low intensity on curve A and a reduction in the normally high neutron yield curve. An interpretation of the combined curves must be made in connection with the known geologic data for the geographic area. In the curves as shown, the zone at a depth of 6200 ft, lying below the shale at 6190 ft, shows high porosity and might reasonably be expected to be productive.

13.12. Zoology. *a. Mutations.* The nucleus of the living cell contains a certain number of threadlike structures known as chromosomes. In the chromosomes are minute entities called "genes." The genes occur in pairs, one member being derived from each parent. When the cell divides, each chromosome and each gene also divide so that each daughter cell resembles the parent. Destruction or alteration of the genes alters the characteristics of the cell. If the change occurs in a germ cell, the alteration is transmitted to all subsequent generations, provided the change is compatible with life. This transmission to a daughter cell of altered characteristics is termed a mutation. This phenomenon undoubtedly plays an important role in evolution.

Mutations in nature occur spontaneously, but not frequently. The effect of ionizing radiation is to increase markedly the frequency of mutations, which might naturally occur. Thus geneticists are able to observe in a short time those changes which by spontaneous mutation would occur only infrequently. This fact was first demonstrated by Muller for X-rays in 1927,[17] using as subject material the fruit fly, Drosophila. The same fundamental principles [18] are applicable to all living beings, including man. A profusion of papers on this subject has appeared, using in some cases gamma rays and in other experiments neutron radiation, all with similar effects.

b. Radiation and Life. The possibility of destroying any living organism by ionizing radiation is well established. The amount of radiation required is dependent upon the nature of the specimen and the kind of radiation employed. A sufficiently large dosage will produce immediate death, while lesser amounts may result in a survival for some fraction of the normal life. This is illustrated in Figure 13.8 which shows the be-

[17] H. J. Muller, *Science*, **67**, 82 (1928).
[18] See G. Failla, *J. Applied Phys.*, **12**, 279 (1941).

havior of fruit flies (*Drosophila melanogaster*) irradiated with large single doses of gamma radiation from cobalt 60.

In spite of the general fear that radiation in any amount is harmful, there exists the possibility that the life-span in certa in simple animal structures may actually be extended by the use of the proper radiation dosage. The flour beetle (*Tribolium con-*

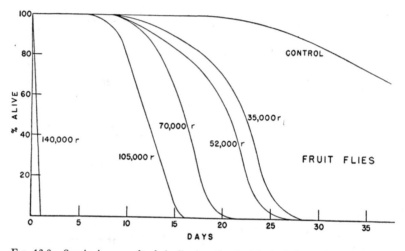

Fig. 13.8. Survival curves for fruit flies irradiated with single large dosage of cobalt 60 gamma rays.

fusum) appears to respond in this way. Under well-controlled laboratory conditions there is evidence that while a single dose of 15,000 r of gamma radiation from cesium 137 (662 kev) is lethal, a chronic dosage of 100 r per day of this same radiation can have a "beneficial" effect. Animals receiving this amount of radiation outlived by about 20% the control specimens which received no gamma rays.

It is not unreasonable to expect an effect of this sort. The slight destructive effect of the irradiation serves as a stimulus to initiate and develop an active repair mechanism within the organism. Many of the everyday catastrophes that might ordinarily lead to disaster may then be safely handled. This is in no sense to be construed as evidence in favor of a similar effect in humans. It is undoubtedly highly desirable to avoid as completely as possible all unnecessary irradiation.

13.13. Safeguards in the Use of Radioactive Materials. The reduction of radiation intensitities to a safe level for the per-

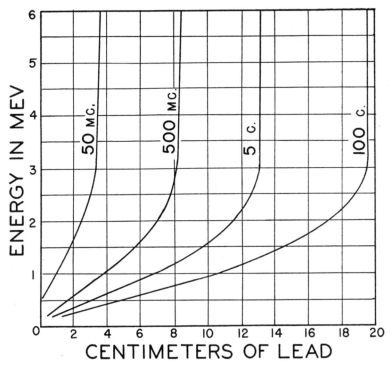

FIG. 13.9. Thickness of lead for tolerance dose at 100 cm as a function of the gamma energy and the source strength.

sonnel involved is not particularly difficult. After surveys have been made, establishing the existing levels and the nature of the radiations, it is easy to introduce the proper safeguards. These will in general consist of (*a*) proper ventilation, (*b*) lead or other dense shielding for gamma or X-rays, (*c*) water or paraffin shielding for neutrons, (*d*) adjustment of maximum distance between source and personnel, and (*e*) limiting the time of exposure, if necessary.

Any airborne radioactive material, such as radon, or other suspended particles which could be inhaled by personnel, must be collected and safely discharged by an adequate ventilating system.

In the shipping of radioactive materials, now usually by air express, adequate protection must be given for the handlers. Figure 13.9 shows the thickness of lead that would be required for sources of different strengths, emitting gamma radiation of a particular energy, for a tolerance dosage of 10 milliroentgens per hour at a distance of 100 centimeters from the source. The recommendations of the U.S. Bureau of Standards for the shielding of radium sources of various strengths at any specific distance is presented Figure 13.10.

United States postal laws permit the acceptance of marked radioactive material, provided among other things that (*a*) the gamma radiation at the surface is less than 0.01 r for 24 hours, (*b*) no package contains more than 0.1 millicurie of radium, or polonium, or that amount of other material which disintegrates at a rate of 5×10^7 atoms per second, and (*c*) liquids are packed in tight-glass or other suitable container, surrounded by sufficient absorbent material to absorb the entire liquid contents.

Neutron shielding is accomplished best by materials which contain hydrogen. Tanks of water containing a small amount of dissolved borax serve very well. In case both neutron and gamma shielding is required, a compromise material such as concrete with as much water content as possible is employed. Some concretes which contain magnetite concentrates will absorb and retain indefinitely up to 10% water by weight, and are thus particularly effective for neutrons.

As an assurance that no individual is receiving an undesirable dosage, it is customary for every person so engaged to carry either a penlike, charged condenser chamber or a photographic monitoring film. At the end of one or two weeks the chamber

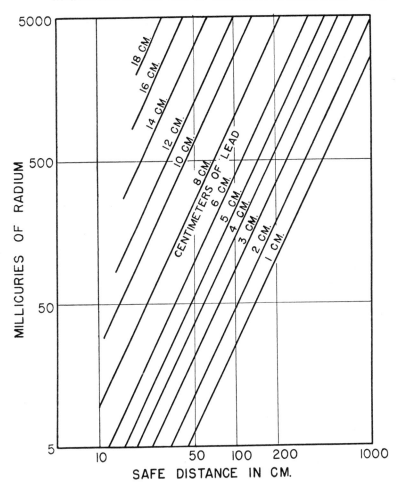

FIG. 13.10.   Safe shielding for radium sources at specified distance.

is checked to note its state of discharge or the film is developed and compared with a calibrated standard, to estimate the dosage. Film meters are not as satisfactory as electrical devices, although they have certain evident advantages in their compactness and their insensitivity to severe temperature and humidity conditions.

An abrupt lowering of the white blood cell count will result from severe exposure to radiation. However, due to the normal variation from one individual to another and the ability of the body quickly to recover normalcy in this regard, too much faith must not be placed in a single observation of the blood.

QUESTIONS AND PROBLEMS

1. A dosage of 10 millicuries of P^{32} is applied intravenously to a patient. One per cent of the material is selectively absorbed by a brain tumor whose mass is 60 gm. How many disintegrations per second will occur in each gram of the diseased tissue two days after the application?

Answer: 515 per sec.

2. A source of radiosodium is assayed as 90 millicuries. It is administered to a patient 45 hr later. What is the activity at that time?

Answer: 10.9 millicuries.

3. The cross section for the reaction $_4Be^9(d, n)_5B^{10}$ is 1.2×10^{-25} cm². A deuteron beam of 60 microamperes traverses a thin beryllium target, 5 mils (0.005″) in thickness. How many neutrons per second will pass through a normal area 10 cm on edge, situated 60 cm from the target, assuming a uniform distribution?

Answer: 15.6×10^7 per sec.

4. The absorption coefficient of neutrons in tissue is 0.14 cm⁻¹. What is the cross section for the absorption process, assuming the tissue to behave as water, and hydrogen to be the absorbing agent?

Answer: 2.085×10^{-24} cm².

5. The average specific gravity of the sun is 1.4 and its diameter is 860,000 miles. The solar radiation constant at the earth is 0.135 joule per cm² per sec and the average distance to the sun is 93 million miles. At what total rate does the sun lose radiation? At what rate does the total mass change?

Answer: 3.8×10^{26} joules/sec or 4.2×10^{12} gm/sec or 4.6×10^6 tons/sec.

6. If the above energy is derived from the synthesis of helium from hydrogen, at what rate is helium being produced in the sun?

Answer: 6.1×10^{14} gm/sec.

7. A gram of carbon taken from the tomb of Cleopatra (30 B.C.) is more radioactive than a gram of carbon from Confucius (478 B.C.) by what factor?

Answer: 1.056.

8. Carbon from the tomb of King Raneb of the Second Egyptian Dynasty is found to be only 0.458 as radioactive as carbon from a growing plant. It is thus probable that Raneb died about what year?

Answer: 4460 B.C.

9. A shipment of 200 millicuries of radium is sent air express and is to be shielded so that the gamma activity is not greater than 10 milliroentgens per hr at a distance of 1 meter. How thick should the lead absorbing layer be?

Answer: ∼5 cm.

10. Twenty-five per cent of an administered dose of 10 millicuries of iodine 131 is taken up by a mass of thyroid tissue of 30 gm. How many disintegrations will occur in 1 gm of the tissue in 1 sec, two days after the administration? Estimate the energy per second set free in each gram of tissue.

Answer: 2.6×10^6 disintegrations/sec; ∼4 ergs.

11. In an agricultural experiment 100 millicuries of phosphorus 32 are mixed with 20 tons of phosphate. If two months later 2.3 counts per second are observed from the total residue of a tomato, how much of the treated phosphate did the the tomato absorb?

Answer: 0.2 gm.

CHAPTER 14

TABLE OF ISOTOPES

By using various modes of excitation, over five hundred radioactive isotopes of the 101 elements have been created. It is frequently desirable to know the half-life, the atomic mass, or the type of radiation emitted by certain of these, without too much searching in the literature. This information is assembled in the following table.

The information presented has been derived in part from the original papers and in part from other previously prepared summarizing tables. The values of the isotopic masses are reproduced through the courtesy of Dr. A. H. Wapstra from the recently assembled tables [1] of Wapstra and Huizenga.

In the following table, the energy of each type of radiation is shown in the accompanying parentheses. The symbol K is used to denote the "K" electron capture process by the nucleus. The number of gamma rays for many isotopes is too numerous to present completely, and it is then represented by the symbol γs. The designations γ, e^-, and e^+ are for gamma rays, electrons, and positrons, respectively. The percentage abundance of the stable isotopes is presented in the column headed as %. Half-lives are designated as S, M, H, D, and Y for seconds, minutes, hours, days, and years, and the energies are in Mev.

[1] A. H. Wapstra and J. R. Huizenga, *Physica*, **21**, 367, 385, 410 (1955).

Handwritten annotation in top right:
1.008145
1.000548
1.007597 mass of p

Z	Element Name	A	Mass	% Abundance	Half-life	Radiation (Mev)
0	Electron........	0	0.000548			
0	Neutron........	1	1.008986			
1	Hydrogen......	1	1.008145	99.98		
		2	2.014740	0.0156		
		3	3.017005		12.4 Y	e^- (0.018)
2	Helium........	3	3.016986	$\sim 10^{-5}$		
		4	4.003873	~ 100		
		5	5.013888		10^{-5} S	α; n
		6	6.020831		0.85 S	e^- (3.7)
3	Lithium........	6	6.017034	7.4		
		7	7.018232	92.6		
		8	8.025033		0.88 S	e^- (12.0)
		9			0.17 S	
4	Beryllium......	7	7.019159		54 D	γ (0.485); K
		8	8.007849		10^{-16} S	2α
		9	8.015046	100		
		10	10.016716		2.7×10^6 Y	e^- (0.56)
5	Boron..........	9	9.016195		10^{-18} S	
		10	10.016119	18.8		
		11	11.012795	81.2		
		12	12.018168		0.027 S	e^- (13.4)
6	Carbon........	10	10.020240		19.1 S	e^+ (2.2)
		11	11.014922		20.5 M	e^+ (0.95)
		12	12.003803	98.9		
		13	13.007478	1.1		
		14	14.007687		5720 Y	e^- (0.155)
7	Nitrogen.......	12	12.022776		0.0125 S	e^+ (16.6)
		13	13.009864		10.0 M	e^+ (0.92, 1.24)
		14	14.007520	99.62		
		15	15.004862	0.38		
		16	16.011171		7.4 S	e^- (10.0); γ (6.4)
		17	17.013984		4.14 S	e^- (3.7)
8	Oxygen........	14	14.013069		76.5 S	e^+ (1.8); γ (2.3)
		15	15.007767		126 S	e^+ (1.7)
		16	16.000000	99.76		
		17	17.004534	0.04		
		18	18.004855	0.20		
		19	19.009591		29.5 S	e^- (3.0, 4.5); γ
9	Fluorine........	17	17.007506		66 S	e^+ (1.7)
		18	18.006646		112 M	e^+ (0.6)

Z	Element Name	A	Mass	% Abundance	Half-life	Radiation (Mev)
9	Fluorine........	19	19.004448	100		
		20	20.006340		12 S	e^- (5.0); γ (2.2)
10	Neon..........	19	19.007945		18.2 S	e^+ (2.20)
		20	19.998769	90.52		
		21	21.000499	0.27		
		22	21.998354	9.21		
		23	23.001764		40 S	e^- (4.1)
11	Sodium........	21	21.004281		23 S	e^+ (2.53)
		22	22.001404		2.6 Y	e^+ (1.8, 0.54); γ (1.28)
		23	22.997053	100		
		24	23.998565		14.8 H	e^- (1.39); γ (2.758, 1.38)
		25	24.997781		62 S	e^- (3.7, 2.7); γ
12	Magnesium.....	23	23.001452		11.9 S	e^+ (2.82)
		24	23.992640	78.6		
		25	24.993752	10.1		
		26	25.990798	11.3		
		27	26.992868		9.6 M	e^- (1.8, 0.8); γs
13	Aluminum......	25	24.998312		7.3 S	e^+
		26	25.995120		6.3 S	e^+ (2.99)
		27	26.990081	100		
		28	27.990771		2.4 M	e^- (3.0); γ (1.8)
		29	28.989925		6.7 M	e^- (2.5, 1.4); γ (2.3, 1.2)
14	Silicon........	27	26.995265		4.92 S	e^+ (3.64)
		28	27.985775	92.3		
		29	28.985660	4.7		
		30	29.983252	3.0		
		31	30.985153		170 M	e^- (1.486)
15	Phosphorus.....	29	28.990994		4.6 S	e^+ (3.63)
		30	29.987885		2.55 M	e^+ (3.5)
		31	30.983561	100		
		32	31.984028		14.3 D	e^- (1.718)
		33	32.982156		25 D	e^- (0.26)
16	Sulfur..........	31	30.989405		2.8 S	e^+ (3.9)
		32	31.982196	95.1		
		33	32.981889	0.74		
		34	33.978640	4.2		
		35	34.980085		87.1 D	e^- (0.17)
		36	35.978440	0.0136		
		37	36.982050		5.0 M	e^- (4.3, 1.6); γ (2.7)
17	Chlorine........	33	32.987744		2.8 S	e^+ (4.13)
		34	33.984570		33 M	e^+ (4.5, 2.6, 1.3); γs
		35	34.979905	75.4		
		36	35.979688		4×10^5 Y	e^+; e^- (0.66); K
		37	36.977540	24.6		

Z	Element Name	A	Mass	% Abundance	Half-life	Radiation (Mev)
17	Chlorine........	38	37.979965		38 M	e^- (4.81, 2.77, 1.11); γs
		39	38.979820		56 M	e^- (2.5)
18	Argon.........	35	34.985715		1.86 S	e^+ (4.38)
		36	35.978921	0.307		
		37	36.978416		34 D	K
		38	37.974790	0.061		
		39	38.976644		2.4 M; 265 Y	e^- (2.1, 0.565)
		40	39.975050	99.632		
		41	40.977530		110 M	e^- (2.55, 1.25); γ (1.3)
19	Potassium......	37	36.985000		1.3 S	e^+ (4.57)
		38	37.981100		7.5 M	e^+ (2.53); γ (2.1)
		39	38.976037	93.1		
		40	39.976653	0.011	1.25×10^9 Y	e^- (1.33); γ (1.46); K
		41	40.974760	6.9		
		42	41.975830		12.4 H	e^- (3.55, 1.99); γ (1.53, 0.31)
		43	42.974330		22 H	e^- (1.84, 1.22); γs
		44	43.975900		22 M	e^- (4.9, 1.5); γ (1.16)
20	Calcium........	39	38.983400		1.1 S	e^+ (5.13)
		40	39.975230	96.97		
		41	40.975230		1.1×10^5 Y	K
		42	41.971890	0.64		
		43	42.972350	0.145		
		44	43.969340	2.06		
		45	44.970350		164 D	e^- (0.256)
		46		0.0033		
		47	46.969460		5.35 D	e^- (1.4, 0.46); γs
		48	47.967700	0.185		
		49	48.971160		8.5 M	e^- (2.0); γ (3.0)
21	Scandium......	40	39.990250		0.3 S	e^+ (9.0); γ (3.75)
		41	40.981630		0.87 S	e^+ (4.94)
		42			13.5 D	e^+ (1.4)
		43	42.974730		4 H	e^+ (1.18, 0.80, 0.39); γs
		44	43.973260		3.9 H	e^+ (1.47); γ (2.54, 1.17)
		.45	44.970075	100		
		46	45.969490		85 D	e^- (0.36); γ; K
		47	46.967240		80 H	e^- (0.61, 0.45); γ (0.159)
		48	47.967410		44 H	e^- (0.64); γs
		49	48.965540		57 M	e^- (2.1)
22	Titanium.......	43			0.58 S	
		45	44.972270		3.0 H	e^+ (1.02)
		46	45.966954	7.94		
		47	46.966500	7.75		
		48	47.963120	73.45		
		49	48.963390	5.52		
		50	49.960580	5.34		
		51	50.962660		5.9 M	e^- (2.13, 1.5); γs

Z	Element Name	A	Mass	% Abundance	Half-life	Radiation (Mev)
23	Vanadium......	46	45.974900		0.4 S	e^+ (6.2)
		47	46.969627		33 M	e^+ (1.9)
		48	47.967453		16 D	e^+ (0.7); γ (1.04); K
		49	48.964043		330 D	K
		50	49.963120	0.23		
		51	50.960040	100		
		52	51.961184		3.8 M	e^- (2.73); γ (1.45)
24	Chromium......	49	48.966794		42 M	e^+ (1.54, 1.45, 1.39); γs
		50	49.961640	4.49		
		51	50.960844		27.5 D	e^+ (0.75, 0.43); γ (0.32)
		52	51.956990	83.78		
		53	52.957460	9.43		
		54	53.956020	2.30		
		55	54.958430		3.5 M	e^- (2.85)
25	Manganese.....	50	49.970000		0.28 S	e^+ (6.5)
		51	50.964300		46 M	e^+ (2.0)
		52	51.962070		21 M; 5.7 D	e^+ (2.6); γ (1.4)
		53	52.962250		140 Y	e^+ (0.57)
		54	53.957310		290 D	K; γ (0.84)
		55	54.955400	100		
		56	55.956590		2.59 H	e^- (0.7, 1.09, 2.88); γs
		57			1.7 M	e^- (2.6); γs
26	Iron..........	52	51.964210		8.3 H	e^+ (0.80)
		53	52.962250		8.9 M	e^+ (2.7); γs
		54	53.956640	5.81		
		55	54.955646		2.9 Y	K
		56	55.952640	91.64		
		57	56.953420	2.21		
		58	57.951470	0.34		
		59	58.953615		46 D	e^- (1.56, 0.46, 0.27); γs
27	Cobalt.........	54	53.966200		0.18 S	e^+ (7.7)
		55	54.959360		18.2 H	e^+ (1.5, 1.03, 0.53); γs
		56	55.957610		77 D	e^+ (1.5, 0.98, 0.32); γ
		57	56.953980		270 D	K; γ (0.137, 0.123, 0.014)
		58	57.953940		72 D	e^+ (0.47); γ (0.805)
		59	58.951940	100		
		60	59.952868		5.3 Y	e^- (1.48, 0.31); γ (1.332,1.172)
		60			10.5 M	e^- (1.54); γ (1.332)
		61	60.951290		1.7 H	e^- (1.42, 1.0); γ
		62	61.952940		13.8 M	e^- (2.5); γ (1.17)
28	Nickel.........	57	56.957460		36 H	e^+ (0.84); γs
		58	57.953770	67.7		
		59	58.953093		7.5×10^4 Y	K
		60	59.949840	26.2		
		61	60.949690	1.2		
		62	61.947570	3.7		

Z	Element Name	A	Mass	% Abundance	Half-life	Radiation (Mev)
28	Nickel..........	63	62.949508		85 Y	e^- (0.062)
		64	63.948130	1.2		
		65	64.950650		2.6 H	e^- (2.10, 1.01, 0.60); γs
		66			56.0 H	e^- (0.3)
29	Copper........	58	57.964000		3 S	e^+ (8.2)
		59			81 S	e^+
		60	59.956580		24.6 M	e^+ (3.92, 3.0, 2.0); γs
		61	60.952084		3.4 H	e^+ (1.21, 1.11, 0.55, 0.23); γs
		62	61.951793		9.8 M	e^+ (2.9)
		63	62.949440	69.1		
		64	63.949934		12.8 H	e^- (0.573); e^+ (0.656); K
		65	64.948400	30.9		
		66	65.949760		5 M	e^- (2.63, 1.65); γ (1.05)
		67	66.949114		59 H	e^- (0.577, 0.484, 0.395); γs
		68			38 S	e^- (3.0)
30	Zinc..........	62	61.953615		9.3 H	e^+ (0.69, 0.64); γ (0.042)
		63	62.953029		38 M	e^+ (2.32); γ
		64	63.949320	48.9		
		65	64.949847		250 D	e^+ (0.33); K; γ (1.11)
		66	65.946940	27.8		
		67	66.948500	4.0		
		68	67.946520	18.6		
		69	68.948533		51 M	e^- (0.90)
		70	69.947430	0.7		
		71	70.949840		2.2 M; 3 H	e^- (2.4, 1.5); γs
		72			49 H	e^- (1.6, 0.3)
31	Gallium........	64	63.957100		2.6 M	e^+
		65	64.953200		15 M	e^+ (2.1); γs
		66	65.952490		9.4 H	e^+ (4.15, 1.38, 0.90, 0.40); γs
		67	66.949576		78 H	K; γs
		68	67.949640		68 M	e^+ (1.9)
		69	68.947570	60.2		
		70	69.948140		21 M	e^- (1.65, 0.6, 0.4); γs
		71	70.947370	39.8		
		72	71.948900		14.2 H	e^- (3.16, 2.53, 1.51, 0.96); γs
		73	72.947950		5 H	e^- (1.4); γs
32	Germanium.....	66			140 M	e^+
		67	66.954330		20 M	e^+ (3.4)
		68			250 D	e^+
		69	68.949970		40 H	e^+ (1.22, 0.61, 0.22); γs
		70	69.946370	20.6		
		71	70.947634		11 D	K
		72	71.944600	27.4		
		73	72.946450	7.6		
		74	73.944590	36.8		
		75	74.946620		82 M	e^- (1.19, 0.98, 0.92, 0.55); γs
		76	75.945330	7.6		

Z	Element Name	A	Mass	% Abundance	Half-life	Radiation (Mev)
32	Germanium.....	77	76.948020		12 H	e^- (2.9, 2.7, 2.2, 0.74); γs
		78			86 M	e^- (0.9)
33	Arsenic........	71	70.949690		62 H	e^+ (0.81)
		72	71.949280		26 H	e^+ (3.34, 2.5, 1.84, 0.67); γs
		73	72.946850		76 D	K; γ (0.052)
		74	73.947345		17 D	e^- (1.36, 0.69); e^+ (1.53, 0.92); γs
		75	74.945400	100		
		76	75.946530		26.8 H	e^- (2.97, 2.41, 1.76, 0.36); γs
		77	76.945095		40 H	e^- (0.68, 0.43, 0.16); γs
		78	77.946490		90 M	e^- (4.1, 1.4); γs
		79	78.946050		9 M	e^- (2.2)
34	Selenium.......	70			44 M	e^+
		72			9.5 D	K
		73	72.949830		7.1 H	e^- (1.68, 1.32); γ
		74	73.945890	0.9		
		75	74.946333		125 D	K; γs
		76	75.943340	9.0		
		77	76.944360	7.6	17.5 S	γ (0.14)
		78	77.942090	23.5		
		79	78.943580		6.5×10^4 Y	e^- (0.16)
		80	79.941980	49.8		
		81	80.943580		19 M	e^- (1.38)
		82	81.942610	9.2		
		83			25 M	e^- (1.5); γs
		84			3 M	e^-
35	Bromine.......	75	74.949260		1.7 H	e^+ (1.7, 0.8, 0.6, 0.3)
		76	75.948270		17 H	e^+ (3.5, 1.7, 1.1, 0.8, 0.6); γs
		77	76.945818		57 H	e^+ (0.36); K; γs
		78	77.945850		6.4 M	e^+ (2.3)
		79	78.943410	50.6		
		80	79.944010		4.4 H	γ (0.048, 0.036)
		80			18 M	e^- (2.0, 1.38); e^+ (0.886)
		81	80.942080	49.4		
		82	81.942680		36 H	e^- (0.465); γs
		83	82.941302		140 M	e^- (0.96); γ (0.051)
		84	83.943085		33 M	e^- (4.68, 3.56, 2.53, 1.72); γs
		85	84.942610		3.0 M	e^- (2.5)
		87	86.949870		55 S	e^- (8.0, 2.6); γs
		88			16.0 S	e^- (2.7, 0.52); γs
36	Krypton........	77	76.948910		1.1 H	e^+ (1.86, 1.67, 0.85); γs
		78	77.944890	0.35		
		79	78.945150		34 H	e^+ (0.60, 0.34); K; γs
		80	79.941860	2.22		
		81	80.942250		2×10^5 Y	K
		82	81.939400	11.53		
		83	82.940340	11.55	1.89 H	γ (0.032, 0.009)

Z	Element Name	A	Mass	% Abundance	Half-life	Radiation (Mev)
36	Krypton........	84	83.938060	57.00		
		85	84.939600		4 H; 10.6 H	e^- (0.85); (0.672, 0.15); γs
		86	85.938210	17.37		
		87	86.941280		78 M	e^- (3.8, 3.3, 1.3); γs
		88	87.942470		2.8 H	e^- (2.7, 0.9, 0.52); γs
		89	88.944790		3.2 M	e^- (4.0, 2.0)
		90			0.5 M	e^- (3.2)
		91			9.3 S	e^- (3.6)
		92			2.3 S	e^-
		93			2.2 S	e^-
		94			1.4 S	e^-
37	Rubidium......	81	80.944610		4.7 H	e^+ (0.9); γ (0.95)
		82	81.943550		1.3 M	e^+ (3.15)
		82			6.4 H	e^+ (0.775); γs
		83			83 D	K; γ (0.525)
		84	83.940900		34 D	e^+ (1.63, 0.82); e^- (0.44)
		85	84.938880	72.3		
		86	85.938521		19.5 D	e^- (1.77, 0.68); γ (1.08)
		87	86.936870	27.7	5×10^{10} Y	e^- (0.275)
		88	87.939300		18 M	e^- (5.3, 3.6, 2.5); γs
		89	88.940490		15 M	e^- (3.8); γ
		90	89.940490		2.7 M	e^- (5.7)
		91	89.941900		1.7 M	e^- (4.6, 3.0)
38	Strontium......	83			38 H	e^+ (1.15)
		84	83.939860	0.56		
		85	84.940000		65 D	K; γ (0.513)
		85			70 M	K; γs
		86	85.936620	9.86		
		87	86.936576	7.02	2.7 H	γ (0.386)
		88	87.933750	82.56		
		89	88.935655		51 D	e^- (1.48)
		90	89.935773		28 Y	e^- (0.6)
		91	90.938667		9.8 H	e^- (2.67, 2.03, 1.36, 1.09, 0.61)
		92	91.939650		2.7 H	e^- (0.55)
		93			7 M	e^-
39	Yttrium........	86	85.941130		15 H	e^+ (1.8, 1.19); γs
		87	86.938390		14 H	K; γ (0.38)
		87			80 H	e^+ (0.7)
		88	87.937770		105 D	e^+ (0.83); γs
		89	88.934080	100		
		90	89.935200		64 H	e^- (2.4)
		91	90.935805		61 D; 50 M	e^- (1.6); γ (1.22, 0.55)
		92	91.937580		3.5 H	e^- (3.6, 2.68, 1.3); γs
		93	92.938660		10.5 H	e^- (3.1)
		94	93.941600		16.5 M	e^- (5.4); γ (1.4)
40	Zirconium......	87	86.942160		94 M	e^+ (2.10); γ (3.81)
		88			85 D	K

Z	Element Name	A	Mass	% Abundance	Half-life	Radiation (Mev)
40	Zirconium	89	88.937131		4.5 M; 79 H	K; e^+ (0.90); γs
		90	89.932840	51.4		
		91	90.934140	11.2		
		92	91.933820	17.1		
		93	92.935327		5 $\times$ 10^6 Y	e^- (0.060)
		94	93.935800	17.4		
		95	94.937906		63 D	e^- (1.0); γs
		96	95.938530	2.8		
		97	96.941420		17 H	e^- (2.5); γs
41	Niobium	89			1.9 H	e^+ (2.9)
		90	89.937610		15.6 H	e^+ (1.5, 0.86, 0.55); γs
		91	90.935630		62 D	K
		92	91.935610		11 D	K; γs
		93	92.935260	100	42 D	γ (0.15)
		94	93.936520		6.6 M	e^- (1.4), (0.4)
		95	94.936700		35 D; 90 H	e^- (0.163); γs
		96	95.938261		22.9 H	e^- (0.75, 0.37); γs
		97	96.938550		74 M	e^- (1.267); γ (0.665)
		98			30 M	e^-
42	Molybdenum ...	91			15.5 M; 75 S	e^+ (3.7, 2.6); γs
		92	91.935210	15.9		
		93	92.935730		2 Y; 6.8 H	K; γs
		94	93.934330	9.1		
		95	94.935700	15.7		
		96	95.934900	16.5		
		97	96.936470	9.5		
		98	97.936560	23.8		
		99	98.939997		68.3 H	e^- (1.23, 0.445); γs
		100	99.938280	9.5		
		101			15 M	e^- (2.2, 1.0); γs
		102			12 M	e^-
43	Technetium	92	91.942080		4.5 M	K; γ (1.51)
		93	92.939100		44 M	e^+ (0.8); γ (1.32)
		94	93.938980		53 M	e^+ (2.41); γs
		95	94.937451		62 D; 20 H	e^+ (0.4); K; γs
		96	95.938230		4.3 D	K; γs
		97			93 D	γ (0.097)
		98			2.7 D	e^-; e^+; γs
		99	98.939515		5 $\times$ 10^5 Y	e^- (0.32)
		100			16 S	e^- (2.8); γ
		101			14 M	e^- (1.3); γ
		102			1 M	e^- (3.7); γ
44	Ruthenium	94			57 M	e^+
		95	94.939700		1.6 H	e^+ (1.1); γ (0.95)
		96	95.937920	5.68		
		98	97.937130	2.22		
		99	98.938200	12.81		

Z	Element Name	A	Mass	% Abundance	Half-life	Radiation (Mev)
44	Ruthenium	100		12.70		
		101		16.98		
		102	101.936410	31.34		
		103	102.938704		40 D	e^- (6.84, 0.22); γs
		104	103.937800	18.27		
		105	104.940845		4.4 H	e^- (1.15); γs
		106	105.940232		1 Y	e^- (0.03)
		107			4 M	e^- (4.0)
45	Rhodium.......	100			21 H	e^+ (3.0, 1.3); γ (1.8)
		101		0.08		
		102	101.938750		210 D	e^- (1.1); e^+; γ
		103	102.937900	99.92	57 M	γ
		104	103.939600		4.2 M	γ (0.055, 0.080)
		104			44 S	e^- (2.3); γs
		105	104.938692		36 H	e^- (0.57, 0.25); γs
		106	105.940190		30 S	e^- (3.5)
		107	106.940240		24 M	e^- (1.2)
46	Palladium......	100			4.0 D	γ (1.8); K
		101			9 H	e^+ (2.3)
		102	101.937530	0.8		
		103	102.938500		17 D	
		104	103.936870	9.3		
		105	104.938080	22.6		
		106	105.936400	27.2		
		107	106.938948		7×10^6 Y	e^- (0.035)
		108	107.937800	26.8		
		109	108.940510		13 H	e^- (1.03)
		110	109.939600	13.5		
		111	110.942890		22 M	e^- (2.15); γs
		112	111.942770		21 H	e^- (0.2)
47	Silver..........	102			73 M	e^+
		104	103.940870		16.3 M	e^+
		105	104.940500		40 D	K; γs
		106	105.939590		24.5 M	e^+ (2.04)
		106			8.6 D	K; γs
		107	106.938910	51.9	42 S	γ (0.093)
		108	107.940090		2.3 M	e^- (1.49, 0.83); γs
		109	108.939340	48.1	40 S	γ (0.0875)
		110	109.941390		24 S	e^- (2.8)
		110			282 D	e^- (0.53, 0.087); γs
		111	110.940580		7.5 D	e^- (1.04, 0.80, 0.70); γs
		112	111.942450		3.2 H	e^- (3.5); γ (0.86)
		113	112.942280		5.3 H	e^- (2.1)
		115	114.945280		20 M	e^- (3.0)
48	Cadmium.......	105	104.943720		38 M	e^+ (1.5); γ
		106	105.939520	1.21		
		107	106.940451		6.7 H	e^+ (0.32); γ (0.847)

Z	Element Name	A	Mass	% Abundance	Half-life	Radiation (Mev)
48	Cadmium.......	108	107.938200	0.87		
		109	108.939510		330 D	K; γ (0.080)
		110	109.938300	12.40		
		111	110.939450	12.75	48.7 M	γ (0.243)
		112	111.938230	24.07		
		113	112.940280	12.26		
		114	113.939550	28.86		
		115	114.942060		2.3 D	e^- (1.11); γs
					43 D	e^- (1.41); γ (1.10)
		116	115.941850	7.58		
		117	116.944800		2.8 H	e^- (1.5)
49	Indium........	107	106.944030		33 M	e^+
		109	108.941410		4.2 H	e^+ (0.75); γ (0.5)
		110	109.942520		65 M	e^+ (2.25); γ (0.65)
		111	110.940400		2.8 D	K; γ (0.33, 0.246, 0.172)
		112	111.940960		9 M	e^+ (1.5); e^- (1.0)
		112			23 M	γ (0.095)
		113	112.940120	4.3	105 M	γ (0.39)
		114	113.941600		48 D	γ (0.1909)
		114			72 S	e^- (1.98); e^+ (0.65); γs
		115	114.940500	95.7	4.5 H	γ (0.34)
		116	115.942530		13 S	e^- (2.8)
		116			54 M	e^- (1.0, 0.87, 0.6); γs
		117	116.941790		117 M	e^- (1.95)
		118			4.5M	e^- (1.5)
50	Tin............	111	110.943110		35 M	e^+ (1.51)
		112	111.940256	0.9		
		113			118 D	K; γ (0.401, 0.255)
		114	113.939468	0.6		
		115	114.939960	0.4		
		116	115.938970	14.1		
		117	116.940200	7.5	14.5 D	γ (0.162)
		118	117.939300	24.0		
		119	118.941000	8.6	245 D	γ
		120	119.940060	33.0		
		121	120.942411		27 H	e^- (0.4)
		122	121.942100	4.8		
		123	122.944620		125 D; 40 M	e^- (1.42, 1.26); γs
		124	123.944540	6.1		
		125	124.947420		10 M; 9.5 D	e^- (2.3, 2.0, 1.17); γs
		126			70 M	e^- (2.7, 0.7); γ (1.2)
51	Antimony......	116	115.944040		60 M	e^+ (1.45); γ
		117			2.9 H	e^+, γ
		118	117.943700		3.5 M	e^+ (3.1)
		119			39 H	K
		120	119.942980		17 M; 6 D	e^+ (1.7); K; γs
		121	120.942000	57.2		
		122	121.943680		2.8 D; 3.5 M	e^- (1.94, 1.36); γs

Z	Element Name	A	Mass	% Abundance	Half-life	Radiation (Mev)
51	Antimony.......	123	122.943100	42.8		
		124	123.945235		60 D; 21 M	e^- (3.2, 2.5, 0.60); γs
		125	124.944900		2.7 Y	e^- (0.616, 0.299, 0.128); γs
		126			9 H	e^- (1.0); γs
		127			90 H	e^- (1.2); γs
		129			4.2 H	e^-
		132			2.2 M	e^-
		133			4.5 M	e^-
52	Tellurium......	118			6.0 D	K
		119			4.5 D	K; γ (1.6)
		120	119.942520	0.1		
		121			17 D; 154 D	K; γ (0.575, 0.213)
		122	121.941560	2.5		
		123	122.943300	0.9	121 D	γ
		124	123.942110	4.6		
		125	124.944080	7.0	58 D	γ
		126	125.943600	18.7		
		127	126.945660		113 D	e^-; γ (0.086)
		127			9.3 H	e^- (0.70)
		128	127.946100	31.7		
		129	128.947580		32 D	e^-; γ
		129			72 M	e^- (1.8); γ (0.3)
		130	129.947800	34.5		
		131	130.950020		30 H	e^-; γ
		131			25 M	e^- (2.0); γ
		132	131.950260		77 H	e^- (0.35); γ (0.22)
		133	132.952850		60 M; 2 M	e^- (2.4; 1.3); γs
		134			43 M	e^-
		135			2 M	e^-
53	Iodine.........	122	121.946010		3.6 M	e^+ (3.1)
		124	123.945570		4.0 D	e^+ (2.2, 1.5, 0.67); γs
		125	124.944240		56 D	K; γ
		126	125.945850		13.0 D	e^- (1.24, 0.85); e^+; γs
		127	126.944800	100		
		128	127.946670		25.0 M	e^- (2.02, 1.59); γ (0.428)
		129	128.945752		1.7×10^7 Y	e^- (0.13); γ (0.039)
		130	129.947810		12.6 H	e^- (0.61, 1.03); γs
		131	130.947660		8.0	e^- (0.60, 0.32); γs
		132	131.949820		2.4 H	e^- (2.2, 1.5); γs
		133	132.949630		22 H	e^- (1.4, 0.5); γs
		134	133.951270		54 M	e^- (3.9, 1.6); γs
		135			6.6 H	e^- (1.4, 1.0, 0.47); γs
		136	135.956920		1.5 M	e^- (6.5); γ
		137			22 S	e^-
		138			5.9 S	e^-
54	Xenon.........	124	123.945390	0.094		
		125			18 H	K, γs
		126	125.944500	0.088		

Z	Element Name	A	Mass	% Abundance	Half-life	Radiation (Mev)
54	Xenon..........	127	126.945880		75 S	γ (0.175, 0.125)
		127			34 D	K; γs
		128	127.944500	1.90		
		129	128.945550	25.23		
		130	129.944620	4.07		
		131	130.946620	21.17	12 D	γ
		132	131.946000	26.96		
		133	132.947660		5.3 D; 2.3 D	e^- (0.346); γs
		134	133.947620	10.54		
		135			9.4 H	e^- (0.9)
		135			15.6 M	e^- (0.65); γ
		136	135.950050	8.95		
		137	136.955200		3.9 M	e^- (4.0)
		138			17 M	e^-
		139			40 S	e^-
		140			16 S	e^-
		141			3 S	e^-
		143			1.3 S	e^-
		145			0.8 S	e^-
55	Cesium.........	128	127.948900		3.1 M	e^+ (3.0)
		129	128.946740		31 H	K; γ
		130	129.947830		30 M	e^+; K
		131	130.946996		10.2 D	e^+; K
		132	131.947930		7.1 D	K; γ (0.62)
		133	132.947200	100		
		134	133.948960		3 H	e^- (2.4); γ (0.7)
		134			2.3 Y	e^- (0.648, 0.092); γs
		135			2.9×10^6 Y	e^- (0.19)
		136			13.3 D	e^- (0.35, 0.28); γs
		137	136.950899		35 Y	e^- (1.17, 0.518); γ (0.662)
		138	137.953900		33 M	e^- (2.6); γ
		139			9.5 M	e^-
		140			66 S	e^-
56	Barium........	129	128.949530		2 H	e^+
		130	129.947355	0.10		
		131			13 D	K; γs
		132		0.09		
		133			38.8 H	γ (0.276)
		133			10 Y	K; γ (0.32, 0.085)
		134	133.946757	2.42		
		135		6.59		
		136		7.81		
		137	136.949630	11.32	2.6 M	γ
		138	137.948700	71.66		
		139	138.952060		85 M	e^- (2.27); γs
		140	139.954370		12.8 D	e^- (1.02, 0.48); γs
		141			18 M	e^- (2.8); γ
		142			30 S	e^-

Z	Element Name	A	Mass	% Abundance	Half-life	Radiation (Mev)
57	Lanthanum.....	134	133.950730		6.5 M	e^+ (2.7); K
		135			18.5 H	K; γ (0.76)
		136			9.5 M	e^+ (2.1); K
		137			400 Y	e^-
		138	137.950100	0.09		
		139	138.949500	99.91		
		140	139.952970		41.4 H	e^- (2.26, 1.67, 1.32); γs
		141	140.954330		3.6 H	e^- (2.8)
		142			74 M	e^-; γ
		143			20 M	e^-
		144			1 S	e^-
58	Cerium.........	135			22 H	e^+ (0.8)
		136		0.19		
		137			36 H	K; γ (0.75, 0.28)
		138	137.949030	0.25		
		139	138.949630		140 D	K; γ (0.137, 0.144)
		140	139.948900	88.49		
		141	140.951724		32 D	e^- (0.56, 0.41); γ (1.41)
		142	141.953020	11.07		
		143	142.956538		33 H	e^- (1.36); γs
		144	143.958445		290 D	e^- (0.45, 0.307); γs
		145			1.8 H	e^-
		146	145.964300		14.6 M	e^-
59	Praseodymium..	138	137.952790		2.0 H	e^+ (1.4); γs
		140	139.952390		3.5 M	e^+ (2.40); γ
		141	140.951100	100		
		142	141.953836		19.2 H	e^- (2.14); γs
		143	142.955050		13.5 D	e^- (0.95)
		144	143.958120		17 M	e^- (2.87); γs
		145			4.5 H	e^- (3.2)
		146	145.963210		24.7 M	e^- (3); γ
60	Neodymium....	140	139.952500		3.3 D	K; γ
		141	140.952980		2.5 H	e^+ (0.78); γ (1.05)
		142	141.951510	27.13		
		143	142.954052	12.20		
		144	143.954930	23.87		
		145		8.30		
		146	145.958700	17.18		
		147	146.961530		11.8 D	e^- (0.78, 0.35); γs
		148	147.964000	5.72		
		149	148.966700		1.8 H	e^- (1.5, 1.1, 0.95); γs
		150	149.967900	5.60		
		151			12 M	e^- (1.93); γs
61	Prometheum....	141			20 M	e^+ (2.6); γ
		142			2 M	e^+
		143			285 D	K; γ
		146	145.958950		2.7 H	e^- (2.0); γ

Z	Element Name	A	Mass	% Abundance	Half-life	Radiation (Mev)
61	Prometheum....	147	146.960552		2.7 Y	e^- (0.2)
		148	147.964200		5.3 D	e^- (2.5); γ (0.8)
		149	148.964900		47 H	e^- (1.1); γ (0.25)
		150	149.969100		2.7 H	e^- (3.0, 2.01); γs
62	Samarium......	143			8 M	e^+
		144	143.956000	3.16		
		145			410 D	K; γ (0.061)
		147	146.960810	15.07	6.7×10^{11} Y	α (2.1)
		148	147.961300	11.27		
		149	148.963460	13.84		
		150	149.963400	7.47		
		151			70 Y	e^- (0.75)
		152	151.967300	26.63		
		153			50 H	e^- (0.82); γs
		154	153.970520	22.53		
		155	154.973510		23 M	e^- (1.8); γs
		156	155.975050		10 H	e^- (0.8)
63	Europium......	146			38 H	e^+ (0.4)
		147			24 D	e^+ (1.0, 0.4); K; γ
		148			58.6 D	K; γ (0.69)
		149			14 D	K; γ (1.0)
		150	149.966200		13.1 H	e^+ (1.8); e^- (1.1, 0.8)
		151		47.8		
		152			9.2 H; 5.3 Y	e^- (1.8, 0.9, 0.36); γs
		153		52.2		
		154	153.972920		5.4 Y	e^- (1.9, 0.7, 0.3); γs
		155	154.971146		1.7 Y	e^- (2.23, 0.24); γs
		156	155.974080		15.4 D	e^-; γ
		157	156.973030		15.4 H	e^-; γ
64	Gadolinium.....	149			9 D	K; γ (3.0)
		150	149.965050		10^4 Y	α (2.7)
		151			150 D	K; γ (2.65)
		152		0.20		
		153			236 D	K; e^-; γ
		154	153.969720	2.15		
		155	154.970880	14.78		
		156	155.971500	20.59		
		157	156.971200	15.71		
		158	157.973420	24.78		
		159			18 H	e^- (1.1, 0.9); γs
		160	159.977750	21.79		
		161			3.7 M	e^- (1.6); γs
65	Terbium.......	152			4.5 H	K
		153			5.1 D	e^+
		154			17.2 H	e^+ (2.6); γ
		155			190 D	K; γ
		157			4.7 D	K; γ (1.4)

Z	Element Name	A	Mass	% Abundance	Half-life	Radiation (Mev)
65	Terbium........	159		100		
		160	159.977755		76 D	e^- (0.59)
		161			6.8 D	e^- (0.5); γ (0.049)
66	Dysprosium....	156		0.05		
		158		0.09		
		159			134 D	e^+; K
		160	195.975800	2.29		
		161		18.88		
		162	161.976960	25.53		
		163		24.97		
		164	163.980420	28.19		
		165	164.982440		145 M	e^- (1.25, 0.88, 0.42); γs
		166			81 H	e^- (0.4); γ
67	Holmium.......	160			20 M	e^+ (1.3); γ (1.2)
		161			4.6 H	K; γ
		162			65 D	e^+ (0.8); γ
		163			5.2 D	K; γs
		164	163.982770		34 M	e^- (0.95)
		165	164.981100	100		
		166			28 H	e^- (1.8, 0.55); γs
68	Erbium........	162		0.1		
		163			11.2 H	K; γ (1.1)
		164	163.981720	1.5		
		165			10 H	K
		166		32.9		
		167		24.4		
		168	167.983920	26.9		
		169			9 D	e^- (0.33)
		170	169.989360	14.2		
		171			7.6 H	e^- (1.49, 1.05, 0.67); γs
69	Thulium.......	166			7.7 H	e^+ (2.1); γ
		167			9 D	K; γ (0.95, 0.22)
		168			85 D	e^- (0.5); K; γs
		169		100		
		170			120 D	e^- (0.99, 0.87); γ
70	Ytterbium......	168		0.14		
		169			30.6 D	K; γs
		170		3.03		
		171		14.24		
		172	171.983840	21.68		
		173		16.18		
		174	173.980750	31.77		
		175			4.2 D	e^- (0.47, 0.37); γs
		176		12.65		
		177			1.88 H	e^- (1.3); γs

Z	Element Name	A	Mass	% Abundance	Half-life	Radiation (Mev)
71	Lutecium.......	170			1.72 D	e^+; K; γ
		171			8.5 D	K; γs
		172			6.7 D	K
		175		97.5		
		176	175.997370	2.5	7.3×10^{10} Y	e^- (0.40); γ (0.26)
		176			3.7 H	e^- (1.15)
		177			6.7 D	e^- (0.44); γs
72	Hafnium.......	173			23.6 H	K; γ (1.0)
		174		0.18		
		176	175.996300	5.30		
		177		18.47		
		178	177.999760	27.13		
		179		13.85	19 S	γ (0.215)
		180	179.998000	35.14	5.5 H	e^- (0.44, 0.33); γ
		181	181.004000		43 D	e^- (0.41); γs
73	Tantalum......	176			8.0 H	e^+; K; γ (1.3)
		177			2.2 D	K; γ
		178			9.3 M; 2.1 H	K; γs
		180	180.002200		8.2 H	e^- (0.7, 0.6); γs
		181	181.002900	100		
		182	182.005370		115 D	e^- (0.53); γs
		182			16.2 M	e^- (0.2); γ
		183			4.8 D	e^- (0.6)
74	Wolfram.......	178			21.5 D	e^+; γ
		179			5.2 M; 30 M	K; e^-
		180	180.001450	0.13		
		182	182.003510	26.3		
		183	183.005300	14.2		
		184	184.006300	30 6		
		185			74 D	e^- (0.43); γ (0.134)
		186	186.010400	28.6		
		187	187.012460		24.1 H	e^- (1.32, 0.63); γs
		188			65 D	e^-
75	Rhenium.......	182			14 H	K; γs
		183			240 D	K; γs
		183			67 H	K; γs
		184			52 D; 2 D	K; γs
		185		37.1		
		186	186.010697		91 H	e^- (1.07, 0.93, 0.3); γs
		187	187.011052	62.9	4×10^{12} Y	e^- (0.043)
		188	188.016330		16 H	e^- (2.1); γs
76	Osmium........	184		0.018		
		185			96 D	K; γ
		186	186.009550	1.59		
		187	187.011045	1.64		
		188	188.014100	13.3		

Z	Element Name	A	Mass	% Abundance	Half-life	Radiation (Mev)
76	Osmium	189	189.018120	16.1		
		190	190.017400	26.4		
		191	191.021500		16 D; 14 H	e^- (0.15); γs
		192	192.022500	41.0		
		193	193.026370		32 H	e^- (1.10); γ (1.5)
77	Iridium	188			41.5 H	e^+ (2.0); γ (1.8)
		190			12.6 D; 3 H	K; γ
		191	191.021240	38.5		
		192	192.024700			e^-; γs
		193	193.025200	61.5		
		194	194.026400		19 H	e^- (2.18); γ (1.35)
		195	195.028660		2.3 H	e^- (1.0)
78	Platinum	190		0.01		
		191			3.0 D	K; γs
		192	192.023100	0.8		
		193	193.025300		4.3 D	K; γs
		194	194.024000	32.8		
		195	195.026400	33.7	3.8 D	γ (0.337, 0.126)
		196	196.026880	25.4		
		197	197.029280		17.4 H	e^- (0.68); γs
		197			82 M	γs
		198	198.029000	7.3		
		199			31 M	e^- (1.8)
79	Gold	190			4.3 M	e^+
		191			18 H	e^+
		192			4.0 H	e^- (1.9); K; γ
		193			15.8 H	K; γ
		194			39.2 H	K; γ
		195			182 D	K; γ
		196	196.028100		14 H	K; γ
		196			5.6 D	e^- (0.36); γs
		197	197.028470	100	7.5 S	e^-; γ
		198	198.030480		2.7 D	e^- (1.38, 0.96, 0.29); γs
		199	199.031033		3.3 D	e^- (0.46, 0.30, 0.25); γs
		200	200.034380		48 M	e^- (2.5)
		201	201.035600			
80	Mercury	196	196.027350	0.15		
		197			23 H	γ (0.275); e^- (0.165); K.
		197			64 H	γ (0.191, 0.077); K
		198	198.029000	10.1		
		199	199.030550	17.0	43 M	γ (0.53)
		200	200.031910	23.1		
		201	201.034000	13.2		
		202	202.035341	29.7		
		203	203.036474		46.5 D	e^- (0.208); γ (0.279)
		204	204.037323	6.8		
		205	205.040359		5.5 M	e^- (1.75)

Z	Element Name	A	Mass	% Abundance	Half-life	Radiation (Mev)
81	Thallium.......	198			1.8 H	$K; \gamma; e^-$
		199			7.2 H	$K; \gamma; e^-$
		200			27 H	e^- (0.40); γs
		201			72 H	$K; \gamma$
		202	202.036415		11.4 D	$K; \gamma$ (0.435); e^- (0.35)
		203	203.035951	29.5		
		204	204.037678		2.7 Y	e^- (0.76); K
		205	205.038480	70.5		
		206	206.040447		4.2 M	e^- (1.8)
	(Ac C'')	207	207.042138		4.76 M	e^- (1.47); γ
	(Th C'')	208	208.047006		3.1 M	e^- (1.82); γ (2.62)
		209	209.050676		2.2 M	e^- (1.8)
	(Ra C'')	210	210.055615		1.32 M	e^- (1.80)
82	Lead..........	199			1.5 H	K
		200			18 H	K
		201			7 H	e^+; K
		202	202.036501		500 Y	K
		203	203.037347		52 H	$K; \gamma$s
		204	204.036859	13	68 M	γ (0.90)
		205	205.038539		10 M	e^+
		206	206.038826	26.3		
		207	207.040580	20.8		
		208	208.041640	51.6		
		209	209.046471		3.3 H	e^- (0.72)
	(Ra D)	210	210.049830		25 Y	e^- (0.025); γs
	(Ac B)	211	211.054754		36.1 M	e^- (0.5, 1.4); γ (0.83)
	(Th B)	212	212.058170		10.6 H	e^- (0.59, 0.36); γ
	(Ra B)	214	214.066581		26.8 M	e^- (0.65); γs
83	Bismuth.......	197			2 M	α (6.2)
		198			7 M	α (5.8); K
		199			27 M	α (5.47); K
		200			90 M	α (5.1)
		204			12 H	K
		206	206.042692		6.4 D	γ (0.93); K
		207	207.043160		50 Y	γs; K
		208	208.044787			K
		209	209.045794	100		
	(Ra E)	210	210.049761		4.8 D	α (5.0); e^- (1.65, 1.080); γ
	(Ac C)	211	211.053261		2.16 M	α (6.619); e^-; γ
	(Th C)	212	212.057545		60.5 M	α (6.054); e^- (2.25); γ
		213	213.060966		46.5 M	α; e^- (1.2)
	(Ra C)	214	214.065518		19.7 M	α (5.502); e^- (3.15)
		215	215.068911		8 M	α (8.3)
		216	216.073802			
84	Polonium.......	203			47 M	α; K
		205			4 H	α (5.17); K
		206			9 D	α (5.2); K; γ
		207			5.7 H	α (5.1); γ; K

Z	Element Name	A	Mass	% Abundance	Half-life	Radiation (Mev)
84	Polonium	208	208.046330		3 Y	α (5.1)
		209	209.047756		200 Y	α (4.09)
		210	210.048505		140 D	α (5.298); γ
	(Ac C′)	211	211.052605		0.5 S	α (7.434)
	(Th C′)	212	212.055129		3×10^{-7} S	α (8.776)
		213	213.059473		3.2×10^{-6}	α (8.3)
	(Ra C′)	214	214.062114		1.6×10^{-4} S	α (7.68)
	(Ac A)	215	215.066711		1.83×10^{-3} S	α (7.365)
	(Th A)	216	216.069462		1.58×10^{-1} S	α (6.774); e^-
		217	217.074058		1 S	α (6.5)
	(Ra A)	218	218.077021		3.05 M	α (5.998)
		219	219.082111			
		220	220.085026			
85	Astatine	207			1.7 H	α (5.7)
		208			6.5 H	α (5.6)
		210	210.052611		8.3 H	K
		211	211.053453		7.5 H	α (5.94); γ; K
		212	212.056934		0.25 S	α
		213	213.059746			
		214	214.063251			α (8.78)
		215	215.065892		10^{-4} S	α (8.04)
		216	216.069950		3×10^{-4} S	α (7.64)
		217	217.072512		0.02 S	α (7.0)
		218	218.076645		2 S	α (6.63)
		219	219.079651		54 S	α (6.27); e^-
		220	220.084124			
86	Radon	212	212.057062		23 M	α (6.17); K
		214	214.062370		1 S	α (8.6)
		215	215.065891		1 S	α (8.0)
		216	216.067770		1 S	α (8.1)
		217	217.071825		1×10^{-3} S	α (7.7)
		218	218.073788		0.019 S	α (7.1)
	(An)	219	219.078036		3.92 S	α (6.824)
	(Tn)	220	220.080211		54.5 S	α (6.282)
		221	221.084508		24 M	α; e^-
	(Rn)	222	222.086899		3.825 D	α (5.486)
		223	223.091574			
		224	224.094113			
87	Francium	219	219.077760		0.02 S	α (7.3)
		220	220.081142		27.5 S	α (6.7)
		221	221.083284		4.8 M	α (6.3)
		222	222.087074		14.8 M	e^-
		223	223.089597		21 M	e^- (1.2); γ
		224	224.093586			
		225	225.095933			
		226	226.100005			

Z	Element Name	A	Mass	% Abundance	Half-life	Radiation (Mev)
88	Radium........	218	218.075506			
		219	219.078521			α (8.0)
		220	220.079778			α (7.49)
		221	221.083037		30 S	α (6.71)
		222	222.084834		38 S	α (6.51)
		223	223.088322		11.2 D	α (5.719, 5.607); γs.
		224	224.090300		3.6 D	α (5.66, 5.44); γ (0.25)
		225	225.093885		14.8 D	e^- (0.2)
		226	226.095999		1.620 Y	α (4.79, 4.61, 4.21); γ (0.188)
		227	227.100177		41.2 M	e^-
		228	228.102558		6.7 Y	e^- (0.030)
		229	229.106415			
		230	230.109141		1 H	e^- (1.2)
89	Actinium.......	221	221.084899			
		222	222.087213		5.5 S	α (6.96)
		223	223.088898		2.2 M	α (6.64); K
		224	224.091764		2.9 H	α (6.17); K
		225	225.087062		10.0	α (5.8)
		226	226.096891		22 H	e^-
		227	227.098878		27.7 Y	α (4.94); e^- (0.02); γ
		228	228.102512		6.13 H	α (4.54); e^- (1.5, 2.0); γ
		229	229.104482		66 M	α
		230	230.108179		1 M	e^- (2.2)
		231	231.110826			
		232	232.114859			
90	Thorium.......	222	222.088082			
		223	223.090658		0.1 S	α (7.55)
		224	224.091452		1 S	α (7.13)
		225	225.094143		8.0 M	α (6.57); K
		226	226.095639		30.9 M	α (6.30)
		227	227.098792		18.6 D	α (6.05, 5.67); γ
		228	228.100106		1.9 Y	α (5.42, 5.34); γ
		229	229.103251		7.340 Y	α (5.02, 4.94, 4.85)
		230	230.104995		8×10^4 Y	α (4.68, 4.61); γ
		231	231.108614		25.6 Y	e^- (0.302, 0.216); γ
		232	232.110797	100	1.39×10^{10} Y	α (3.98); γ (0.055)
		233	233.114321		23.5 M	e^- (1.23)
		234	234.116778		24.1 D	e (0.192, 0.104); γ
91	Protactinium ...	225	225.096617		2.0 S	α
		226	226.098533		1.8 M	α (6.81)
		227	227.099842		38.3 M	α (6.46); K
		228	228.102300		22 H	α (6.09, 5.85); K
		229	229.103594		1.5 D	α (5.69); K
		230	230.106622		17.7 D	α; e^- (1.1); K
		231	231.108266		34,300 Y	α (4.66, 5.04)
		232	232.111180		1.32 D	e^- (0.28)
		233	233.113000		27.4 D	e^- (0.53)
		234	234.116567		1.14 M	e^- (2.32, 0.8)

Z	Element Name	A	Mass	% Abundance	Half-life	Radiation (Mev)
91	Protactinium...	235	235.119000		23.7 M	e^- (1.4)
		236	236.122871			
92	Uranium.......	226	226.099907			
		227	227.101967			
		228	228.102622		9.3 M	α (6.72)
		229	229.104990		58 M	α (6.42)
		230	230.105951		20.8 D	α (5.85)
		231	231.108630		4.2 D	K
		232	232.109795		70 Y	α (5.31)
		233	233.112398		1.63×10^5 Y	α (4.83), e^-, γ, K
		234	234.114064	0.006	2.5×10^5 Y	α (4.76)
		235	235,117496	0.71	7.1×10^8 Y	α (4.52)
		236	236.119590		2.46×10^7 Y	α (4.49); γ (0.05)
		237	237.122752		6.7 D	e^- (0.26), γ (0.5)
		238	238.125223	99.28	4.50×10^9 Y	α (4.18); γ (0.045)
		239	239.129160		23.5 M	e^- (0.56, 1.2); γ
		240	240.131807		18 H	e^-
		241	241.135466			
		242	242.138444			
93	Neptunium.....	229	229.108088			
		230	230.109660			
		231	231.110580		50 M	α (6.2); K
		232	232.112643		13 M	γ; K
		233	233.113518		35 M	α (5.53); γ; K
		234	234.116352		4.4 D	γ (1.9); K
		235	235.117674		435 D	α (5.06); K
		236	236.120503		22 H	e^- (0.51, 0.36); γ (0.15)
		237	237.122204		2.2×10^7 Y	α (4.77); γ (0.065)
		238	238.125356		2.1 D	e^- (0.258, 1.272); γs
		239	239.127769		2.33 D	e^- (0.676); γ (0.023)
		240	240.131421		7.3 M	e^- (1.30)
		241	241.133555		60 M	e^- (0.89); γ
		242	242.137746			
94	Plutonium......	232	232.113696		36 M	α (6.6); K
		233	233.115849			
		234	234.116595		8.5 H	α (6.2); K
		235	235.118898		26 M	α (5.85); K
		236	236.119955		2.7 Y	α (5.75); γ (0.045)
		237	237.122430		40.0 D	K
		238	238.123956		90 Y	γ (0.0436, 0.100)
		239	239.126999		100 Y	α (5.1); γ (0.035, 0.050)
		240	240.129105		6.580 Y	α (5.16)
		241	241.132148		14 Y	α (4.91); e^- (0.01)
		242	242.134449		5×10^5 Y	α (4.88)
		243	243.138087		5 H	e^- (0.39); γ (0.095, 0.12)
		244	244.140647			
		245	245.144123			
		246	246.147123			

Z	Element Name	A	Mass	% Abundance	Half-life	Radiation (Mev)
95	Americium......	236	236.123394			
		237	237.123958		1.3 H	α (6.01); K
		238	238.126642		2.1 H	e^-; K
		239	239.127835		12 H	α (5.77); γ (0.285)
		240	240.130556		47.0 H	γ (0.92, 1.02, 1.40)
		241	241.132126		470 Y	γ (0.026, 0.033, 0.043)
		242	242.135187		16.0 H; 100 Y	e^- (0.626); γ (0.041, 0.043)
		243	243.137479		10^4 Y	α (5.21)
		244	244.140925		25 M	e^-
		245	245.142834		119 M	
		246	246.146800			
		247	247.149299			
		248	248.154051			
96	Curium........	236	236.125359			
		237	237.127158			
		238	238.127572		2.5 H	α (6.5)
		239	239.129756		3 H	K
		240	240.130664		26.8 D	α (6.26); K
		241	241.133074		35 D	α (5.95); γ (0.47, 0.59)
		242	242.134506		162 D	α (6.08); γ (0.045)
		243	243.137483		100 Y	α (5.89, 5.79); γ
		244	244.139314		19 Y	α (5.78)
		245	245.142093		500 Y	α
		246	246.144126			
97	Berkelium......	240	240.135273			
		241	241.135590			
		242	242.138059			
		243	243.139048		4.5 H	γ (0.07, 0.22); α (6.72)
		244	244.141544		~4.5 H	K
		245	245.142920		4.9 D	α (6.15, 5.9)
		246	246.145723			
		247	247.147639			
		248	248.150677			
		249	249.152522		290 D	α (5.40); e^- (0.080)
		250			3.13 H	e^- (1.9, 0.9)
98	Californium.....	242	242.139687			
		243	243.141689			
		244	244,142349		45 M	α (7.15); K
		245	245.144576			
		246	246.145757		1.5 D	γ (0.043); α (6.75)
		247	247.148470			
		248	248.150022			
		249	249.152522		470 Y	α (5.81)
		250	250.154598		12 Y	α (6.024, 5.98); γ
		253			20 D	e^-
99	Einsteinium.....	244	244.147796			
		245	245.147898			

Z	Element Name	A	Mass	% Abundance	Half-life	Radiation (Mev)
99	Einsteinium	246	246.150174			
		247	247.150894			
		248	248.153122			
		249	249.154187			
		250	250.156689			
		253			20 D	α (6.63)
		254			36 H	e^- (1.1)
100	Fermium	246	246.152586			
		247	247.154373			
		248	248.154818			
		249	249.156863			
		250	250.157689			
		251	251.160027			
		252	252.161632			
		254			3.2 H	α (7.22)
		255			15.0 H	α (7.1)
101	Mendelevium . . .	250	250.162912			
		251	251.163364			
		252	252.165322			
		253	253.166420			
		254	254.168965			
		255	255.170935			
		256	256.173833		3 H	Fission

APPENDIX

TABLE A I.   FUNDAMENTAL CONSTANTS [1]

Electronic

Charge of electron $(4.80286 \pm 0.00016) \times 10^{-10}$ esu.
$(1.60206 \pm 0.00003) \times 10^{-20}$ emu.

Specific charge of electron $\left(\dfrac{e}{m_0}\right)$ $(1.75890 \pm 0.00002) \times 10^7$ emu per gm.

Atomic weight of electron (Aston) 0.0005486.

Mass of electron $(9.1083 \pm 0.0003) \times 10^{-28}$ gm.

1 ampere $= 6.242 \times 10^{18}$ electrons per sec.

Atomic

Mass of hydrogen atom $(1.67330) \times 10^{-24}$ gm.

Avogadro's number $(6.02486 \pm 0.00016) \times 10^{23}$ per gm mol.

Loschmidt's number (NPT) $(2.68719 \pm 0.00010) \times 10^{19}$ per cm^3.

Volume 1 gm mol gas (NPT) $(22,420.7 \pm 0.6)$ cm^3.

Boltzmann's gas constant $(1.38044 \pm 0.0005) \times 10^{-16}$ erg per deg C. per particle.

Specific charge of proton (e/m) (9579.0 ± 0.5) emu per gm.

Specific charge of alpha particle (e/m) (4817.8 ± 0.5) emu per gm.

Radiation

Planck constant (h) $(6.62517 \pm 0.00023) \times 10^{-27}$ erg sec.

Solar constant 1.353×10^6 ergs per cm^2 per sec.

Velocity of radiation (vacuum) $(299,793.0 \pm 0.3) \times 10^5$ cm per sec.

Curie of radioactive material: 37.0×10^9 disintegrations per sec.

Energy Transformations

1 Mev $= 1.07 \times 10^{-3}$ mass units $= 1.6 \times 10^{-6}$ ergs $= 4.45 \times 10^{-20}$ kwh.

1 mass unit $= 931$ Mev $= 1.49 \times 10^{-3}$ ergs $= 4.15 \times 10^{-17}$ kwh.

1 erg $= 671$ mass units $= 6.24 \times 10^5$ Mev $= 2.78 \times 10^{-14}$ kwh.

1 kwh $= 2.41 \times 10^{16}$ mass units $= 2.25 \times 10^{19}$ Mev $= 3.60 \times 10^{13}$ ergs.

1 gm $(mc^2) = 9 \times 10^{20}$ ergs $= 25.01 \times 10^6$ kwh.

[1] E. Cohen, J. DuMond, T. Layton, and J. Rollett, *Rev. Mod. Phys.*, **27**, 363 (1955).

Equations

The energy W, from relativity, is:

1. $W = mc^2 - m_0c^2 = m_0c^2 \left[\dfrac{1}{\sqrt{1 - \beta^2}} - 1 \right] = m_0c^2 \left[\dfrac{1}{2}\beta^2 + \dfrac{3}{8}\beta^4 + \dfrac{5}{16}\beta^6 + \cdots \right]$

$= \dfrac{1}{2}m_0v^2 \left[1 + \dfrac{3}{4}\beta^2 + \dfrac{5}{8}\beta^4 + \cdots \right]$ ergs, where m is the mass and m_0 the rest mass of

the electron and β is the ratio of its velocity v to that of light c.

The ratio of the mass m to the rest mass m_0 from equation 1 is:

2. $\dfrac{m}{m_0} = \dfrac{W}{m_0c^2} + 1 = \dfrac{W(\text{Mev})}{0.51} + 1.$

The momentum, $P = Mv$, from equation 1 is:

3. $P = mv = \dfrac{1}{c}\sqrt{W(W + 2m_0c^2)}$ (gm cm per sec).

In a field of B Gauss the central forces on the electron whose radius is ρ are:

4. $\text{Bev} = \dfrac{mv^2}{\rho}$, or $B\rho = \dfrac{mv}{e(\text{emu})}$ (Gauss-cm).

Hence from equation 3:

5. $B\rho = \dfrac{1}{ce}\sqrt{W(W + 2m_0c^2)} = \dfrac{10^4}{3}\sqrt{W'(W' + 1.02)}$ where W' is in Mev.

The energy may be explicitly expressed in terms of B and ρ as:

6. $W = m_0c^2 \pm c\sqrt{m_0^2c^2 + B^2\rho^2e^2}.$

TABLE A III. DATA ON ELECTRONS

β	W (Kev)	$B\rho$	m/m_0	β	W (Kev)	$B\rho$	m/m_0
0.00198	0.001	3.37	1.00000	0.22	12.83	384.2	1.02512
0.00280	0.002	4.76	1.00000	0.23	14.07	402.6	1.02755
0.00343	0.003	5.84	1.00000	0.24	15.38	421.3	1.03011
0.00396	0.004	6.74	1.00000	0.25	16.75	440.0	1.03280
0.00443	0.005	7.53	1.00001	0.26	18.18	458.8	1.0356
0.00485	0.006	8.25	1.00001	0.27	19.69	477.8	1.0385
0.005	0.00638	8.50	1.00001	0.28	21.28	496.8	1.0416
0.00524	0.007	8.91	1.00001	0.29	22.94	516.2	1.0449
0.00560	0.008	9.53	1.00001	0.30	24.66	535.9	1.0482
0.00594	0.009	10.10	1.00001	0.31	26.47	555.7	1.0518
0.00626	0.010	10.65	1.00002	0.32	28.36	575.3	1.0555
0.00886	0.020	15.06	1.00004	0.33	30.31	595.6	1.0593
0.0100	0.02554	17.0	1.00005	0.34	32.37	616.0	1.0633
0.0109	0.030	18.45	1.00006	0.35	34.49	636.6	1.0675
0.0125	0.040	21.3	1.00008	0.36	36.70	657.5	1.0718
0.0140	0.050	24.6	1.00010	0.37	39.01	678.7	1.0763
0.0198	0.100	33.7	1.00019	0.38	41.42	700.0	1.0811
0.0200	0.1022	34.06	1.00020	0.39	43.92	721.5	1.0860
0.0280	0.200	47.6	1.00039	0.40	46.53	743.5	1.0910
0.0300	0.230	51.04	1.00045	0.41	49.23	766.0	1.0963
0.0343	0.300	58.3	1.00059	0.414	50.00	775.0	1.0983
0.0400	0.4087	68.1	1.00080	0.42	52.05	788.3	1.1019
0.0442	0.500	75.3	1.00098	0.43	54.97	811.4	1.1076
0.0500	0.6385	85.0	1.00125	0.44	58.03	834.9	1.1135
0.0560	0.800	95.2	1.00157	0.45	61.19	858.6	1.1197
0.060	0.9248	102.3	1.00181	0.46	64.50	882.5	1.1262
0.0626	1.00	106.6	1.00196	0.47	67.91	907.3	1.1329
0.07	1.257	119.6	1.00246	0.48	71.43	932.2	1.1399
0.08	1.644	136.7	1.00322	0.49	75.17	957.6	1.1471
0.0883	2.000	151.0	1.00391	0.50	79.03	983.6	1.1547
0.09	2.083	154.0	1.00408	0.51	83.04	1010.	1.1625
0.10	2.575	171.3	1.00504	0.52	87.20	1038.	1.1707
0.11	3.122	188.5	1.00611	0.53	91.57	1065.	1.1792
0.12	3.720	205.9	1.00728	0.54	96.08	1093.	1.1881
0.124	4.000	214.0	1.00783	0.548	100.0	1116.	1.1955
0.13	4.373	223.4	1.00856	0.55	100.8	1122.	1.1973
0.138	5.00	239.0	1.00967	0.56	105.8	1151.	1.2070
0.14	5.083	241.0	1.00995	0.57	110.9	1182.	1.2170
0.15	5.844	258.4	1.01144	0.58	116.2	1214.	1.2275
0.16	6.668	276.1	1.01305	0.59	121.9	1245.	1.2385
0.17	7.546	293.9	1.01477	0.60	127.7	1278.	1.2500
0.18	8.479	311.9	1.01660	0.61	133.8	1312.	1.2619
0.19	9.478	329.7	1.01855	0.62	140.2	1346.	1.2745
0.195	10.00	340.0	1.01958	0.63	147.0	1382.	1.2876
0.20	10.53	347.8	1.02062	0.64	154.1	1420.	1.3014
0.21	11.66	366.0	1.02281	0.65	161.3	1458.	1.3159

TABLE A III.   DATA ON ELECTRONS (*Continued*)

β	W (Kev)	$B\rho$	m/m_0	β	W (Kev)	$B\rho$	m/m_0
0.66	169.2	1497.	1.3310	0.938	962.8	4610.	2.8848
0.67	177.2	1538.	1.3470	0.940	986.4	4694.	2.9310
0.68	185.8	1580.	1.3638	0.9411	1000.	4739.	2.9577
0.69	194.9	1623.	1.3815	0.942	1010.	4782.	2.9796
0.695	200.0	1646.	1.3920	0.944	1038.	4874.	3.0308
0.70	204.3	1669.	1.4002	0.946	1065.	4971.	3.0848
0.71	214.4	1718.	1.4200	0.948	1094.	5074.	3.1419
0.72	225.3	1768.	1.4409	0.95	1125.	5183.	3.2025
0.73	236.4	1820.	1.4631	0.952	1158.	5299.	3.2669
0.74	248.5	1874.	1.4867	0.954	1192.	5420.	3.3354
0.75	261.4	1933.	1.5118	0.956	1231.	5551.	3.4087
0.76	275.2	1992.	1.5386	0.958	1271.	5691.	3.4871
0.77	289.7	2056.	1.5672	0.960	1313.	5841.	3.5714
0.78	305.6	2124.	1.5980	0.962	1360.	6002.	3.6623
0.79	322.3	2195.	1.6310	0.964	1411.	6178.	3.7607
0.80	340.5	2272.	1.6666	0.966	1465.	6365.	3.8678
0.81	360.2	2354.	1.7052	0.968	1525.	6573.	3.9848
0.82	381.8	2441.	1.7471	0.970	1591.	6796.	4.1134
0.83	405.0	2536.	1.7928	0.972	1662.	7048.	4.2556
0.84	430.7	2638.	1.8430	0.974	1743.	7324.	4.4140
0.85	458.9	2749.	1.8983	0.976	1834.	7637.	4.5919
0.86	490.3	2870.	1.9596	0.978	1938.	7990.	4.7937
0.863	500.0	2925.	1.9907	0.980	2057.	8391.	5.0252
0.87	525.3	3006.	2.0281	0.982	2194.	8869.	5.2943
0.88	564.6	3156.	2.1053	0.984	2356.	9410.	5.6126
0.89	609.6	3325.	2.1931	0.986	2553.	10,080.	5.9971
0.90	661.1	3517.	2.2941	0.988	2796.	10,890.	6.4744
0.902	671.2	3559.	2.3162	0.990	3110.	11,960.	7.0888
0.904	684.1	3601.	2.3390	0.991	3305.	12,620.	7.4703
0.906	695.0	3646.	2.3625	0.992	3536.	13,380.	7.9215
0.908	708.3	3693.	2.3868	0.993	3814.	14,320.	8.4664
0.910	721.3	3740.	2.4119	0.994	4160.	15,480.	9.1424
0.912	734.5	3788.	2.4379	0.9950	4604.	16,980.	10.0125
0.914	748.2	3838.	2.4647	0.9955	4881.	17,900.	10.5528
0.916	762.4	3891.	2.4926	0.9960	5206.	18,990.	11.1915
0.918	777.3	3942.	2.5215	0.9965	5600.	20,310.	11.9628
0.92	792.5	3990.	2.5515	0.9970	6090.	21,950.	12.9196
0.922	808.5	4058.	2.5827	0.9975	6718.	24,050.	14.1510
0.924	825.0	4118.	2.6151	0.9980	7571.	26,900.	15.8193
0.926	842.2	4179.	2.6488	0.9985	8119.	31,070.	18.2643
0.928	860.0	4244.	2.6839	0.9990	10,900.	38,080.	22.3663
0.930	879.1	4311.	2.7206	0.9995	15,630.	53,860.	31.6268
0.932	898.5	4381.	2.7589	0.9_4—871	10^5	3.349×10^5	196.77
0.934	918.9	4454.	2.7989	0.9_6—870	10^6	3.33×10^6	1958.7
0.936	940.3	4531.	2.8409	0.9_7—870	10^7	3.33×10^7	19,587.

TABLE A IV.   USEFUL INFORMATION REGARDING PROTONS IN MOTION

V (Cm/sec)	β (V/C)	W (Kev)	$B\rho$ (Gauss-Cm)	Range (Cm Air)
1.0×10^9	0.03333	522	1.044×10^5	0.8
1.1	0.03666	632	1.149	1.1
1.2	0.04000	753	1.253	1.4
1.3	0.04333	884	1.358	1.8
1.4	0.046666	1,025	1.463	2.3
1.5	0.05000	1,177	1.568	2.9
1.6	0.05333	1,340	1.673	3.6
1.7	0.05666	1,513	1.778	4.4
1.8	0.06000	1,697	1.883	5.3
1.9	0.06333	1,891	1.988	6.3
2.0	0.06666	2,095	2.093	7.5
2.1	0.07000	2,310	2.198	8.9
2.2	0.07333	2,536	2.304	10.4
2.3	0.07666	2,773	2.409	12.1
2.4	0.08000	3,021	2.514	14.0
2.5	0.08333	3,280	2.619	16.1
2.6	0.08666	3,649	2.725	18.4
2.7	0.09000	3,929	2.830	21.0
2.8	0.09333	4,120	2.936	23.9
2.9	0.09666	4,422	3.042	27.0
3.0	0.10000	4,734	3.148	30.4
3.1	0.10333	5,057	3.254	34.1
3.2	0.10666	5,391	3.360	38.2
3.3	0.11000	5,736	3.467	42.6
3.4	0.11333	6,092	3.573	47.4
3.5	0.11666	6,460	3.680	52.6
3.6	0.12000	6,838	3.786	58.2
3.7	0.12333	7,227	3.893	64.1
3.8	0.12666	7,628	4.000	70.5
3.9	0.13000	8,040	4.107	77.4
4.0	0.13333	8,463	4.214	84.8
4.1	0.13666	8,897	4.321	92.7
4.2	0.14000	9,343	4.428	101.3
4.3	0.14333	9,800	4.535	110.4
4.4	0.14666	10,270	4.643	119.9
4.5	0.15000	10,750	4.750	130.0
4.6	0.15333	11,240	4.858	140.8
4.7	0.15666	11,740	4.966	152.3
4.8	0.16000	12,250	5.075	164.6
4.9	0.16333	12,770	5.184	177.5
5.0	0.16666	13,310	5.293	191.1

Note:—A deuteron whose range is twice the range of a proton possesses twice the energy, hence Table A IV may be used equally well for the range of deuterons up to 26.6 Mev.

TABLE A V. USEFUL INFORMATION REGARDING ALPHA PARTICLES

V (Cm/sec)	β (V/C)	W (Kev)	$B\rho$ (Gauss-Cm)	Range (Cm Air)	Ion Pairs
0.75×10^9	0.0250	1,167	1.5555×10^5	0.55	0.33×10^5
0.80	0.0266	1,328	1.6593	0.62	0.38
0.85	0.02833	1,499	1.7631	0.70	0.43
0.90	0.03000	1,681	1.8669	0.80	0.48
0.95	0.03166	1,873	1.9707	0.91	0.53
1.00	0.03333	2,075	2.0745	1.04	0.59
1.05	0.03500	2,288	2.1783	1.18	0.65
1.10	0.03666	2,511	2.2822	1.32	0.72
1.15	0.03833	2,745	2.3862	1.48	0.79
1.20	0.04000	2,989	2.4901	1.67	0.86
1.25	0.04166	3,244	2.5941	1.87	0.93
1.30	0.04333	3,509	2.6980	2.09	1.00
1.35	0.04500	3,785	2.8019	2.33	1.08
1.40	0.04666	4,071	2.9060	2.58	1.17
1.45	0.04833	4,368	3.0100	2.864	1.25
1.50	0.05000	4,674	3.1141	3.169	1.34
1.55	0.05166	4,991	3.2181	3.499	1.43
1.60	0.05333	5,319	3.3221	3.853	1.52
1.65	0.05500	5,658	3.4263	4.240	1.62
1.70	0.05666	6,008	3.5304	4.652	1.72
1.75	0.05833	6,367	3.6346	5.093	1.82
1.80	0.06000	6,737	3.7388	5.569	1.93
1.85	0.06166	7,117	3.8431	6.079	2.03
1.90	0.06333	7,508	3.9474	6.621	2.15
1.95	0.06500	7,910	4.0517	7.202	2.26
2.00	0.06666	8,322	4.1560	7.821	2.38
2.05	0.06833	8,745	4.2604	8.479	2.50
2.10	0.07000	9,178	4.3648	9.177	2.62
2.15	0.07166	9,622	4.4693	9.919	2.76
2.20	0.07333	10,077	4.5739	10.706	2.88
2.25	0.07500	10,543	4.6784	11.536	3.02
2.30	0.07666	11,018	4.7830	12.416	3.16
2.35	0.07833	11,504	4.8876	13.433	3.29
2.40	0.08000	12,001	4.9922	14.322	3.44
2.45	0.08166	12,508	5.1369	15.353	3.58
2.50	0.08333	13,027	5.2016	16.441	3.73

TABLE A VI. EXCITATION POTENTIALS FOR THE ELEMENTS, IN KILOVOLTS

Element	K	L_1	L_2	L_3	M	N	Element	K	L_1	L_2	L_3	M	N
92 U	115	21.7	20.9	17.2	5.54	1.44	52 Te	31.8	4.93	4.61	4.34	1.01	0.17
90 Th	109	20.5	19.6	16.3	5.17	1.33	51 Sb	30.4	4.69	4.38	4.13	0.94	0.15
82 Pb	87.6	15.8	15.2	13.0	3.85	0.89	50 Sn	29.1	4.46	4.16	3.92	0.88	0.13
81 Tl	85.2	15.3	14.7	12.7	3.71	0.86	49 In	27.9	4.23	3.94	3.73	0.83	0.12
80 Hg	82.9	14.8	14.2	12.3	3.57	0.82	48 Cd	26.7	4.02	3.72	3.53	0.77	0.11
79 Au	80.5	14.3	13.7	11.9	3.43	0.79	47 Ag	25.5	3.80	3.52	3.34	0.72	0.10
78 Pt	78.1	13.9	13.3	11.5	3.30	0.71	46 Pd	24.4	3.61	3.32	3.17	0.67	0.08
77 Ir	76.0	13.4	12.8	11.2	3.17	0.67	45 Rh	23.2	3.41	3.14	3.00	0.62	0.07
76 Os	73.8	12.9	12.3	10.9	3.05	0.64	44 Ru	22.1	3.24	2.97	2.84	0.59	0.06
74 W	69.3	12.1	11.5	10.2	2.81	0.59	42 Mo	20.0	2.88	2.62	2.52	0.51	0.06
73 Ta	67.4	11.7	11.1	9.9	2.71	0.57	41 Cb	19.0	2.70	2.45	2.37	0.48	0.05
72 Hf	65.4	11.3	10.7	9.6	2.60	0.54	40 Zr	18.0	2.54	2.30	2.22	0.43	0.05
71 Lu	63.4	10.9	10.3	9.2	2.50	0.51	39 Y	17.0	2.37	2.15	2.08		
70 Yb	61.4	10.5	10.0	8.9	2.41	0.50	38 Sr	16.1	2.21	2.00	1.94		
69 Tm	59.5	10.1	9.6	8.6	2.31	0.47	37 Rb	15.2	2.06	1.86	1.81		
68 Er	57.5	9.76	9.25	8.35	2.22	0.45	36 Kr	14.3	1.91				
67 Ho	55.8	9.39	8.91	8.06	2.13	0.43	35 Br	13.5	1.77				
66 Dy	53.8	9.05	8.57	7.78	2.04	0.42	34 Se	12.7	1.64				
65 Tb	52.0	8.71	8.25	7.51	1.96	0.40	33 As	11.9	1.52				
64 Gd	50.3	8.38	7.93	7.24	1.88	0.38	32 Ge	11.1	1.41				
63 Eu	48.6	8.06	7.61	6.97	1.80	0.36	31 Ga	10.4	1.31				
62 Sm	46.8	7.74	7.31	6.71	1.72	0.35	30 Zn	9.65	1.20				
60 Nd	43.6	7.13	6.72	6.21	1.58	0.32	29 Cu	8.86					
59 Pr	41.9	6.84	6.43	5.96	1.51	0.30	28 Ni	8.29					
58 Ce	40.3	6.55	6.16	5.72	1.43	0.29	27 Co	7.71					
57 La	38.7	6.28	5.89	5.48	1.36	0.27	26 Fe	7.10					
56 Ba	37.4	5.99	5.62	5.24	1.29	0.25	25 Mn	6.54					
55 Cs	35.9	5.72	5.35	5.00	1.21	0.23	24 Cr	5.98					
54 Xe	34.5	5.44	5.09	4.77	1.14	0.21	23 Va	5.45					
53 I	33.2	5.18	4.85	4.55	1.08	0.19	22 Ti	4.95					

AUTHOR INDEX

403

SUBJECT INDEX

411